D1196198

# The Method of Second Quantization

# PURE AND APPLIED PHYSICS

## A SERIES OF MONOGRAPHS AND TEXTBOOKS

### CONSULTING EDITORS

H. S. W. MASSEY

*University College, London, England*

KEITH A. BRUECKNER

*University of California, San Diego
La Jolla, California*

# The Method
# of Second Quantization

By **F. A. Berezin**

*Moscow State University*
*Moscow, U.S.S.R.*


Translated by **Nobumichi Mugibayashi**

*Department of Physics*
*Kobe University*
*Kobe, Japan*


and **Alan Jeffrey**

*Department of Engineering Mathematics*
*University of Newcastle-upon-Tyne*
*Newcastle-upon-Tyne, England*

ACADEMIC PRESS   NEW YORK and LONDON   1966

ACADEMIC PRESS INC.
111 Fifth Avenue, New York, New York 10003

*United Kingdom Edition published by*
ACADEMIC PRESS INC. (LONDON) LTD.
Berkeley Square House, London W.1

LIBRARY OF CONGRESS CATALOG CARD NUMBER: 66-26260

PRINTED IN THE UNITED STATES OF AMERICA

# Preface to the English Edition

For every author it is a great honor for his book to be translated into a foreign language, particularly so when the translator is a specialist in the field in question. When the book is on mathematical physics and the language into which it is translated is English it becomes a special honor, for, to a remarkable extent, this language has become international for the study of physics and modern mathematical physics.

Compared with the Russian edition, the presentation of certain results has been somewhat revised in the English translation. These revisions are chiefly concerned with Chapter IV which deals with the Thirring model, and also with some results in Sections 1 and 7.

Since the appearance of the Russian edition, I have received a number of critical remarks thereon from Professors M. G. Kreĭn, O. A. Lady-ženskaya, and A. S. Švarc. Their suggestions have been utilized in the preparation of this English edition and I take this opportunity to express my gratitude to them. A considerable number of misprints that occurred in the Russian edition have been corrected by Professor N. Mugibayashi. I am deeply grateful to him for this.

I also wish to thank Professor N. Mugibayashi for taking the initiative in organizing the English translation of this book.

*September, 1966*                                          F. A. BEREZIN

# Preface

In problems of quantum mechanics dealing with an indefinite number of particles, mainly in field theory and quantum statistics, the use of the so-called method of second quantization is customary.

This method arose almost at the same time as the definitive mathematical formulation of quantum mechanics in the works of Dirac, Fock, Jordan, and Wigner,[1] but only recently has it begun to be developed intensively.

This delay is apparently connected with the fact that the mathematical problems occurring in the method of second quantization are somewhat removed from the traditional problems of mathematical physics which are formulated in terms of partial differential equations. In particular, major roles in the method of second quantization are taken by purely algebraic questions, strange to classical mathematical physics, which are close to the representation theory of Lie groups, and by some questions in measure theory. Most attention in this book is paid to this aspect of the method of second quantization.

In the method of second quantization, just as in ordinary quantum mechanics, states of a physical system are described by vectors of a Hilbert space, called a *state space*, and the evolution of the system is determined by the Schrödinger equation

$$ i\hbar \frac{\partial \Psi}{\partial t} = H\Psi , $$

where $H$ is the energy operator, also called the *Hamiltonian*, and $\Psi$ is a vector in the state space.

[1] Cf. Dirac [1], Fock [1, 2], and Jordan-Wigner [1].

However, whereas in the quantum mechanics of a single particle

$$H\Psi = -\frac{\hbar^2}{2m}\Delta\Psi + V\Psi,$$

$H$ is an operator realized in a natural way in a function space of three real variables, the state space in the method of second quantization is the direct sum of function spaces of one, two, etc., variables, and there exists no natural realization of the Hamiltonian in the Hilbert space of functions with a fixed number of variables.

There are, however, natural realizations of the state space as *functional* spaces of functions with a definite number of variables. Depending on the sort of particles described, these functionals are either those of ordinary complex-valued functions or of functions with anticommuting values. The particles are called *bosons* in the first case and *fermions* in the second. Like state vectors, operators too are often conveniently given by means of functionals.[2]

It is noted that functionals form not only a linear space, but also a ring with respect to ordinary multiplication. This situation turns out to be exceedingly advantageous, because many calculations are much simplified as a result. When bosons are considered, the ring of functionals is shown to be commutative, and when fermions are considered, this is an anticommutative ring or, in other terminology, a Grassmann algebra with an infinite number of generators. In spite of an evident algebraic difference between these rings, all the basic formulas for them surprisingly show an almost complete coincidence.

Another reason which makes the realization of the state space in terms of functionals attractive is that functionals can be represented, roughly speaking, as functions of an infinite number of variables. In ordinary quantum mechanics the number of variables in functions forming a state space is the number of degrees of freedom. Thus there arises an interpretation of problems in second quantization as problems in quantum mechanics with an infinite number of degrees of freedom, and then there follows a natural desire to approximate these problems by those with a finite but large number of degrees of freedom. A series of interesting results have been obtained in this way (cf. an article by Gel'fand and Yaglom [1] and the bibliography at the end of that article).

---

[2] Fock [2] first applied functionals to describe the state space for bosons.

In this book state spaces and the simplest operators therein are described. In the Introduction, we recall fundamental statements of the method of second quantization and introduce notations to be used in the sequel. In Chapter I the connections between vectors and functionals and between operators and functionals are established, and fundamental rules for operating on functionals are also established (for each two functionals corresponding to operators $A$, $B$, there is a functional corresponding to their product $AB$, etc.).

In Chapters II and III, so-called quadratic operators and linear canonical transformations closely connected with them are considered.

In Chapter IV, Thirring's four-fermion model, one of the simplest models in quantum field theory, is studied.

The present book is an extended version of my article prepared for *Uspehi Matematičeskih Nauk*, September 1962. The Appendices of that article have been included in this book.

*Moscow, 1965*                                      F. A. BEREZIN

# Contents

# Introduction

1. STATE SPACE. According to the fundamental principle of quantum mechanics, the state of a particle is described by a vector of a complex Hilbert space. We denote this space by $L$. Let us realize it by means of square-integrable functions on a certain set $M$ provided with a measure.

If a system consists of $n$ particles, and the states of the $k$th particle are described by the aid of the space $L_k$ of square-integrable functions on the set $M_k$, then the states of the system are described by square-integrable functions of $n$ variables $x_1,\ldots, x_n$, where $x_k \in M_k$. This space is denoted by $\mathfrak{H}^n$. The inner product in $\mathfrak{H}^n$ is given by the formula

$$(f_1, f_2) = \int f_1(x_1,\ldots, x_n)\overline{f_2(x_1,\ldots, x_n)}\, d^n x,$$

where $x_k \in M_k$; $d^n x$ here and in what follows signifies the product of differentials $d^n x = dx_1 \cdots dx_n$, with $dx_k$ representing the differential of the measure on $M_k$.

If a system consists of $n$ identical particles, the sets $M_k$ coincide with each other. In this case it turns out to be unnecessary to consider the whole space $\mathfrak{H}^n$. Depending on the sort of particles, the system is described by the subspace $\mathscr{H}_B{}^n \subset \mathfrak{H}^n$ consisting of symmetric functions, or by the subspace $\mathscr{H}_F{}^n \subset \mathfrak{H}^n$ consisting of antisymmetric functions. The particles are called *bosons* in the first case and *fermions* in the second.

States of a system consisting of an indefinite number of particles are described by vectors of the space $\mathfrak{H}$, which is the direct sum of all $\mathfrak{H}^n$ and the one-dimensional space $\mathfrak{H}^0$ corresponding to the state from which the particle is absent.

1

A system consisting of an indefinite number of bosons is described by means of the subspace $\mathscr{H}_B \subset \mathfrak{H}$, where $\mathscr{H}_B = \sum_{n=0}^{\infty} \oplus \mathscr{H}_B^n$, $\mathscr{H}_B^0 = \mathfrak{H}^0$; a system consisting of an indefinite number of fermions is described by the subspace $\mathscr{H}_F \subset \mathfrak{H}$, where $\mathscr{H}_F = \sum_{n=0}^{\infty} \oplus \mathscr{H}_F^n$, $\mathscr{H}_F^0 = \mathfrak{H}^0$.

In what follows we shall deal mainly with the subspaces $\mathscr{H}_B$ and $\mathscr{H}_F$. Elements of these spaces describe states of real physical systems. Hence $\mathscr{H}_B$ and $\mathscr{H}_F$ are called *state spaces*.[1]

Vectors of the space $\mathfrak{H}$ are naturally written in the form of column vectors[2]:

$$\hat{\Phi} = \begin{pmatrix} K_0 \\ K_1(x) \\ K_2(x_1, x_2) \\ \vdots \\ K_n(x_1,\ldots, x_n) \\ \vdots \end{pmatrix},$$

(0.1)

$$(\hat{\Phi}, \hat{\Phi}) = |K_0|^2 + \sum_{n=1}^{\infty} \int |K_n(x_1,\ldots, x_n)|^2 \, d^n x.$$

In such a method of writing vectors whose components all vanish except for the $n$th form the subspace $\mathfrak{H}^n \subset \mathfrak{H}$.

Vectors belonging to the spaces $\mathscr{H}_B$ and $\mathscr{H}_F$, and the inner product in these spaces, are also given by formulas (0.1), but all the functions $K_n(x_1,\ldots, x_n)$ are symmetric in the first case and antisymmetric in the second.

Vectors for which all components, beginning with one, are equal to zero will be called *finite*. It is evident that finite vectors form a dense set in each of the three spaces $\mathfrak{H}$, $\mathscr{H}_B$, and $\mathscr{H}_F$.

Let $\hat{A}$ be an operator in the space $\mathfrak{H}$ such that its domain of definition contains everywhere-dense sets $\tilde{\mathfrak{H}}^n$ belonging to the subspace $\mathfrak{H}^n$. Evidently, the operator $\hat{A}$ allows the matrix representation

$$\hat{A} = \begin{pmatrix} A_{00} & A_{01} & A_{02} & \cdots \\ A_{10} & A_{11} & A_{12} & \cdots \\ A_{20} & A_{21} & A_{22} & \cdots \\ \cdots\cdots\cdots\cdots\cdots\cdots \end{pmatrix},$$

(0.2)

[1] For the reason which will be explained at the end of the next subsection, these spaces are sometimes also referred to as *occupation-number spaces*.

[2] Vectors and operators in the spaces $\mathfrak{H}$, $\mathscr{H}_B$, and $\mathscr{H}_F$ will be denoted by letters with a caret: $\hat{\Phi}$, $\hat{A}$, etc.

where $A_{ik}$ is an operator mapping $\tilde{\mathfrak{H}}^k$ into $\mathfrak{H}^i$. In particular, any bounded operator allows a matrix representation. The operation of an operator allowing a matrix representation on a vector $\hat{f} = \sum_k \hat{f}_k$, $\hat{f}_k \in \tilde{\mathfrak{H}}^k$, is defined by the natural formula: If $\hat{\Phi} = \hat{A}\hat{f} = \sum_k \hat{\Phi}_k$, $\hat{\Phi}_k \in \mathfrak{H}_k$, then

$$\hat{\Phi}_k = \sum_p A_{kp}\hat{f}_p; \qquad (0.3)$$

the product $\hat{C} = \hat{A}\hat{B}$ of such operators is defined by the formula[3]

$$C_{nk} = \sum_p A_{np}B_{pk}. \qquad (0.4)$$

The trace of $\hat{A}$, if it exists, is equal to

$$\operatorname{Sp} \hat{A} = \sum_k \operatorname{sp} A_{kk}. \qquad (0.5)$$

Since the spaces $\mathfrak{H}^n$ are realized by means of functions, the operators $A_{nk}$ can be provided by kernels which are, in general, generalized functions of $n + k$ variables[4]:

$$A_{nk} = A_{nk}(x_1,\ldots, x_n \,|\, y_1,\ldots, y_k). \qquad (0.6)$$

Furthermore, if

$$\hat{f}_p = \begin{pmatrix} 0 \\ \vdots \\ K_p(x_1,\ldots, x_p) \\ 0 \\ \vdots \end{pmatrix} \in \mathfrak{H}^p,$$

then

$$A_{np}\hat{f}_p = \int A_{np}(x_1,\ldots, x_n \,|\, y_1,\ldots, y_p)K_p(y_1,\ldots, y_p)\,d^p y. \qquad (0.7)$$

[3] Of course, the formula is correct under the condition that all the operators $A_{np}B_{pk}$ have meaning. This condition is *a fortiori* satisfied if the whole space $\mathfrak{H}^p$ is the domain of definition of $A_{np}$.

[4] We are not interested in the functional nature of the generalized functions $A_{nk}(x_1,\ldots, x_n \,|\, y_1,\ldots, y_k)$; these are only ways of expression which are effective when, by the use of them, some formula or argument can be made clearer. The same applies to all the other generalized functions encountered in the book.

The summands in formulas (0.4) and (0.5) take the form

$$A_{ni}B_{ik} = \int A_{ni}(x_1,\ldots, x_n | \xi_1,\ldots, \xi_i)$$

$$\times B_{ik}(\xi_1,\ldots, \xi_i | y_1,\ldots, y_k)\, d^i\xi, \tag{0.8}$$

$$\mathrm{sp}\, A_{kk} = \int A_{kk}(x_1,\ldots, x_k | x_1,\ldots, x_k)\, d^k x. \tag{0.9}$$

All that we have stated above on operators allowing a matrix representation may be transferred without any alteration to the spaces $\mathscr{H}_B$ and $\mathscr{H}_F$. When $\hat{A}$ is an operator in $\mathscr{H}_B$ or in $\mathscr{H}_F$, the kernel $A_{nk}(x_1,\ldots, x_n | y_1,\ldots, y_k)$ is not uniquely defined by the operator $A_{nk}$. Such a uniqueness, however, can be achieved if it is required that the function $A_{nk}(x_1,\ldots, x_n | y_1,\ldots, y_k)$ be symmetric with respect to $x_1,\ldots, x_n$ and $y_1,\ldots, y_k$, separately, in the first case, and antisymmetric in the second. In what follows, this requirement is always assumed to be satisfied.

2. GENERATING FUNCTIONALS. Let $\hat{\Phi} \in \mathscr{H}_B$ be of the form (0.1). We assign to the vector $\hat{\Phi}$ the functional

$$\Phi(a^*) = \sum_n \frac{1}{(n!)^{1/2}} \int K_n(x_1,\ldots, x_n)a^*(x_1) \cdots a^*(x_n)\, d^n x, \tag{0.10}$$

where $K_n(x_1,\ldots, x_n)$ are the same functions as in (0.1) and $a^*(x) \in L$. To each operator $\hat{A}$ in $\mathscr{H}_B$, which is given by a matrix of the form (0.2), we assign the functional

$$\tilde{A}(a^*, a) = \sum \frac{1}{(m!n!)^{1/2}} \int A_{mn}(x_1,\ldots, x_m | y_1,\ldots, y_n)$$

$$\times a^*(x_1) \cdots a^*(x_m)a(y_n) \cdots a(y_1)\, d^m x\, d^n y, \tag{0.11}$$

where $a(x) \in L$ and $a^*(x)$ is the complex-conjugate function to $a(x)$.

In the next section it will be proved that the series (0.10) and (0.11) converge. [Convergence of the series (0.11) will be proved under the assumption that $\|A\| < \infty$.]

It is shown that the functional (0.11) is very simply connected with the so-called normal form of the operator $\hat{A}$.

Knowing the functionals $\Phi(a^*)$ and $\tilde{A}(a^*, a)$, one can obviously reconstruct the vector $\hat{\Phi}$ and the operator $\hat{A}$.

In the Fermi case we shall also assign to vectors and operators functionals of the form (0.10) and (0.11). The difference is that, for fermions, $a(x)$ and $a^*(x)$ are not complex-valued functions, but serve as generators of a Grassmann algebra:

$$\{a(x), a(x')\} = \{a(x), a^*(x')\} = \{a^*(x), a^*(x')\} = 0.$$

($\{A, B\}$ is the abbreviation for the anticommutator $\{A, B\} = AB + BA$.) We shall sometimes refer to $a(x)$ and $a^*(x)$ as functions with anti-commuting values. The series (0.10) and (0.11) for fermions are formal. In spite of this, as we shall see later on, these are useful as the corresponding series for bosons.

The realization of the state spaces in the form of infinite tensor products is connected with the functionals (0.10).

We realize $L$ in the form of a space of sequences. In this case $x = 1, 2,\ldots, k,\ldots$ runs through the numbers of one-particle states, and $a^*(x) = a_k^*$. It is clear from (0.10) that for such a realization one can introduce in the space $\mathcal{H}_B$ an orthonormal basis of vectors $\hat{\Phi}_{n_1,n_2,\cdots}$, to which there correspond functionals of the form

$$\Phi_{n_1,n_2,\cdots, n_k,\cdots} = \frac{1}{(n_1!n_2! \cdots n_k! \cdots)^{1/2}} (a_1{}^*)^{n_1}(a_2{}^*)^{n_2} \cdots (a_k{}^*)^{n_k} \cdots, \quad (0.10')$$

where only a finite number of $n_k$'s are different from zero.

The vectors (0.10′) have a simple physical meaning: If a system is found in the state (0.10′), this means that $n_1$ particles are present in the state with number 1, $n_2$ particles are in the state with number 2, and so forth. The numbers $n_k$ are called *occupation numbers*.

One can also introduce a basis of the form (0.10′) in the space $\mathcal{H}_F$, and the numbers $n_k$ have the same meaning as in the Bose case. However, as $(a_k{}^*)^2 = 0$ for fermions, the vector $\hat{\Phi}_{n_1,n_2,\ldots,n_k,\cdots} \neq 0$ only if $n_k = 0$ or $n_k = 1$. This last situation is simply the expression of the Pauli principle: No more than one Fermi particle can be found in one state. The presence of bases of the form (0.10′) in the spaces $\mathcal{H}_B$ and $\mathcal{H}_F$ allows us to interpret these spaces as tensor products of an infinite number of Hilbert spaces $R_k$. ($R_k$ are infinite-dimensional Hilbert spaces for bosons, and two-dimensional spaces for fermions.)

We finally note that if the degree of freedom of a system (i.e., the dimension of the space $L$) is finite and equal to $N$, then $\mathcal{H}_B$ and $\mathcal{H}_F$

are tensor products of $N$ spaces $R_k$. (Evidently, the space $\mathcal{H}_F$ in this case is finite-dimensional, its dimension being equal to $2^N$.) The spaces $\mathcal{H}_B$ and $\mathcal{H}_F$ are very special examples of infinite tensor products. The general theory of infinite tensor products of Hilbert spaces was constructed by von Neumann [2].

3. HILBERT SPACE WITH INVOLUTION. In a Hilbert space describing the states of some kind of particle or a physical system, an involution is usually given.[5] A mapping $f \to f^*$ of the space onto itself is called an *involution* if it possesses the properties

(1) $(f^*)^* = f$,
(2) $(f_1 + f_2)^* = f_1{}^* + f_2{}^*$,
(3) $(\lambda f)^* = \bar{\lambda} f^*$     ($\lambda$ is a complex number),
(4) $(f_1, f_2) = (f_2{}^*, f_1{}^*)$.

Vectors are said to be *real* or *purely imaginary* if they satisfy, correspondingly, the condition $f = f^*$ or $f = -f^*$. The set of real vectors, and that of purely imaginary vectors as well, are real subspaces of the original Hilbert space.

If the Hilbert space is realized by means of square-integrable functions $f = f(x)$, for which $f^* = \bar{f}(x)$, where $\bar{f}(x)$ is the function complex conjugate to $f(x)$, then we say that such a realization is *concordant with involution*.

We shall always assume that the space $L$ used for the starting point to construct the spaces $\mathfrak{H}$, $\mathcal{H}_B$, and $\mathcal{H}_F$ is provided with an involution. The involution given in $L$ is carried over in a natural way into the spaces $\mathfrak{H}$, $\mathcal{H}_B$, and $\mathcal{H}_F$. [Let the realization of the space $L$ effective for the construction of the spaces be concordant with the involution and $\hat{\Phi} \in \mathfrak{H}$ with components $K_n(x_1, \ldots, x_n)$. Then $\hat{\Phi}^*$ has components $\bar{K}_n(x_1, \ldots, x_n)$.] We note some properties of the space $L$ connected with the involution:

(1) In $L$ there is a bilinear form

$$f_1 f_2 = (f_1, f_2{}^*). \tag{0.11}$$

Evidently, $(f_1, f_2) = f_1 f_2{}^*$.

---

[5] Commutability of the Hamiltonian and the involution implies the so-called *principle of detailed balance* (cf., for instance, Landau and Lifshitz [1]).

(2) In $L$ one can define complex-conjugate and transposed operators: The operator $\bar{A}$ defined by the equality $(Af)^* = \bar{A}f^*$ is said to be *complex conjugate* to $A$.

The operator $A' = \bar{A}^*$ is said to be the transpose of $A$. Evidently, $A^* = \bar{A}'$. ($A^*$ here and in what follows signifies the operator which is the hermitian conjugate of $A$.) An operator $A$ is called *real* or *symmetric*, respectively, if $A = \bar{A}$ or $A = A'$. The real operator can be differently defined as an operator transforming real vectors into real vectors.

(3) We define the right operation of an operator on a vector by the formula $gA = A'g$.

It is readily seen that the following relation holds:

$$(gA)f = g(Af). \tag{0.12}$$

Equation (0.12) coincides in form with the associative law in matrix algebra. Here $f$ plays the role of a one-column matrix and $g$ that of a one-row matrix.

It will often be necessary for us to deal with the Hilbert space $\mathscr{E}$ consisting of pairs $f = \binom{a_1}{a_2}$, $a_1, a_2 \in L$, $(f,f) = (a_1, a_1) + (a_2, a_2)$. As a rule we shall be interested in the case when $a_2 = a_1{}^*$. In this connection we shall sometimes write $\mathscr{E} = L \oplus L^*$.

Operators in the space $\mathscr{E}$ are naturally written in terms of matrices $\mathscr{A} = \binom{A_{11}\ \ A_{12}}{A_{21}\ \ A_{22}}$, where $A_{ik}$ are operators in $L$. Every operator $\mathscr{A}$ in $\mathscr{E}$ generates a bilinear form which is conveniently written in the matrix form:

$$(a_1\ a_2) \begin{pmatrix} A_{11} & A_{12} \\ A_{21} & A_{22} \end{pmatrix} \begin{pmatrix} b_1 \\ b_2 \end{pmatrix} = a_1 A_{11} b_1 + a_1 A_{12} b_2 + a_2 A_{21} b_1 + a_2 A_{22} b_2. \tag{0.13}$$

We shall frequently encounter Fredholm determinants of operators in $\mathscr{E}$ which are regularized in a definite way. We give the corresponding definition.

Consider a monotonic sequence of orthogonal projection operators $P(n)$ onto complex $n$-dimensional subspaces in $L$, and suppose the sequence converges strongly to the identity operator. We put in correspondence to each operator $P(n)$ the projection operator $\mathscr{P}(n)$ in $\mathscr{E}$: $\mathscr{P}(n) = \binom{P(n)\ \ 0}{0\ \ \bar{P}(n)}$, where $\bar{P}(n)$ is the operator complex conjugate to $P(n)$. Denote the subspace $\mathscr{P}(n)\mathscr{E}$ by $\mathscr{E}_n$.

Let $\mathscr{A}$ be an arbitrary bounded operator in $\mathscr{E}$. We denote by $\mathscr{A}_n$ the operator $\mathscr{P}(n)\mathscr{A}\mathscr{P}(n)$ which is bounded on $\mathscr{E}_n$.

We shall call the limit det $\mathscr{A} = \lim_{n \to \infty}$ det $\mathscr{A}_n$ a *regularized Fredholm determinant* of the operator $\mathscr{A}$ or simply a *determinant* of $\mathscr{A}$, if this limit exists and does not depend on the choice of the sequence $\{P(n)\}$. Evidently, if $\mathscr{A} - E$ is a trace-class operator,[6] det $\mathscr{A}$ coincides with the Fredholm determinant of $\mathscr{A}$. However, det $\mathscr{A}$ can exist even if $\mathscr{A} - E$ is not a trace-class operator, and so the Fredholm determinant of $\mathscr{A}$ in the usual sense does not exist. We mention without proof two such cases which we shall meet in the sequel.

(1) $\mathscr{A} = \begin{pmatrix} A_{11} & A_{12} \\ A_{21} & A_{22} \end{pmatrix}$, where $A_{11} - E$, $A_{22} - E$ are trace-class operators and $A_{12}$, $A_{21}$ are Hilbert-Schmidt operators.[7]

(2) $\mathscr{A} = \begin{pmatrix} 0 & E \\ -E & 0 \end{pmatrix}$. In this case det $\mathscr{A} = 1$.

In closing this subsection we shall prove the following theorem.

**Theorem 0.1.** *Let A be a self-adjoint operator in a Hilbert space L with involution. Then there exists in L a unitary operator U such that $UAU^{-1}$ is a real operator.*

According to Hellinger's theorem on spectral types (cf., for example, the article by Plessner and Rohlin [1]), the space $L$ is realizable in the form of vector functions of a real variable such that $f(x) = (f_1(x), f_2(x), \ldots)$, $(f, f) = \sum_k \int |f_k(x)|^2 \, d\sigma_k$, $Af = xf(x)$. We denote by $R_A$ the space of real vector functions.

Consider the operator $U$ which induces a one-to-one isometric mapping of $R_A$ onto the space of real vectors $R \subset L$. We extend this operator to a unitary operator in the whole space by putting $\dot{U}i\xi = iU\xi$, $\xi \in R_A$. It is evident that the space $R$ is invariant with respect to $UAU^{-1}$, and accordingly the operator $U$ has the required property.

---

[6] An operator $A$ is said to be a trace-class operator or an operator with absolutely convergent trace if $\sum |(A\xi_i, \xi_i)| < \infty$ whatever orthonormal basis $\{\xi_i\}$ may be chosen. If $A$ is a trace-class operator and $\lambda_p$ are its eigenvalues, then $\sum |\lambda_p| < \infty$, and $\sum (A\xi_i, \xi_i) - \sum \lambda_p =$ Sp $A$ for every orthonormal basis $\{\xi_i\}$.

In order that an operator $E + A$ should have a Fredholm determinant, it is necessary and sufficient that the operator $A$ should be a trace-class operator. (For details on trace-class operators, cf. the books by Gel'fand and Vilenkin [1] and by Dunford and Schwartz [1].)

[7] $A$ is called a Hilbert-Schmidt operator if $AA^*$ is a trace-class operator. If the space is realized as a space of square-integrable functions, then Hilbert-Schmidt operators are given by kernels which are square-integrable as functions of two variables. In that case, if the kernel $A(x, y)$ corresponds to the operator $A$, then Sp $AA^* = \int |A(x, y)|^2 \, dx \, dy$ (cf. Dunford and Schwartz [1]).

*Chapter I*

# Generating Functionals

In Section 1 of this chapter creation and annihilation operators are introduced; they play a fundamental role in the method of second quantization. These operators are generators in the algebra of all operators in the state space. With their aid one can write down, in the form of functionals, vectors of the state space and a definite class of operators therein (so-called *operators representable in the normal form*).

Sections 2 and 3 are devoted to the operations on functionals; for each pair of functionals corresponding to the operators, there is a functional corresponding to their product, and so forth.

In Section 2 these problems are solved for bosons, and in Section 3 for fermions.

## 1. Creation and Annihilation Operators. Generating Functionals

1. OPERATOR-GENERALIZED FUNCTIONS. In the method of second quantization an important role is played by operator-generalized functions. In this connection we shall give the general definition.

Let $L$ be a Hilbert space with involution *. We assign to each $f \in L$ an operator $B(f)$ in a Hilbert space $H$.

The function $B(f)$ is called an *operator linear functional* on $L$ if it satisfies the following conditions:

(1) Operators $B(f)$ are defined on a dense domain $D \subset H$ common to all of them.

(2) $B(\alpha_1 f_1 + \alpha_2 f_2) = \alpha_1 B(f_1) + \alpha_2 B(f_2)$ for all complex numbers $\alpha_1, \alpha_2$.

An operator linear functional $B^*(f)$ is said to be *adjoint* to $B(f)$ if $(B(f)\xi, \eta) = (\xi, B^*(f^*)\eta)$ for every $\xi \in D$, $\eta \in D^*$ [$D^* \subset H$ is a dense set on which all the operators $B^*(f)$ are defined].

If the space $L$ consists of functions on a set $M$ provided with a measure, then operator functionals on $L$ are naturally written in the symbolic form $B(f) = \int B(x)f(x)\, dx$ ($x \in M$, $dx$ is the differential of the measure on $M$). $B(x)$ will be called an *operator-generalized function*.

If operator functionals $B(f)$ and $B^*(f)$ are adjoint, the corresponding generalized functions $B(x)$ and $B^*(x)$ will be called *adjoint*.

2. CREATION AND ANNIHILATION OPERATORS. Consider the spaces $\mathfrak{H}$, $\mathscr{H}_B$, and $\mathscr{H}_F$ described in the Introduction, Subsection 1.

Consider the matrices consisting of generalized functions

$$\hat{a}(\xi) = \begin{pmatrix} 0 & \delta(y, \xi) & 0 & 0 & \cdots \\ 0 & 0 & \sqrt{2}\,\delta(x_1, y_1)\delta(y_2, \xi) & 0 & \cdots \\ 0 & 0 & 0 & \sqrt{3}\,\delta(x_1, y_1)\delta(x_2, y_2)\delta(y_3, \xi) & \cdots \\ & & & & \end{pmatrix},$$

$$(1.1)$$

$$\hat{a}^*(\xi) = \begin{pmatrix} 0 & 0 & 0 & \cdots \\ \delta(x, \xi) & 0 & 0 & \cdots \\ 0 & \sqrt{2}\,\delta(x_1, y_1)\delta(x_2, \xi) & 0 & \cdots \\ 0 & 0 & \sqrt{3}\,\delta(x_1, y_1)\delta(x_2, y_2)\delta(x_3, \xi) & \cdots \\ & & & \end{pmatrix},$$

where $\delta(\xi, \eta)$ is Dirac's $\delta$ function.

It is not difficult to see that if $f(\xi)$ is a square-integrable function, then

$$\hat{a}(f) = \int \hat{a}(\xi)f(\xi)\, d\xi, \qquad \hat{a}^*(f) = \int \hat{a}^*(\xi)f(\xi)\, d\xi$$

are operators in $\mathfrak{H}$, whose domain of definition contains the set of all finite vectors.

Thus the matrices $\hat{a}(\xi)$ and $\hat{a}^*(\xi)$ are operator-generalized functions on the Hilbert space of square-integrable functions. In the space $L$ there is a natural involution comprising the passage to the complex-conjugate function.

It can be readily seen that $\hat{a}(\xi)$ and $\hat{a}^*(\xi)$ are operator-generalized functions adjoint to each other.[1]

We denote by $P_B$ and $P_F$ the projection operators from $\mathfrak{H}$ onto the subspaces $\mathscr{H}_B$ and $\mathscr{H}_F$, respectively.

Let us consider in the spaces $\mathscr{H}_B$ and $\mathscr{H}_F$ the operators

$$\hat{a}_B(f) = P_B\hat{a}(f)P_B, \qquad \hat{a}_B^*(f) = P_B\hat{a}^*(f)P_B,$$
$$\hat{a}_F(f) = P_F\hat{a}(f)P_F, \qquad \hat{a}_F^*(f) = P_F\hat{a}^*(f)P_F. \tag{1.2}$$

The operators $\hat{a}_B(f)$ and $\hat{a}_F(f)$ are called *annihilation operators* of Bose (correspondingly, Fermi) particles, and the operators $\hat{a}_B^*(f)$, $\hat{a}_F^*(f)$ are called *creation operators* of Bose (correspondingly, Fermi) particles.

It is not difficult to see that all these operators are defined on finite vectors and in addition that the operator functionals $\hat{a}_B(f)$ and $\hat{a}_B^*(f)$, as well as $\hat{a}_F(f)$ and $\hat{a}_F^*(f)$, are conjugate to each other.

By the use of formulas (1.1) and (1.2) we easily find that the following relations hold for the operators $\hat{a}_B(f)$, $\hat{a}_B^*(f)$, $\hat{a}_F(f)$, and $\hat{a}_F^*(f)$,

$$[\hat{a}_B(f_1), \hat{a}_B(f_2)] = [\hat{a}_B^*(f_1), \hat{a}_B^*(f_2)] = 0,$$
$$[\hat{a}_B(f_1), \hat{a}_B^*(f_2)] = (f_1, f_2^*), \tag{1.3}$$

$$\{\hat{a}_F(f_1), \hat{a}_F(f_2)\} = \{\hat{a}_F^*(f_1), \hat{a}_F^*(f_2)\} = 0,$$
$$\{\hat{a}_F(f_1), \hat{a}^*(f_2)\} = (f_1, f_2^*). \tag{1.4}$$

---

[1] We turn our attention to the fact that if the measure of every isolated point in $M$ is equal to zero, then $\hat{a}^*(\xi)$ is not an operator; no matter how one may formally apply $\hat{a}^*(\xi)$ to a vector $\Phi \neq 0$, it is impossible to obtain an element of the Hilbert space. On the contrary, $\hat{a}(\xi)$ is an operator, and in any case the vector

$$\begin{pmatrix} 1 \\ 0 \\ 0 \\ \vdots \end{pmatrix}$$

is contained in its domain of definition.

It is not difficult to show that the domain of definition of $\hat{a}(\xi)$ is indeed dense. Thus in this case $\hat{a}(\xi)$ supplies an example of the operator which does not have an adjoint operator.

On the contrary, when the measure of a point $\xi \in M$ is finite, $\hat{a}^*(\xi)$ is an operator adjoint to $\hat{a}(\xi)$. It should be remarked that in both cases one can associate with $\hat{a}^*(\xi)$ a bilinear form, whose domain of definition coincides with that of $\hat{a}(\xi)$: $(\hat{a}^*(\xi)\hat{\Phi}, \hat{\Psi}) = (\hat{\Phi}, \hat{a}(\xi)\hat{\Psi})$.

All that we have stated applies also to the operator-generalized functions $\hat{a}_B(\xi)$, $\hat{a}_B^*(\xi)$, $\hat{a}_F(\xi)$, and $\hat{a}_F^*(\xi)$ defined below.

Here, as everywhere in the sequel, $[A, B] = AB - BA$ is the commutator of operators $A$ and $B$, whereas $\{A, B\} = AB + BA$ is the anticommutator of operators $A$ and $B$.

If one passes from operator functionals to operator-generalized functions, it is evident that relations (1.3) and (1.4) are replaced by

$$[\hat{a}_B(\xi), \hat{a}_B(\eta)] = [\hat{a}_B^*(\xi), \hat{a}_B^*(\eta)] = 0,$$

$$[\hat{a}_B(\xi), \hat{a}_B^*(\eta)] = \delta(\xi, \eta),$$

(1.3′)

$$\{\hat{a}_F(\xi), \hat{a}_F(\eta)\} = \{\hat{a}_F^*(\xi), \hat{a}_F^*(\eta)\} = 0,$$

$$\{\hat{a}_F(\xi), \hat{a}_F^*(\eta)\} = \delta(\xi, \eta).$$

(1.4′)

where $\delta(\xi, \eta)$ is Dirac's $\delta$ function.

Relations (1.3), (1.4) and (1.3′), (1.4′) are called *commutation relations*.

Let a vector $\hat{\Phi} \in \mathcal{H}_B$ describe the state of a system in which just $n$ particles are present,

$$\hat{\Phi} = \begin{pmatrix} 0 \\ 0 \\ \vdots \\ \Phi_n(x_1 \cdots x_n) \\ 0 \\ \vdots \end{pmatrix}$$

It is not difficult to see that the operator $\hat{a}_B^*(f)$ carries over the system from the state $\hat{\Phi}$ to the state in which there are $n + 1$ particles (creating a particle), whereas the operator $\hat{a}_B(f)$ carries over to the state in which there are $n - 1$ particles (annihilating a particle). The operators $\hat{a}_F$, $\hat{a}_F^*$ have analogous properties. It is this property that gives the operators $\hat{a}_B(f)$, $\hat{a}_B^*(f)$, $\hat{a}_F(f)$, and $\hat{a}_F^*(f)$ their names.

3. WRITING VECTORS IN TERMS OF CREATION OPERATORS. Let us consider in the space $\mathcal{H}_B$ the vector

$$\hat{\Phi}_0 = \begin{pmatrix} 1 \\ 0 \\ 0 \\ \vdots \end{pmatrix}$$

It is easy to see that this vector is annihilated by any one of the operators $\hat{a}_B(f)$, and moreover that it is the unique solution, up to a multiplier, of the equations $\hat{a}_B(f)\hat{\Phi} = 0$ for all $f$. Conversely, by applying operators $\hat{a}_B{}^*(f)$ to $\hat{\Phi}_0$, one can obtain any vector of the Hilbert space:

$$\hat{\Phi} = \begin{pmatrix} K_0 \\ K_1(x_1) \\ K_2(x_1, x_2) \\ \vdots \end{pmatrix}$$

$$= \sum_{n=0}^{\infty} \frac{1}{(n!)^{1/2}} \int K_n(x_1, \ldots, x_n) \hat{a}_B{}^*(x_1) \cdots \hat{a}_B{}^*(x_n) \, d^n x \, \hat{\Phi}_0 . \qquad (1.5)$$

A similar formula is valid for fermions. We again stress that the functions $K_n(x_1, \ldots, x_n)$ are symmetric for bosons and antisymmetric for fermions.

The vector $\hat{\Phi}_0$ describes the state of the system in which no particle is present. It is called the *vacuum vector*.

Creation operators, as distinguished from annihilation operators, generally do not carry over vectors into the zero vector. More precisely, we have the statements:

If a vector $\hat{\Phi} \in \mathcal{H}_B$ satisfies the equations $\hat{a}_B{}^*(f)\hat{\Phi} = 0$ for all $f \in L$, then $\hat{\Phi} = 0$.

If a vector $\hat{\Phi} \in \mathcal{H}_F$, $\hat{\Phi} \neq 0$, satisfies the equations $\hat{a}_F{}^*(f)\hat{\Phi} = 0$ for all $f \in L$, then the space $L$ is finite-dimensional.

The proofs of both statements are very simple, so we shall not discuss them.

### 4. DOMAIN OF DEFINITION OF CREATION AND ANNIHILATION OPERATORS.

We have seen above that the set of finite vectors is contained in the domain of definition of creation operators for bosons, as well as for fermions. We begin with the Fermi case.

**Theorem 1.1.** *Operators $\hat{a}_F(f)$ and $\hat{a}_F{}^*(f)$ are bounded.*

Let $f \in L$, $(f, f) = 1$. Consider the operators

$$\hat{P} = \hat{a}_F(f)\hat{a}_F{}^*(f^*), \qquad \hat{Q} = \hat{a}_F{}^*(f)\hat{a}_F(f^*). \qquad (1.6)$$

The operators $\hat{P}$ and $\hat{Q}$ are defined and symmetric on a dense set of finite vectors. Further, it follows from the commutation relations (1.4) that

$$\hat{P}^2 = \hat{P}, \qquad \hat{Q}^2 = \hat{Q}, \qquad \hat{P} + \hat{Q} = E. \qquad (1.7)$$

Let $\hat{f}$ be a finite vector. According to (1.7), $(\hat{P}\hat{f}, \hat{P}\hat{f}) + (\hat{Q}\hat{f}, \hat{Q}\hat{f}) = (\hat{f},\hat{f})$. Consequently, $(\hat{P}\hat{f}, \hat{P}\hat{f}) \leq (\hat{f},\hat{f})$ and $(\hat{Q}\hat{f}, \hat{Q}\hat{f}) \leq (\hat{f},\hat{f})$. Since finite vectors form a dense set, we have $\|\hat{P}\| \leq 1$, $\|\hat{Q}\| \leq 1$. Hence it follows that $\|\hat{a}_F(f)\| \leq 1$, $\|\hat{a}_F^*(f)\| \leq 1$.

Finally we remark that from the symmetry of the operators $\hat{P}$ and $\hat{Q}$, and from equations (1.7), it follows, besides the boundedness of $\hat{P}$ and $\hat{Q}$, that $\hat{P}$ and $\hat{Q}$ are operators of orthogonal projection.

From the proof of the theorem there evidently follows

**Corollary 1.1.** (1) *The operators $\hat{a}_F(f)$ and $\hat{a}_F^*(f^*)$ are adjoint to each other.*

(2) *The operators $\hat{\mathscr{P}}(f) = (\hat{a}_F(f) + \hat{a}_F^*(f^*))$ and $\hat{\mathscr{Q}}(f) = (1/i)(\hat{a}_F(f) - \hat{a}_F^*(f^*))$ are self-adjoint.*

We now pass to the Bose case.

Consider, on the set of finite vectors in $\mathscr{H}_B$, the operators $\hat{\mathscr{Q}}(f) = (a_B(f) + a_B^*(f^*))/\sqrt{2}$ and $\hat{\mathscr{P}}(f) = (\hat{a}_B(f) - a_B^*(f^*))/i\sqrt{2}$. Evidently these operators are symmetric.[2] We prove the following theorem:

[2] If $\|f\| = 1$, the operators $\hat{\mathscr{P}}(f)$ and $\hat{\mathscr{Q}}(f)$ satisfy the commutation relations characteristic of momentum and coordinate operators in ordinary quantum mechanics, namely, in the units in which Planck's constant $\hbar = 1$, we have

$$|\hat{\mathscr{P}}(f), \hat{\mathscr{Q}}(f)| = \frac{1}{i}.$$

Without effort we can show that in the case when the degrees of freedom are finite (equal to $N$) the space $\mathscr{H}_B$ is realizable as the space of square-integrable functions of $N$ real variables in such a way that

$$\hat{a}_n = \frac{1}{\sqrt{2}}\left(x_n + \frac{\partial}{\partial x_n}\right), \qquad \hat{a}_n^* = \frac{1}{\sqrt{2}}\left(x_n - \frac{\partial}{\partial x_n}\right)$$

$[\hat{a}_n = \hat{a}(f_n)$ and $\{f_n\}$ is an orthonormal basis in $L]$. To the vacuum vector in such an interpretation there corresponds the vector

$$\Phi_0 = \frac{1}{\pi^{n/4}} \exp\left(-\frac{1}{2}\sum_1^N x_n^2\right),$$

and the following relations hold:

$$\hat{\mathscr{Q}}_n f = x_n f, \qquad \hat{\mathscr{P}}_n f = \frac{1}{i}\frac{\partial}{\partial x_n} f.$$

i.e., $\hat{\mathscr{Q}}_n$ and $\hat{\mathscr{P}}_n$ are coordinate and momentum operators in ordinary quantum mechanics (cf., for instance, the book by Landau and Lifshitz [1], p. 94 (English transl., Pergamon Press, p. 67), or Bargmann [2]).

**Theorem 1.2.** *The operators $\hat{\mathscr{P}}(f)$ and $\hat{\mathscr{Q}}(f)$ have the deficiency indices $(0, 0)$.*

**Proof.** Let $z$, $\operatorname{Im} z \neq 0$, be a complex number. Let us show that if a vector $\hat{\Phi} \in \mathscr{H}_B$ satisfies the equations

$$((\hat{\mathscr{P}}(f) - z)\hat{F}, \hat{\Phi}) = 0, \tag{1.8}$$

where $\hat{F}$ is an arbitrary finite vector, then $\hat{\Phi} = 0$.

Without loss of generality we may assume that $\|f\| = 1$.

Consider in the space $L$ the subspace $L_f$ consisting of elements orthogonal to $f$. We denote by $\mathscr{H}_f$ the subspace of $\mathscr{H}_B$, which is generated by vectors $\hat{a}_B^*(f_1) \cdots \hat{a}_B^*(f_n)\hat{\Phi}_0$, where $f_k \in L_f$ and $0 \leq n < \infty$. Elements of $\mathscr{H}_f$ have the obvious property: If $\hat{F} \in \mathscr{H}_f$, then $\hat{a}_B(f)\hat{F} = 0$.

We consider in $\mathscr{H}_f$ an orthonormal basis $\{\hat{F}_k\}$ consisting of finite vectors. By applying operators $\hat{a}_B^*(f)$ to $\hat{F}_k$, we obtain the subspace $\mathscr{H}_k$ consisting of vectors of the form

$$\hat{\Phi} = \sum_{n=0}^{\infty} \frac{c_n}{\sqrt{n!}} (\hat{a}_B^*(f))^n \hat{F}_k. \tag{1.9}$$

From the commutation relations it follows immediately that

$$(\hat{\Phi}, \hat{\Phi}) = \sum_n |c_n|^2 < \infty. \tag{1.9'}$$

Evidently, all $\mathscr{H}_k$ are orthogonal to each other and amount to giving $\mathscr{H}_B$.[3]

Suppose a vector $\hat{\Phi}$ satisfies equation (1.8). Denote by $\hat{\Phi}_k$ the projection of $\hat{\Phi}$ on $\mathscr{H}_k$. We shall show that $\hat{\Phi}_k = 0$. Let $\hat{\Phi}_k = \sum_n (c_n/\sqrt{n!}) (\hat{a}_B^*(f))^n \hat{F}_k$. Put $\hat{\Phi}_k$ in (1.8) and take as $\hat{F}$ the sequence $\hat{F}_k$, $\hat{a}_B^*(f) \hat{F}_k$, $(\hat{a}_B^*(f))^2 \hat{F}_k$, and so on. Then we obtain the recursion formula to determine $c_n$:

$$(n + 1)^{1/2} c_{n+1} + \sqrt{n}\, c_{n-1} = z c_n. \tag{1.10}$$

The coefficients of relations (1.10) form a symmetric Jacobi matrix, for which the sum of inverses of the side elements is equal to $\sum_n (1/\sqrt{n})$ $= \infty$. Therefore, by virtue of the well-known theorem of Carleman,[4] relation (1.10) is consistent with (1.9') only if $c_n = 0$.

---

[3] It is readily verified that $\mathscr{H}_B$ is a tensor product of $\mathscr{H}_f$ by any one of $\mathscr{H}_k$.

[4] Cf. Carleman [1]. The proof of this theorem in the Russian language is found in an article by Ahiezer [1].

Thus $\hat{\Phi}_k = 0$. Since clearly $\hat{\Phi} = \sum_k \hat{\Phi}_k$, we have $\hat{\Phi} = 0$. The theorem is proved.

The set of finite vectors may be included in a wider set, on which all $\hat{a}_B(f)$, $\hat{a}_B^*(f)$ are defined.

We consider the operator

$$\hat{N} = \int \hat{a}_B^*(x)\hat{a}_B(x)\, dx. \tag{1.11}$$

The operator $\hat{N}$ is called the *number operator of particles*, since a state with a fixed number of particles is an eigenstate of $\hat{N}$: If

$$\hat{\Phi} = \begin{pmatrix} 0 \\ \vdots \\ \Phi_n(x_1, \ldots, x_n) \\ \vdots \\ 0 \end{pmatrix},$$

then $\hat{N}\hat{\Phi} = n\hat{\Phi}$ (this property of the operator $\hat{N}$ follows from the commutation relations).

It is not difficult to see that the set of vectors $\hat{\Phi}$ having the property

$$(\hat{\Phi}, \hat{N}\hat{\Phi}) < \infty \tag{1.12}$$

is contained in the domain of definition of the operators $\hat{a}_B(f)$, $\hat{a}_B^*(f)$ for all $f \in L$. It would be interesting to know whether this set is the maximal common domain of definition of the operators $\hat{a}_B(f)$, $\hat{a}_B^*(f)$ for all $f$.

5. OPERATORS COMMUTING WITH CREATION AND ANNIHILATION OPERATORS. We shall find the general form of the operator in the spaces $\mathscr{H}_B$ and $\mathscr{H}_F$ commuting, respectively, with all operators $\hat{a}_B(f)$, $\hat{a}_B^*(f)$ or $\hat{a}_F(f)$, $\hat{a}_F^*(f)$. Recall that operators $\hat{B}$ and $\hat{C}$ commute if every vector $\hat{\Phi}$ entering the domain of definition of $\hat{B}\hat{C}$ enters also into the domain of definition of $\hat{C}\hat{B}$, and, moreover, $\hat{B}\hat{C}\hat{\Phi} = \hat{C}\hat{B}\hat{\Phi}$.

**Theorem 1.3.** (1) *Every closed operator in the space $\mathscr{H}_B$ which commutes with all operators $\hat{a}_B(f)$, $\hat{a}_B^*(f)$, and is defined on the vacuum vector, is a multiple of the identity.*

(2) *Every closed operator in the space $\mathscr{H}_F$, which commutes with all operators $\hat{a}_F(f)$, $\hat{a}_F^*(f)$ and is defined on the vacuum vector, is a multiple of the identity.*

The proof of both assertions is identical, so we shall confine ourselves to the case of the space $\mathcal{H}_B$. Let $\hat{A}$ be an operator commuting with all operators $\hat{a}_B(f)$ and $\hat{a}_B{}^*(f)$. Let $\hat{\Phi}_0$ be the vacuum vector. Since $\hat{a}_B(f) \hat{\Phi}_0 = 0$, we have $\hat{a}_B(f)\hat{A}\hat{\Phi}_0 = \hat{A}\hat{a}_B(f)\hat{\Phi}_0 = 0$. Further, since $\hat{\Phi}_0$ is the unique solution of the equations $\hat{a}_B(f)\hat{\Phi} = 0$ for all $f$, we have $\hat{A}\hat{\Phi}_0 = \alpha\hat{\Phi}_0$, where $\alpha$ is a number.

We now remark that the vector $\hat{\Phi}_0$ is in the domain of definition of the operator $\hat{A}\hat{a}_B{}^*(f)$ [this follows from the commutability of $\hat{A}$ and $\hat{a}_B{}^*(f)$ and the fact that $\hat{\Phi}_0$ is in the domain of definition of $\hat{a}_B{}^*(f)\hat{A}$]. Consequently, the vector $\hat{a}_B{}^*(f)\hat{\Phi}_0$ enters into the domain of definition of the operator $\hat{A}$.

We apply the operator $\hat{A}$ to $\hat{a}_B{}^*(f)\hat{\Phi}_0$:

$$\hat{A}\hat{a}_B{}^*(f)\hat{\Phi}_0 = \hat{a}_B{}^*(f)\hat{A}\hat{\Phi}_0 = \alpha\hat{a}_B{}^*(f)\hat{\Phi}_0. \tag{1.13}$$

Continuing this reasoning further, we find that whatever the functions $f_1, \ldots, f_n$ may be, the vector $\hat{a}_B{}^*(f_1) \cdots \hat{a}_B{}^*(f_n)\hat{\Phi}_0$ is an eigenvector for $\hat{A}$ with eigenvalue $\alpha$.

Evidently linear combinations of such vectors $\hat{a}_B{}^*(f_1) \cdots \hat{a}_B{}^*(f_n)\hat{\Phi}_0$ for all possible $f_n$ and $n$ form a dense set in $\mathcal{H}_B$ [cf. (1.5)]. Thus the operator $\hat{A}$ is a multiple of the identity on an everywhere-dense set. The fact that $\hat{A}$ is closed implies that it is a multiple of the identity operator in the whole $\mathcal{H}_B$.

There follows from the proof of the theorem a series of important corollaries.

**Corollary 1.2.** *Every bounded operator commuting with all $\hat{a}_B(f)$, $\hat{a}_B{}^*(f)$ is a multiple of the identity.*

In fact, every bounded operator is defined on the vacuum vector.

Consider the set $\tilde{\mathcal{H}}_B$ of finite vectors. It is evident that all possible products of operators $\hat{a}_B(f)$, $\hat{a}_B{}^*(f)$ for different $f$, and sums of these products are defined on $\tilde{\mathcal{H}}_B$. Thus the operators $\hat{a}_B(f)$, $\hat{a}_B{}^*(f)$ generate on $\tilde{\mathcal{H}}_B$ a ring of operators. We denote this ring by $\mathfrak{A}$. We shall say that a sequence of operators $\hat{C}_n$ *converges weakly* to $\hat{C}$ on $\tilde{\mathcal{H}}_B$, if $(\hat{C}_n\hat{f}, \hat{g}) \to (\hat{C}\hat{f}, \hat{g})$ holds for every $\hat{f}, \hat{g} \in \tilde{\mathcal{H}}_B$. The set of operators which are limits in this sense of a sequence of operators from $\mathfrak{A}$ is called the *weak closure* of the ring $\mathfrak{A}$.

**Corollary 1.3.** *All bounded operators are contained in the weak closure of $\mathfrak{A}$.*

According to Theorem 1.2 the operators $\hat{a}_B(f) + \hat{a}_B{}^*(f^*)$ and $i(\hat{a}_B(f)$ $- \hat{a}_B{}^*(f^*))$ have zero deficiency indices. Therefore the operators $\hat{b}_1(s, f)$ $= \exp is(\hat{a}_B(f) + \hat{a}_B{}^*(f^*))$ and $\hat{b}_2(s, f) = \exp s(\hat{a}_B(f) - \hat{a}_B{}^*(f^*))$, where $s$ is a real number, are unitary and are accordingly bounded. Evidently, any bounded operator commuting with all $\hat{b}_1(s, f)$ and $\hat{b}_2(s, f)$ commutes also with $\hat{a}_B(f)$ and $\hat{a}_B{}^*(f)$, and so it is a multiple of the identity.

Consider the ring $\mathfrak{B}$ generated by the operators $\hat{b}_1(s, f)$ and $\hat{b}_2(s, f)$. Since any bounded operator commuting with all elements of $\mathfrak{B}$ is a multiple of the identity, the weak closure of $\mathfrak{B}$ coincides with the set of all operators in $\mathcal{H}_B$ by virtue of a well-known theorem of functional analysis.[5]

On the other hand, it is easy to see that the ring $\mathfrak{B}$ lies in the weak closure of the ring $\mathfrak{A}$. The corollary is thus proved.

Let $\mathcal{H}_1$ be a subspace of $\mathcal{H}_B$. We shall say that $\mathcal{H}_1$ is *invariant with respect to operators* $\hat{a}_B(f), \hat{a}_B{}^*(f)$, if (1) from the fact that an element $\hat{\Phi}$ belongs to $D \cap \mathcal{H}_1$, where $D$ is the common domain of definition of $\hat{a}_B(f)$ and $\hat{a}_B{}^*(f)$, it follows that $\hat{a}_B(f)\hat{\Phi} \in \mathcal{H}_1$, $\hat{a}_B{}^*(f)\hat{\Phi} \in \mathcal{H}_1$, and if (2) the symmetric operators $\hat{a}_B(f) + \hat{a}_B{}^*(f^*)$ and $i(\hat{a}_B(f) - \hat{a}_B{}^*(f^*))$ with the domain of definition $D \cap \mathcal{H}_1$ have zero deficiency indices as operators in $\mathcal{H}_1$.

**Corollary 1.4.** *The family of operators* $\hat{a}_B(f), \hat{a}_B{}^*(f)$ *are irreducible in the sense that there does not exist a proper subspace* $\mathcal{H}_1 \subset \mathcal{H}_B$ *invariant with respect to all* $\hat{a}_B(f), \hat{a}_B{}^*(f)$.

In fact, the subspace $\mathcal{H}_1$ invariant with respect to all $\hat{a}_B(f), \hat{a}_B{}^*(f)$ is evidently invariant with respect to the ring $\mathfrak{B}$ constructed in the course of the proof of Corollary 1.3. $\mathfrak{B}$ is a ring of bounded operators in which, along with every operator, its adjoint is contained. Therefore the orthogonal complement of $\mathcal{H}_1$ is also invariant with respect to $\mathfrak{B}$. Consequently, the operator $\hat{P}$ of orthogonal projection onto $\mathcal{H}_1$ commutes with all elements of $\mathfrak{B}$, and hence $\hat{P} = \lambda E$, which implies that either $\hat{P} = 0$ or $\hat{P} = E$.

Corollaries 1.2 through 1.4 all remain valid for fermions.

In this case, since the operators $\hat{a}_F(f)$ and $\hat{a}_F{}^*(f)$ are bounded, the ring $\mathfrak{A}$ participating in the formulation of the corollary may be under-

[5] Cf. Naimark's book [1].

stood simply as a ring of bounded operators generated by $\hat{a}_F(f)$, $\hat{a}_F{}^*(f)$, and the weak closure is to be understood in the usual sense.

It should also be remarked that if a subspace $\mathscr{H}_1 \subset \mathscr{H}_F$ is invariant with respect to $\hat{a}_F(f), \hat{a}_F{}^*(f)$, then the restrictions of the operators $\hat{a}_F(f) + \hat{a}_F{}^*(f^*)$ and $i(\hat{a}_F(f) - \hat{a}_F{}^*(f^*))$ on $\mathscr{H}_1$ are self-adjoint operators in $\mathscr{H}_1$. Therefore requirement (2) in the definition of an invariant space is fulfilled automatically.

6. REMARKS ON THE COMMUTATION RELATIONS. We shall prove the following important theorem.

**Theorem 1.4.** *Let $L$ be a Hilbert space with involution, and $\alpha(f)$ and $\alpha^*(f)$ be operator functionals on $L$ which are adjoint to each other and are defined in a Hilbert space $H$. Suppose the operators $\alpha(f), \alpha^*(f)$ satisfy the following conditions:*

(1) *In $H$ there does not exist a proper subspace invariant[6] with respect to all $\alpha(f), \alpha^*(f)$.*

(2) *In $H$ there exists a vector $\mathscr{F}_0$ such that $\alpha(f)\,\mathscr{F}_0 = 0$ for all f.*

$(3_B)$   $[\alpha(f_1), \alpha(f_2)] = [\alpha^*(f_1), \alpha^*(f_2)] = 0, \quad [\alpha(f_1), \alpha^*(f_2)] = (f_1, f_2{}^*).$

*Then there exists a one-to-one isometric mapping $U$ of the space $H$ onto $\mathscr{H}_B$ such that*

$$\hat{a}_B(f) = U\alpha(f)U^{-1}, \qquad \hat{a}_B{}^*(f) = U\alpha^*(f)U^{-1}.$$

*If, in place of $(3_B)$, the condition*

$(3_F)$   $\{\alpha(f_1), \alpha(f_2)\} = \{\alpha^*(f_1), \alpha^*(f_2)\} = 0, \qquad \{\alpha(f_1), \alpha^*(f_2)\} = (f_1, f_2{}^*)$

*is satisfied, then there exists a one-to-one isometric mapping $U$ of the space $H$ onto $\mathscr{H}_F$ such that*

$$\hat{a}_F(f) = U\alpha(f)U^{-1}, \qquad \hat{a}_F{}^*(f) = U\alpha^*(f)U^{-1}.$$

Both assertions are proved in exactly the same way, so we restrict ourselves to the first.

---

[6] The definition of the invariant subspace is the same as for $\hat{a}_B(f), \hat{a}_B{}^*(f)$ (cf. p. 18). It is obvious that if $\alpha(f), \alpha^*(f)$ are bounded operators, then the second requirement of this definition follows from the first.

Consider a realization of $L$, concordant with involution, in terms of square-integrable functions on a set $M$. Let $\mathscr{F}_0 \in H$ be a vector satisfying the equations $\alpha(f)\mathscr{F}_0 = 0$ for all $f$.

Let us consider the subspace $H_1$ of the space $H$ consisting of vectors of the form

$$\mathscr{F} = \sum_{n=0}^{\infty} \frac{1}{(n!)^{1/2}} \int K_n(x_1,\ldots, x_n)\alpha^*(x_1) \cdots \alpha^*(x_n)\, d^n x\, \mathscr{F}_0. \quad (1.14)$$

From condition $(3_B)$ it follows that

$$(\mathscr{F}, \mathscr{F}) = \sum_n \int |K_n(x_1,\ldots, x_n)|^2\, d^n x. \quad (1.15)$$

We put in correspondence to each vector (1.14) the vector (1.5) with the same functions $K_n(x_1,\ldots, x_n)$. Denote by $U$ the mapping thus obtained of the space $H_1$ onto $\mathscr{H}_B$. It is easily seen that $U$ is a one-to-one isometric mapping satisfying the condition $U\alpha^*(f)U^{-1} = \hat{a}_B^*(f)$ and $U\alpha(f)U^{-1} = \hat{a}_B(f)$.

We shall prove that the space $H_1$ coincides with $H$. Let $D$ be the common domain of definition of operators $\alpha(f)$, $\alpha^*(f)$ for all $f \in L$. Evidently, $D \cap H_1$ contains all vectors of the form (1.14), in which the sum on the right is finite. From the commutation relations $(3_B)$ it follows that if $F \in D \cap H_1$, then $\alpha(f)F \in H_1$ and $\alpha^*(f)F \in H_1$. Under the mapping $U$ the set $D$ goes over into the set of all finite vectors. According to Theorem 1.2 the operators $\hat{a}_B(f) + \hat{a}_B^*(f^*)$ and $i(\hat{a}_B(f) - \hat{a}_B^*(f^*))$, defined on the set of finite vectors, are symmetric and have zero deficiency indices. Consequently, the operators $\alpha(f) + \alpha^*(f^*)$ and $i(\alpha(f) - \alpha^*(f^*))$ defined on $D \cap H_1$ possess the same property. Therefore $H_1$ is an invariant subspace, and since $H_1 \neq 0$, we have $H_1 = H$. The theorem just proved is sometimes briefly stated as follows: Irreducible representations of commutation relations with a vacuum vector are equivalent. The problem of describing irreducible commutation relations without the vacuum vector can only be partly solved.[7] It is not difficult to show that if the degrees of freedom are finite (i.e., $L$ is a finite-dimensional space), then the vacuum vector always exists. Thus the irreducible commutation relations in the

---

[7] Cf., in this connection, Gårding and Wightman [1, 2], Siegel [1], and Gel'fand and Vilenkin [1].

case of a finite (fixed) number of degrees of freedom are equivalent.[8]

In the case of an infinite number of degrees of freedom, the representation of commutation relations, having the vacuum vector, is sometimes called the *Fock representation*.

### 7. NORMAL FORM OF AN OPERATOR. Consider the function

$$K(x_1,\ldots, x_m \,|\, y_1,\ldots, y_n) = \sum f_{i_1}(x_1) \cdots f_{i_m}(x_m) g_{j_1}(y_1) \cdots g_{j_n}(y_n),$$

where $f_i(x)$, $g_j(y)$ are square-integrable functions and the sum is finite. We assign to the function $K$ an operator in the Hilbert space $\mathscr{H}_B$:

$$\hat{A} = \int K(x_1,\ldots, x_m \,|\, y_1,\ldots, y_n)$$
$$\times \hat{a}_B{}^*(x_1) \cdots \hat{a}_B{}^*(x_m)\hat{a}_B(y_1) \cdots \hat{a}_B(y_n)\, d^m x\, d^n y$$
$$= \sum \hat{a}_B{}^*(f_{i_1}) \cdots \hat{a}_B{}^*(f_{i_m})\hat{a}_B(g_{j_1}) \cdots \hat{a}_B(g_{j_n}).$$

Now let $K(x_1,\ldots, x_m \,|\, y_1,\ldots, y_n)$ be a generalized function: For some linear set $\tilde{L}$ of square-integrable functions of $m + n$ variables, the functional

$$(K, \varphi^*) = \int K(x_1,\ldots, x_m \,|\, y_1,\ldots, y_n)\varphi(x_1,\ldots, x_m \,|\, y_1,\ldots, y_n)\, d^m x\, d^n y$$

is defined. Let $K_N(x_1,\ldots, x_m \,|\, y_1,\ldots, y_n)$ be a sequence of functions which are represented in the form of finite linear combinations of the products of square-integrable functions with a single variable. Suppose that the sequence $K_N$ approximates the generalized function $K$ in such a sense that $\lim_{N \to \infty}(K_N, \varphi^*) = (K, \varphi^*)$ for every function $\varphi \in \tilde{L}$.

We assign to each function $K_N$ an operator $\hat{A}_N$ written as above. If the sequence of the operators $\hat{A}_N$ for $N \to \infty$ converges strongly on a dense set $D$ of finite vectors[9] to an operator $\hat{A}$ and this limit is reached independent of the choice of the sequence $K_N$ approximating $K$, then we assign $\hat{A}$ to the function $K$ and agree to write it in the form

$$\hat{A} = \int K(x_1,\ldots, x_m \,|\, y_1,\ldots, y_n)$$
$$\times \hat{a}_B{}^*(x_1) \cdots \hat{a}_B{}^*(x_m)\hat{a}_B(y_1) \cdots \hat{a}_B(y_n)\, d^m x\, d^n y. \qquad (1.16_B)$$

---

[8] Equivalence of the irreducible representations of commutation relations in the case of a finite number of degrees of freedom was first proved by von Neumann [1] for bosons, and by Jordan and Wigner [1] for fermions.

[9] It is not necessary for $D$ to exhaust all finite vectors.

Similarly for fermions we define the operator of the form

$$\hat{A} = \int K(x_1,\dots, x_m \,|\, y_1,\dots, y_n)$$

$$\times \hat{a}_F{}^*(x_1) \cdots \hat{a}_F{}^*(x_m)\hat{a}_F(y_1) \cdots \hat{a}_F(y_n) \, d^m x \, d^n y. \quad (1.16_F)$$

It is noted that, without changing the operator $\hat{A}$, we may replace the function $K$ by a function symmetric in $x_1,\dots, x_m$ and $y_1,\dots, y_n$, separately, for bosons, and antisymmetric for fermions. By the condition that the function $K$ has the stated properties of symmetry, it is uniquely determined by the operator $\hat{A}$ for bosons as well as for fermions.

It happens that although it is impossible to associate an operator written as above with the generalized function $K(x_1,\dots, x_m \,|\, y_1,\dots, y_n)$, there is an everywhere-dense set $D$ consisting of finite vectors such that the limit

$$\lim_{N \to \infty} (\hat{A}_N\hat{\Phi}, \hat{\Psi}) \qquad \hat{\Phi} \in D, \quad \hat{\Psi} \in D$$

exists. The $\hat{A}_N$ are, as above, operators generated by functions $K_N$ which approximate $K$, and the limit is supposed to be independent of the choice of approximating sequence.

In this case we shall say that the function $K$ gives a bilinear form. The bilinear form generated by $K$ will be written, as before, in the form $(1.16_B)$ or $(1.16_F)$. All remarks on the symmetry of the function $K$ that have been stated concerning operators apply to the bilinear forms.

It is readily verified that if the set $\tilde{L}$ on which the function $K$ defines the functional contains the dense subset consisting of finite linear combinations of functions of the form $f_1(x_1,\dots, x_m)f_2(y_1,\dots, y_n)$, then there corresponds to the function $K$ a bilinear form. The question whether there also corresponds to it an operator with a nonvoid domain of definition is in general not so simple.[10]

---

[10] We mention a very simple example of the generalized function, to which a bilinear form corresponds but an operator with nonvoid domain of definition does not. Let $x$ run along the real axis, let $dx$ be the Lebesgue measure, and let

$$K(x \,|\, ) = \delta(x - \xi).$$

The corresponding bilinear form $\int K(x \,|\, )\hat{a}_B{}^*(x) \, dx = \hat{a}_B{}^*(\xi)$ or $\int K(x \,|\, )\hat{a}_F{}^*(x) \, dx = \hat{a}_F{}^*(\xi)$ is not an operator (cf. the footnote on p. 11).

We proceed to define the normal form of the operator. Let $K_{mn}(x_1,\ldots,$ $x_m \mid y_1,\ldots, y_n)$ be generalized functions which correspond to the operators $(1.16_B)$ or $(1.16_F)$.

Denote by $\mathcal{H}_n$ the subspace of the state space, consisting of vectors of the form

$$\hat{\Phi} = (n!)^{-1/2} \int K(x_1,\ldots, x_n) a^*(x_1) \cdots a^*(x_n)\, d^n x\, \hat{\Phi}_0$$

$$(a^*(x) = a_B^*(x) \qquad \text{or} \qquad a^*(x) = a_F^*(x))$$

(the so-called $n$-particle subspace).

An operator $\hat{A}$ in the space $\mathcal{H}$ ($\mathcal{H} = \mathcal{H}_B$ or $\mathcal{H} = \mathcal{H}_F$) is said to be *representable in normal form* if its domain of definition contains a set $D$ such that $D \cap \mathcal{H}_n$ is dense in $\mathcal{H}_n$ and if it can be written as a sum of weakly convergent series on that set.[11]

$$\hat{A} = \sum \int K_{mn}(x_1,\ldots, x_m \mid y_1,\ldots, y_n)$$

$$\times\, \hat{a}^*(x_1) \cdots \hat{a}^*(x_m)\hat{a}(y_1) \cdots \hat{a}(y_n) d^m x d^n y, \qquad (1.16)$$

where $\hat{a}(x) = \hat{a}_B(x)$, $\hat{a}^*(x) = \hat{a}_B^*(x)$ if the space $\mathcal{H}_B$ is involved, and $\hat{a}(x) = \hat{a}_F(x)$, $\hat{a}^*(x) = \hat{a}_F^*(x)$ if the space $\mathcal{H}_F$ is involved. The functions $K_{mn}$ are, generally speaking, generalized functions and are supposed to be symmetric in $x_1,\ldots, x_m$ and $y_1,\ldots, y_n$, separately, for bosons, and antisymmetric for fermions.

The series (1.16) is called the *normal form of the operator* $\hat{A}$.

It is characteristic of the normal form that in every summand, creation operators stand to the left of annihilation operators.[12] It will be proved in Subsection 10 that bounded operators are representable in the normal form. Some unbounded operators are also represented in the normal form.

Note that if the operator $\hat{A}$ is represented in the normal form, then the vacuum vector enters into its domain of definition.

---

[11] The set $D$ need not consist of *all* finite vectors.

[12] In the physics literature, for operators reducible to the normal form, one thinks of all operators that are representable in the form (1.16), without saying anything about the character of convergence of the series (1.16) and the domain of definition of individual summands.

The precise definition of this notion, given above, seems to be natural, although it is not the only possibility.

It often happens that we must deal with bilinear forms, not with operators, defined on some dense set in the state space. By the analogy of an operator reducible to the normal form, we may give the definition of a bilinear form reducible to the normal form. A bilinear form $\hat{A}$ is *representable in normal form* if it can be written in the series (1.16) of bilinear forms, which converges on a dense set consisting of finite vectors.[13] [The sequence of bilinear forms $\hat{A}_N$ converges to a bilinear form $\hat{A}$ on the set $D$ if $\lim_{N \to \infty} (\hat{A}_N \hat{\Phi}, \hat{\Psi}) = (\hat{A}\hat{\Phi}, \hat{\Psi})$ for every $\hat{\Phi}, \hat{\Psi} \in D$.]

8. GENERATING FUNCTIONALS FOR VECTORS AND OPERATORS. BOSE CASE. Let $L$ be a Hilbert space of functions on a set $M$. We put in correspondence to every vector written in the form (1.5) and to every operator written in the form (1.16) functionals on $L$:

$$\Phi(a^*) = \sum_n \frac{1}{(n!)^{1/2}} \int K_n(x_1,\ldots, x_n) a^*(x_1) \cdots a^*(x_n)\, d^n x, \quad (1.17)$$

$$A(a^*, a) = \sum \int K_{mn}(x_1,\ldots, x_m \mid y_1,\ldots, y_n)$$

$$\times\, a^*(x_1) \cdots a^*(x_m) a(y_1) \cdots a(y_n)\, d^m x\, d^n y, \quad (1.18)$$

where $K_n$, $K_{mn}$ are the same functions as in (1.5), (1.16) and $a(x)$, $a^*(x) \in L$.

Unless otherwise stated, the functions $a(x)$ and $a^*(x)$ will be assumed to be complex conjugates.

Let $\|A_{mn}(x_1,\ldots, x_m \mid y_1,\ldots, y_n)\|$ be the matrix corresponding to the operator $\hat{A}$. We assign to this matrix a functional on $L$:

$$\tilde{A}(a^*, a) = \sum \frac{1}{(m!n!)^{1/2}} \int A_{mn}(x_1,\ldots, x_m \mid y_1,\ldots, y_n)$$

$$\times\, a^*(x_1) \cdots a^*(x_m) a(y_n) \cdots a(y_1)\, d^m x\, d^n y. \quad (1.19)$$

In Subsection 11 we shall prove the convergence of the series (1.17) and the convergence of the series (1.18), (1.19) under the assumption that the operator $\hat{A}$ is bounded.

We remark that the functionals (1.17)–(1.19) have the form of power series. Individual summands in (1.17)–(1.19) will be called *homogeneous*

---

[13] This dense set need not consist of all finite vectors.

*functionals of degree n* [in the case of (1.17)] or *of degree m in a\* and n in a*
[in the case of (1.18), (1.19)].

If the series (1.17)–(1.19) represents really finite sums, then the
corresponding functionals will be called *polynomials*. Evidently $\Phi(a^*)$
is a polynomial functional if and only if $\hat{\Phi}$ is a finite vector.

We find variational derivatives of the functional (1.18) with respect
to $a(x)$ and $a^*(x)$:

$$\frac{\delta}{\delta a(x)} A(a^*, a) = \sum n \int K_{mn}(x_1,\dots, x_m \mid y_1,\dots, y_{n-1}, x)$$

$$\times a^*(x_1) \cdots a^*(x_m) a(y_1) \cdots a(y_{n-1}) d^m x \, d^{n-1} y,$$

$$\frac{\delta}{\delta a^*(x)} A(a^*, a) = \sum m \int K_{mn}(x_1,\dots, x_{m-1}, x \mid y_1,\dots, y_n)$$

$$\times a^*(x_1) \cdots a^*(x_{m-1}) a(y_1) \cdots a(y_n) \, d^{m-1} x \, d^n y.$$

The variational derivatives of the functionals $\tilde{A}(a^*, a)$ and $\Phi(a^*)$ are
defined analogously.

It is easy to see that if the functional (1.17) corresponds to the
vector $\hat{\Phi}$ and the functionals (1.18), (1.19) to the operator $\hat{A}$, then there
correspond to the vectors $\hat{a}(x)\hat{\Phi}$, $\hat{a}^*(x)\hat{\Phi}$ and to the operators $\hat{a}(x)\hat{A}$,
$\hat{a}^*(x)\hat{A}$, $\hat{A}\hat{a}(x)$, $\hat{A}\hat{a}^*(x)$ the functionals[14]

$$\hat{a}(x)\hat{\Phi} \leftrightarrow \frac{\delta}{\delta a^*(x)} \Phi(a^*),$$

$$\hat{a}^*(x)\hat{\Phi} \leftrightarrow a^*(x)\Phi(a^*), \tag{1.20}$$

$$\hat{a}(x)\hat{A} \leftrightarrow \left(a(x) + \frac{\delta}{\delta a^*(x)}\right) A(a^*, a),$$

$$\hat{a}^*(x)\hat{A} \leftrightarrow a^*(x)A(a^*, a),$$

$$\hat{A}\hat{a}(x) \leftrightarrow a(x)A(a^*, a), \tag{1.21}$$

$$\hat{A}\hat{a}^*(x) \leftrightarrow \left(a^*(x) + \frac{\delta}{\delta a(x)}\right) A(a^*, a),$$

[14] Strictly speaking, we must consider the vector $\hat{a}(f)\hat{\Phi} = \int \hat{a}(x)f(x)\, dx\, \hat{\Phi}$, etc.,
the corresponding alterations of formulas (1.20)–(1.22) being obvious.

$$\hat{a}(x)\hat{A} \leftrightarrow \frac{\delta}{\delta a^*(x)} \tilde{A}(a^*, a),$$

$$\hat{a}^*(x)\hat{A} \leftrightarrow a^*(x)\tilde{A}(a^*, a),$$

$$\hat{A}\hat{a}(x) \leftrightarrow a(x)\tilde{A}(a^*, a), \qquad\qquad (1.22)$$

$$\hat{A}\hat{a}^*(x) \leftrightarrow \frac{\delta}{\delta a(x)} \tilde{A}(a^*, a).$$

The notations in these formulas do not require explanation.

9. GENERATING FUNCTIONALS FOR VECTORS AND OPERATORS. FERMI CASE. We consider anticommuting symbols $a(x)$, $a^*(x)$:

$$\{a(x), a(x')\} = \{a(x), a^*(x')\} = \{a^*(x), a^*(x')\} = 0.$$

In what follows we shall often refer to these symbols as functions with anticommuting values. To every vector $\hat{\Phi}$ written in the form (1.5), to every operator $\hat{A}$ written in the normal form, and to every matrix $\|A_{mn}(x_1,\ldots, x_m | y_1,\ldots, y_n)\|$ of the operator $\hat{A}$ we assign the generating functionals

$$\Phi(a^*) = \sum_n \frac{1}{(n!)^{1/2}} \int K_n(x_1,\ldots, x_n)a^*(x_1) \cdots a^*(x_n) \, d^n x, \qquad (1.23)$$

$$A(a^*, a) = \sum \int K_{mn}(x_1,\ldots, x_m | y_1,\ldots, y_n)$$
$$\times a^*(x_1) \cdots a^*(x_m)a(y_1) \cdots a(y_n) \, d^m x \, d^n y, \qquad (1.24)$$

$$\tilde{A}(a^*, a) = \sum \frac{1}{(m!n!)^{1/2}} \int A_{mn}(x_1,\ldots, x_m | y_1,\ldots, y_n)$$
$$\times a^*(x_1) \cdots a^*(x_m)a(y_n) \cdots a(y_1) \, d^m x, d^n y, \qquad (1.25)$$

respectively, where the functions $K_n(x_1,\ldots, x_n)$ and $K_{mn}(x_1,\ldots, x_m | y_1,\ldots, y_n)$ are the same as in (1.5) and (1.16).

The series (1.23)–(1.25) is to be understood as a formal power series. It will be shown in Section 3 that the functionals $\Phi$, $A$, $\tilde{A}$ are elements of a Grassmann algebra with an infinite number of generators.[15]

---

[15] It is assumed that the number of degrees of freedom of the system is infinite. If this number is equal to $n < \infty$, then $x$ runs through $n$ values and the symbols $a(x)$, $a^*(x)$ are generators of a finite-dimensional Grassmann algebra.

We define the left derivative by $a^*(x)$ and the right derivative by $a(x)$ of the functional $A(a^*, a)$. Denote these derivatives by $[\delta/\delta a^*(x)]$ $A(a^*, a)$ and $A(a^*, a)[\delta/\delta a(x)]$, respectively:

$$\frac{\delta}{\delta a^*(x)} A(a^*, a) = \sum m \int K_{mn}(x, x_1,\ldots, x_{m-1} \mid y_1,\ldots, y_n)$$
$$\times a^*(x_1) \cdots a^*(x_{m-1}) a(y_1) \cdots a(y_n) \, d^{m-1}x \, d^n y,$$

$$A(a^*, a) \frac{\delta}{\delta a(x)} = \sum n \int K_{mn}(x_1,\ldots, x_m \mid y_1,\ldots, y_{n-1}, x)$$
$$\times a^*(x_1) \cdots a^*(x_m) a(y_1) \cdots a(y_{n-1}) \, d^m x \, d^{n-1} y.$$

Derivatives of the functionals[16] $\tilde{A}$ and $\Phi$ are defined similarly.

Let $\Phi(a^*)$, $A(a^*, a)$, $\tilde{A}(a^*, a)$ be functionals corresponding to the vector $\hat{\Phi}$ and the operator $\hat{A}$. We now find the functionals corresponding to the vectors $\hat{a}(x)\hat{\Phi}$, $\hat{a}^*(x)\hat{\Phi}$ and the operators $\hat{a}(x)\hat{A}$, $\hat{a}^*(x)\hat{A}$, $\hat{A}\hat{a}(x)$, $\hat{A}\hat{a}^*(x)$. It is readily verified that these functionals are equal to[17]

$$\hat{a}(x)\hat{\Phi} \leftrightarrow \frac{\delta}{\delta a^*(x)} \Phi(a^*),$$
$$\hat{a}^*(x)\hat{\Phi} \leftrightarrow a^*(x)\Phi(a^*), \tag{1.26}$$

$$\hat{a}(x)\hat{A} \leftrightarrow \left( a(x) + \frac{\delta}{\delta a^*(x)} \right) A(a^*, a),$$
$$\hat{a}^*(x)\hat{A} \leftrightarrow a^*(x)A(a^*, a),$$
$$\hat{A}\hat{a}(x) \leftrightarrow A(a^*, a)a(x), \tag{1.27}$$
$$\hat{A}\hat{a}^*(x) \leftrightarrow A(a^*, a) \left( a^*(x) + \frac{\delta}{\delta a(x)} \right),$$

$$\hat{a}(x)\hat{A} \leftrightarrow \frac{\delta}{\delta a^*(x)} \tilde{A}(a^*, a),$$
$$\hat{a}^*(x)\hat{A} \leftrightarrow a^*(x)\tilde{A}(a^*, a),$$
$$\hat{A}\hat{a}(x) \leftrightarrow \tilde{A}(a^*, a)a(x), \tag{1.28}$$
$$\hat{A}\hat{a}^*(x) \leftrightarrow \tilde{A}(a^*, a) \frac{\delta}{\delta a(x)}.$$

[16] The general definition of derivatives for the element of a Grassmann algebra will be given in Section 3.

[17] Cf. the footnote on p. 25.

10. Representation of Bounded Operators in the Normal Form.[18]

**Theorem 1.5.** *A bounded operator in either of the spaces $\mathcal{H}_B$ or $\mathcal{H}_F$ is representable in the normal form.*

The proofs for both cases are identical, so we shall confine ourselves to the case of the space $\mathcal{H}_F$.

We denote by $\hat{P}_m$ the projection operator onto $\mathcal{H}_F^m$, and by $\hat{A}_{mn}$ the operator $\hat{P}_m \hat{A} \hat{P}_n$. Evidently the operator $\hat{A}$ is the sum of the strongly convergent series

$$\hat{A} = \sum \hat{A}_{mn}. \qquad (1.29)$$

We remark that the functional

$$\tilde{P}_0 \equiv 1, \qquad (1.30)$$

corresponds to the matrix form of the projection operator $\hat{P}_0$ onto the vacuum, and the functional

$$\tilde{A}_{mn}(a^*, a) = \frac{1}{(m!n!)^{1/2}} \int A_{mn}(x_1,\ldots, x_m \,|\, y_1,\ldots, y_n)$$

$$\times\, a^*(x_1) \cdots a^*(x_m) a(y_n) \cdots a(y_1) \, d^m x \, d^n y, \quad (1.31)$$

to the matrix form of the operator $\hat{A}_{mn}$. Here $A_{mn}(x_1,\ldots, x_m \,|\, y_1,\ldots, y_n)$ is an element of the matrix $\|A_{mn}\|$ corresponding to the operator $\hat{A}$.

It is found from formulas (1.30), (1.31), by the aid of the second and third formulas of (1.28), that

$$\hat{A}_{mn} = \frac{1}{(m!n!)^{1/2}} \int A_{mn}(x_1,\ldots, x_m \,|\, y_1,\ldots, y_n)$$

$$\times\, \hat{a}^*(x_1) \cdots \hat{a}^*(x_m) \hat{P}_0 \hat{a}(y_n) \cdots \hat{a}(y_1) \, d^m x \, d^n y. \quad (1.32)$$

We find the normal form of the operator $\hat{P}_0$. For this purpose we note that $\hat{P}_0$ is the unique operator satisfying the conditions

$$\hat{a}(x)\hat{P}_0 = 0, \qquad \hat{P}_0 \hat{a}^*(x) = 0, \qquad \hat{P}_0 \hat{\Phi}_0 = \hat{\Phi}_0, \qquad (1.33)$$

where $\hat{\Phi}_0$ is the vacuum vector.

[18] A part of the results in this subsection (Theorems 1.5, 1.6, and 1.8) has been presented briefly in the author's work [6]. Theorem 1.7 was formulated by Bargmann [1].

According to (1.27), the first two relations of (1.33) are equivalent to the following equations for a functional $P_0(a^*, a)$, if such a functional exists:

$$\left(a(x) + \frac{\delta}{\delta a^*(x)}\right)P_0 = 0, \qquad P_0\left(a^*(x) + \frac{\delta}{\delta a(x)}\right) = 0. \qquad (1.34)$$

It is easy to verify that the solution of these equations is the functional

$$P_0(a^*, a) = c \exp\left[-\int a^*(x)a(x)\, dx\right].$$

$P_0(a^*, a)$ is the functional corresponding to an operator. In fact, for any finite vector $\hat{\Phi}$ the series[19]

$$c \sum_n \frac{(-1)^n}{n!} \int \hat{a}^*(x_1) \cdots \hat{a}^*(x_n)\hat{a}(x_n) \cdots \hat{a}(x_1)\, d^n x\, \hat{\Phi} \qquad (1.35)$$

contains only a finite number of nonvanishing summands, each of which belongs to $\mathscr{H}_F$, as is easily seen. Consequently, the series (1.35) converges in norm and the functional $P_0(\hat{a}^*, a)$ defines the normal form of a certain operator $\hat{Q}$.

From (1.34) and (1.27) it evidently follows that the operator $\hat{Q}$ satisfies the first two equations of (1.33). In addition, putting $\hat{\Phi} = \hat{\Phi}_0$ in (1.35), it is found that $\hat{Q}\hat{\Phi}_0 = c\hat{\Phi}_0$. Therefore, for $c = 1$ the operator $\hat{Q}$ satisfies all the conditions (1.33), and accordingly $\hat{Q} = \hat{P}_0$. Thus we find that the operator $\hat{P}_0$ is reducible to the normal form and that there corresponds to its normal form the functional

$$P_0(a^*, a) = \exp\left[-\int a^*(x)a(x)\, dx\right]. \qquad (1.36)$$

We put

$$\hat{P}_0 = \sum_n \frac{(-1)^n}{n!} \int \hat{a}^*(x_1) \cdots \hat{a}^*(x_n)\hat{a}(x_n) \cdots \hat{a}(x_1)\, d^n x$$

in (1.32) and apply the series obtained to the finite vector $\hat{\Phi}$. Note that as a result we get the finite sum of elements in the space $\mathscr{H}_F$. Thus the

---

[19] Attention should be paid to the order of factors under the integral of (1.35). It is related to the fact that the functions $a(x)$, $a^*(x)$ anticommute with each other.

operator $\hat{A}_{mn}$ too has been represented in the normal form. Evidently, there corresponds to its normal form the functional[20]

$$A_{mn}(a^*, a) = \frac{1}{(m!n!)^{1/2}} \int A_{mn}(x_1,\ldots, x_m \mid y_1,\ldots, y_n)$$
$$\times a^*(x_1) \cdots a^*(x_m)a(y_n) \cdots a(y_1) \, d^m x \, d^n y \exp\left[-\int a^*(x)a(x) \, dx\right]. \quad (1.37)$$

We put the normal form of the operator $\hat{A}_{mn}$ in (1.29). As a result we obtain for the operator $\hat{A}$ an expression of the form

$$\hat{A} = \sum \int K_{mn}(x_1,\ldots, x_m \mid y_1,\ldots, y_n)$$
$$\times \hat{a}^*(x_1) \cdots a^*(x_m)\hat{a}(y_n) \cdots \hat{a}(y_1) \, d^m x \, d^n y,$$

where

$$K_{mn} = \sum_{\mu+p=m, \nu+p=n} \frac{(-1)^p}{p!} \frac{1}{(\mu!\nu!)^{1/2}} A_{\mu\nu}(x_1,\ldots, x_\mu \mid y_1,\ldots, y_\nu)$$
$$\times \delta(x_{\mu+1}, y_{\nu+1}) \cdots \delta(x_m, y_n).$$

Let us apply the operator $\hat{A}$ to the vector $\hat{\Phi}$ of the form

$$\hat{\Phi} = \frac{1}{(s!)^{1/2}} \int F(\eta_1,\ldots, \eta_s)a^*(\eta_1) \cdots a^*(\eta_s) \, d^s\eta \, \hat{\Phi}_0.$$

As a result we obtain a vector $\hat{\Psi} = \sum \hat{\Psi}_{mn}, 0 \le n \le s$, where

$$\hat{\Psi}_{mn} = \int G_{m+s-n}(x_1,\ldots, x_{m+s-n})\hat{a}^*(x_1) \cdots \hat{a}^*(x_{m+s-n}) \, d^{m+s-n}x\hat{\Phi}_0$$

and

$$G_{m+s-n}$$
$$= \frac{s(s-1) \cdots (s-n+1)}{(s!)^{1/2}} \int K_{mn}(x_1,\ldots, x_m \mid y_1,\ldots, y_n)$$
$$\times F(y_1,\ldots, y_n, x_{m+1},\ldots, x_{m+s-n}) \, d^n y$$
$$= \sum_{\mu+p=m, \nu+p=n} \frac{(-1)^p}{p!} \frac{s(s-1) \cdots (s-n+1)}{(\mu!\nu!s!)^{1/2}} \int A_{\mu\nu}(x_1,\ldots, x_\mu \mid y_1,\ldots, y_\nu)$$
$$\times F(y_1,\ldots, y_\nu, x_{\mu+1},\ldots, x_{m+s-n}) \, d^\nu y.$$

[20] The functional $\exp[-\int a^*(x)a(x) \, dx]$ commutes with any functional, because its expansion in powers of $a(x)$, $a^*(x)$ contains only elements of even powers in $a$, $a^*$ as a whole.

We shall show that the individual term $\hat{\Psi}_{mn}$ belongs to the space $\mathcal{H}_F$. To this end we consider the vector

$$\hat{\Phi}_\nu(x_{\mu+1},\ldots, x_{m+s-n}) = \frac{1}{(\nu!)^{1/2}} \int F(y_1,\ldots, y_\nu, x_{\mu+1},\ldots, x_{m+s-n})$$
$$\times \hat{a}^*(y_1) \cdots \hat{a}^*(y_\nu)\, d^\nu y\, \hat{\Phi}_0.$$

Now we note that the individual term in the sum defining the function $G_{m+s-n}$ has the form of the projection of the vector $\hat{A}\hat{\Phi}_\nu(x_{\mu+1},\ldots, x_{m+s-n})$ onto the $\mu$-particle subspace $\mathcal{H}_F{}^\mu$ of the space $\mathcal{H}_F$. Therefore, the individual term can be easily estimated as

$$\int \left| \int A_{\mu\nu}(x_1,\ldots, x_\mu \,|\, y_1,\ldots, y_\nu) F(y_1,\ldots, y_\nu, x_{\mu+1},\ldots, x_{m+s-n})\, d^\nu y \right|^2 d^\mu x$$
$$\leq \|A\|^2 \int |F(y_1,\ldots, y_\nu, x_{\mu+1},\ldots, x_{m+s-n})|^2\, d^\nu y.$$

Integrating the left and right members of this inequality again with respect to $x_{\mu+1},\ldots, x_{m+s-n}$, we finally obtain

$$\int \left| \int A_{\mu\nu}(x_1,\ldots, x_\mu \,|\, y_1,\ldots, y_\nu) F(y_1,\ldots, y_\nu, x_{\mu+1},\ldots, x_{m+s-n})\, d^\nu y \right|^2 d^{m+s-n} x$$
$$\leq \|A\|^2 \int |F(y_1,\ldots, y_s)|^2\, d^s y.$$

Since the sum defining $G_{m+s-n}$ consists of finite terms, it follows that

$$\int |G_{m+s-n}(x_1,\ldots, x_{m+s-n})|^2\, d^{m+s-n} x < \infty,$$

and hence $\hat{\Psi}_{mn} \in \mathcal{H}_F$.

We shall now show that the series $\sum \hat{\Psi}_{mn}$ converges weakly on the set of finite vectors.

Let us denote by $\hat{P}_N$ the projection operator onto the $N$-particle subspace $\mathcal{H}_F{}^N$ of the space $\mathcal{H}_F$. We observe that $\hat{P}_N \hat{\Psi}_{mn} \neq 0$ only if $N = m + s - n$. By making use of the expression for $\hat{\Psi}_{mn}$ obtained above, and after simple transformations, we find that

$$\hat{P}_N \hat{\Psi}_{mn} = \frac{1}{(N!)^{1/2}} \int \left[ \int A_{Ns}(x_1,\ldots, x_N \,|\, y_1,\ldots, y_s) \right.$$
$$\left. \times F(y_1,\ldots, y_s)\, d^s y \right] \hat{a}^*(x_1) \cdots \hat{a}^*(x_N)\, d^N x\, \hat{\Phi}_0.$$

Evidently there results from this the weak convergence of the series $\sum \hat{\Psi}_{mn}$ on the set of finite vectors.

The theorem is completely proved.

We remark that the connection between the functionals $A(a^*, a)$ and $\tilde{A}(a^*, a)$ follows from formulas (1.29) and (1.37). We formulate the result obtained in the form of an independent theorem.

**Theorem 1.6.** *The functionals* $A(a^*, a)$, $\tilde{A}(a^*, a)$ *corresponding to the normal and matrix forms of the operator* $\hat{A}$ *are connected by the relations*

$$A(a^*, a) = \tilde{A}(a^*, a) \exp\left[ -\int a^*(x)a(x)\,dx \right],$$

$$\tilde{A}(a^*, a) = A(a^*, a) \exp\left[ \int a^*(x)a(x)\,dx \right]. \tag{1.38}$$

11. Convergence of Series (1.17)–(1.19) in the Bose Case. Consider the vectors $\hat{P}_f$ and $\hat{Q}_f$ for which the generating functionals are of the form

$$P_f(a^*) = \exp\left[ \int a^*(x)f(x)\,dx - \tfrac{1}{2}\int f(x)f^*(x)\,dx \right] \tag{1.39}$$

$$Q_f(a^*) = \exp\left[ \int a^*(x)f(x)\,dx \right]. \tag{1.39'}$$

Evidently $(\hat{P}_f, \hat{P}_f) = 1$, $(\hat{Q}_f, \hat{Q}_f) = \exp\left[\int f^*(x)f(x)\,dx\right]$. In case the system has one degree of freedom and is found in the state $\hat{P}_f$ or $\hat{Q}_f$, the probability that $n$ particles are present in the system is evidently equal to $|f|^{2n}\exp(-|f|^2)/n!$ and thus has a Poisson distribution. In this connection the vectors $\hat{P}_f$ and $\hat{Q}_f$ will be called the *normalized and unnormalized Poisson vector with index f.*

We now observe that if $\hat{\Phi}$ is an arbitrary vector, the functional corresponding to it is equal to

$$\Phi(a^*) = (\hat{\Phi}, \hat{Q}_a). \tag{1.40}$$

The convergence of the series (1.17) follows from (1.40).

Further, let the vector $\hat{\Phi}$ have components $K_n(x_1,\ldots, x_n)$. Denote by $|\hat{\Phi}|$ the vector with components $|K_n(x_1,\ldots, x_n)|$. Evidently $(\hat{\Phi}, \hat{\Phi}) = (|\hat{\Phi}|, |\hat{\Phi}|)$.

We note that the series formed by the absolute values of the series (1.17) is equal to $(|\hat{\Phi}|, \hat{Q}_{|a|})$, and hence it also converges. Let us estimate the residual of the series (1.17). To this end, we consider the projection operator $\hat{P}_N$ onto the subspace $\mathcal{H}_N = \sum_{n>N} \mathcal{H}_B{}^n$. Evidently the residual $R_N(a^*)$ of the series (1.17) allows the estimate

$$|R_N(a^*)| \leq (|\hat{\Phi}|, \hat{P}_N \hat{Q}_{|a|}) \leq \|\hat{\Phi}\| \, \|\hat{P}_N \hat{Q}_{|a|}\|.$$

From (1.39′) it is found immediately that if $\int |a(x)|^2 \, dx \leq R^2$, then

$$\|\hat{P}_N \hat{Q}_{|a|}\| \leq c \, \frac{R^N}{(N!)^{1/2}}, \tag{1.41}$$

under the condition that $N + 1 > R^2$.

Thus we have arrived at the following theorem:

**Theorem 1.7.** *The functionals* $\Phi(a^*)$ *corresponding to the vectors are defined on the Hilbert space L of functions which are square-integrable on M. The series* (1.17) *converges absolutely and uniformly for all* $a^* \in L$ *lying in the ball of a fixed radius R.*

We pass to the functionals (1.18), (1.19). We shall investigate the convergence of somewhat more general series, $\tilde{A}(a_1, a_2)$, $A(a_1, a_2)$, where $a_1(x)$, $a_2(x)$ are different functions. We note first of all that the functional $\tilde{A}(a_1, a_2)$ can be represented in the form

$$\tilde{A}(a_1, a_2) = (\hat{A} \hat{Q}_{a_2}, \hat{Q}_{a_1*}). \tag{1.42}$$

The convergence of the series (1.18) follows from (1.42). Let us estimate the residual $R_{MN}$ of this series. Evidently $R_{MN}$ can be represented in the form

$$R_{MN}(a_1, a_2) = (\hat{A} \hat{P}_N \hat{Q}_{a_2}, \hat{Q}_{a_1*}) + (\hat{A} \hat{Q}_{a_2}, \hat{P}_M \hat{Q}_{a_1*}) + (\hat{A} \hat{P}_N \hat{Q}_{a_2}, \hat{P}_M \hat{Q}_{a_1*}).$$

Under the assumption that

$$\int |a_1|^2 \, dx \leq R_1, \qquad \int |a_2|^2 \, dx \leq R_2 \tag{1.43}$$

we obtain, by using (1.41), the estimate for $R_{MN}$:

$$|R_{MN}(a_1, a_2)| \leq \|A\| \left( c_1 \frac{R_1{}^M}{(M!)^{1/2}} + c_2 \frac{R_2{}^N}{(N!)^{1/2}} + c_3 \frac{R_1{}^M R_2{}^N}{(M!N!)^{1/2}} \right).$$

It follows from this estimate that the series (1.18) converges uniformly if $a_1$, $a_2$ satisfy inequalites (1.43).

We now show that the series (1.18) converges absolutely. To this end we choose functions $a_1(x)$ and $a_2(x)$ in an arbitrary way and fix them. We denote

$$\int A_{mn}(x_1,\ldots, x_m \mid y_1,\ldots, y_n)a_1(x_1) \cdots a_1(x_m)a_2(y_1) \cdots a_2(y_n) \, d^m x \, d^n y$$

by $a_{mn}$. Then

$$\tilde{A}(a_1, a_2) = \sum a_{mn}. \tag{1.44}$$

Consider the functions $b_1(x) = \alpha a_1(x)$, $b_2(x) = \beta a_2(x)$, where $\alpha$ and $\beta$ are numbers such that $0 < |\alpha| < 1$, $0 < |\beta| < 1$. It is evident that

$$\tilde{A}(b_1, b_2) = \sum a_{mn}\alpha^m\beta^n. \tag{1.45}$$

Since the series (1.44) converges, the series (1.45) converges absolutely by the well-known theorem on power series. Thus the series (1.18) for $b_1(x)$, $b_2(x)$ converges absolutely. By the use of the connection between $a_1(x)$, $a_2(x)$ and $b_1(x)$, $b_2(x)$ and the fact that $a_1(x)$, $a_2(x)$ are arbitrary square-integrable functions, we obtain the result that $b_1(x)$ and $b_2(x)$ are also such functions.

Since the functionals $A(a^*, a)$ and $\tilde{A}(a^*, a)$ are connected by relations (1.38), all that we have stated can be transferred without alteration to the functional $A(a^*, a)$.

We summarize the result in the following theorem:

**Theorem 1.8.** *Let* $a(x)$, $a^*(x)$ *be two arbitrary square-integrable functions. Then the series* (1.18) *and* (1.19) *converge uniformly and absolutely if* $\|a\| < R_1$, $\|a^*\| < R_2$, *where* $R_1 > 0$, $R_2 > 0$ *are arbitrary numbers.*

By $\|a\|$, $\|a^*\|$ in the formulation of the theorem we mean the norms of $a$, $a^*$ as elements of the Hilbert space $L$:

$$\|a\| = \left(\int |a|^2 \, dx\right)^{1/2}, \qquad \|a^*\| = \left(\int |a^*|^2 \, dx\right)^{1/2}.$$

We remark that if $\hat{A}$ is an unbounded operator, but if the Poisson vectors $\hat{P}_a$ with indices $a(x)$ running through the set $\tilde{L}$ are contained in the domain of definition of $\hat{A}$, then for the operator $\hat{A}$, theorems similar to Theorems 1.7 and 1.8 hold. In that case the functionals $A(a^*, a)$, $\tilde{A}(a^*, a)$ are shown to be defined not on the entire $L$, but on $\tilde{L}$.

In closing this subsection we note that for the functional $A(a^*, a)$ there holds a formula analogous to (1.42),

$$A(a^*, a) = (\hat{A}\hat{P}_{a^*}, \hat{P}_{a^*}),\tag{1.46}$$

where $\hat{P}_a$ is the normalized Poisson vector with index $a$. Formula (1.46) is obtained in an obvious way by comparing (1.42), (1.38), and (1.39).

12. PROJECTION OPERATORS. We find the matrix and normal forms of the projection operator $\hat{P}_{\hat{\Phi}}$ onto a vector $\hat{\Phi}$. Let us consider for definiteness the Fermi case. Let

$$\hat{\Phi} = \begin{pmatrix} K_0 \\ K_1(x) \\ K_2(x_1, x_2) \\ \vdots \end{pmatrix}.$$

Evidently, elements of the matrix $\|A_{mn}\|$ of the operator $\hat{P}_{\hat{\Phi}}$ have the form

$$A_{mn}(x_1, \ldots, x_m \mid y_1, \ldots, y_n) = K_m(x_1, \ldots, x_m)\, \overline{K_n(y_1, \ldots, y_n)}.$$

Thus the functional corresponding to the matrix of the operator $\hat{P}_{\hat{\Phi}}$ is equal to

$$\tilde{P}(a^*, a) = \Phi(a^*)\Phi^*(a),\tag{1.47}$$

where $\Phi(a^*)$ is the functional corresponding to the vector $\hat{\Phi}$, and

$$\Phi^*(a) = \sum \int \overline{K_n(x_1, \ldots, x_n)} a(x_n) \cdots a(x_1)\, d^n x.$$

It follows from (1.38) that the normal form of the operator $\hat{P}_{\hat{\Phi}}$ is defined by the functional

$$P(a^*, a) = \Phi(a^*)\Phi^*(a) \exp\left[ -\int a^*(x)a(x)\, dx \right].\tag{1.48}$$

Formulas (1.47), (1.48) are also valid for bosons.

## 2. Operations on Generating Functionals. Bose Case

At the end of Section 1 we associated functionals with vectors and operators in the Hilbert space $\mathscr{H}_B$. In this section we express a functional corresponding to a product of operators through functionals corresponding to factors, a functional corresponding to the vector $\hat{A}\hat{\Phi}$ through functionals corresponding to the operator $\hat{A}$ and the vector $\hat{\Phi}$, and establish some other formulas of the operational calculus for bosons. All these formulas contain continual integrals.

We note that functionals which have been assigned to vectors and operators are infinite-dimensional analogs of analytic functions. In this connection, before deriving the formulas of the operational calculus, we shall formulate precise definitions of analytic functions and continual integrals.

1. DIFFERENTIABLE AND ANALYTIC FUNCTIONALS. Let $L$ be a real Hilbert space. A functional $\Phi$ is said to be *differentiable at a point* $f \in L$ if for any $h \in L$ there exists an element $\delta\Phi/\delta f \in L$ such that

$$\left| \Phi(f + h) - \Phi(f) - \left( h, \frac{\delta\Phi}{\delta f} \right) \right| = o(\|h\|). \tag{2.1}$$

$\delta\Phi/\delta f$ is called the *variational derivative* of the functional $\Phi$ at the point $f$. When the space $L$ is realized as a space of square-integrable functions of a variable $x$, then $\delta\Phi/\delta f$ is a function usually denoted as $\delta\Phi/\delta f(x)$.

A functional $\Phi$ in a real or complex Hilbert space $L$ is said to be *entire analytic* if it is representable in the form of a series which converges absolutely and uniformly in the interior of a ball of a finite radius in $L$,

$$\Phi(f) = \sum_{n=0}^{\infty} \Phi_n(f), \tag{2.2}$$

where $\Phi_n(f)$ is a bounded homogeneous functional of degree $n$.[21]

---

[21] A functional $\Phi_n(f)$ is called a *bounded homogeneous functional* of degree $n$ if it is equal to the value of a bounded polynomial functional $F(f_1,\ldots,f_n)$ at coinciding arguments:

$$\Phi_n(f) = F(f,\ldots,f).$$

The functional $F(f_1,\ldots,f_n)$ is called a *bounded polynomial* if it has the properties:

(1)     $F(f_1,\ldots,f_{k-1}, \alpha f_k' + \beta f_k'', f_{k+1},\ldots,f_n)$
$$= \alpha F(f_1,\ldots,f_{k-1}, f_k', f_{k+1},\ldots,f_n)$$
$$+ \beta F(f_1,\ldots,f_{k-1}, f_k'', f_{k+1},\ldots,f_n),$$

where $k = 1, 2,\ldots, n$ and $\alpha$, $\beta$ are complex numbers;

(2)     $|F(f_1,\ldots,f_n)| \leq C\|f_1\| \, \|f_2\| \cdots \|f_n\|.$

Let $L$ be a complex Hilbert space with involution. $L$ may be regarded as a real space consisting of elements $u$, $v$, the real and imaginary parts of the element $f = u + iv$. Then the definitions of differentiability and analyticity given above are transferred to functionals in $L$. However, it will always be more convenient for us to use the formal variables $f = u + iv$ and $f^* = u - iv$ rather than the variables $u$, $v$. We define formal derivatives as usual by

$$\frac{\delta\Phi(f^*, f)}{\delta f} = \frac{1}{2}\left(\frac{\delta\Phi}{\delta u} - i\frac{\delta\Phi}{\delta v}\right), \qquad \frac{\delta\Phi}{\delta f^*} = \frac{1}{2}\left(\frac{\delta\Phi}{\delta u} + i\frac{\delta\Phi}{\delta v}\right). \qquad (2.3)$$

Functionals in $L$ which are analytic in the real sense will be written in a series involving $f$, $f^*$ as follows:

$$\Phi(f^*, f) = \sum \Phi_{mn}(f^*, f), \qquad (2.4)$$

where $\Phi_{mn}$ is a homogeneous functional of degree $m$ in $f^*$ and degree $n$ in $f$.

Let $L$ be the state space of a single particle and $\mathscr{H}_B$ be the state space of the system. Evidently, among functionals in $L$ analytic in the real sense, there are contained functionals corresponding to a vector of the space $\mathscr{H}_B$, as well as functionals of both types corresponding to an operator in $\mathscr{H}_B$.

The definitions of differentiability and analyticity of functionals are easily transferable to the case when a functional $\Phi$ is defined not on the whole space $L$, but on a dense set $D \subset L$ in which its own norm $\|f\|_D$ is given. In order to adapt the definitions to this case, it is necessary that everywhere in them $\|f\|$ be replaced by $\|f\|_D$. We need only take into account that in this case $\delta\Phi/\delta f$ is a linear functional defined only on $D$, so that it is not necessarily true that $\delta\Phi/\delta f \in L$.

As an example we consider a Hilbert space of square-integrable functions $f(x)$ on a certain set $M$. Let $D$ be the set of bounded functions which are everywhere defined, and $\|f\|_D = \sup_{x\in M} f(x)$. Consider the functional $\Phi(f) = f(x_0)$. Evidently, $\delta\Phi/\delta f(x) = \delta(x, x_0)$, where $\delta(x, x_0)$ is Dirac's $\delta$ function.

2. CONTINUAL INTEGRAL. Let $L$ be a real Hilbert space, and $\Phi(f)$ a functional in $L$. We consider a sequence of finite-dimensional spaces $L_n$

with dimension $n$ that are successively embedded, and suppose that the closure of the sum of $L_n$ coincides with $L$:

$$\overline{\cup L_n} = L. \tag{2.5}$$

In every one of the subspaces $L_n$ we choose an orthonormal basis $f_1,\ldots,$ $f_n$. Let us consider a functional $\Phi$ on elements of the space $L_n$. Since $f \in L_n$ is representable as $f = x_1 f_1 + \cdots + x_n f_n$, we have $\Phi(f) = \Phi_n(x_1,\ldots,x_n)$. Consider the integral

$$I_n = \frac{1}{\pi^{n/2}} \int \Phi_n(x_1,\ldots,x_n)\, d^n x. \tag{2.6}$$

If the limit $I = \lim_{n\to\infty} I_n$ exists and is independent of the choice of the sequence of subspaces $L_n$, then it will be called the *continual integral* of the functional $\Phi$ and be denoted by

$$I(\Phi) = \int \Phi(f)\Pi\, df. \tag{2.7}$$

Now let $L$ be a Hilbert space with involution. We consider a sequence of embedded $n$-complex-dimensional subspaces $L_n$ satisfying the condition (2.5). In each $L_n$ we choose an orthonormal basis $f_1,\ldots,f_n$. The value of a functional $\Phi$ on the subspace $L_n$ is a function $\Phi_n$ of $2n$ real variables $x_n$, $y_n$, the real and imaginary parts of the coordinate $z$ of the vector $f$ relative to the basis $\{f_k\}$. It will be more convenient to consider the formal variables $z_k$, $\bar{z}_k$ instead of the variables $x_k$, $y_k$. Consider the integral

$$I_n = \frac{1}{(2\pi i)^n} \int \Phi_n(z_1,\ldots,z_n \mid \bar{z}_1,\ldots,\bar{z}_n)\, d^n z\, d^n \bar{z},$$

where, as usual, $dz\, d\bar{z} = 2i\, dx\, dy$.

If there exists a limit of $I_n$ as $n \to \infty$ and this limit is independent of the choice of the sequence of subspaces $L_n$, we shall call it the *continual integral* and denote it by

$$I(\Phi) = \int \Phi(f^*, f)\Pi\, df\, df^*. \tag{2.8}$$

The space $L$ with involution may be regarded as a real space: $L = R \oplus iR$ where $R$ is the space of real elements (i.e., elements such that $f^* = f$).

Evidently, if the integral (2.7) exists for the functional $\Phi$ in a complex space $L$ when $L$ is considered as a real space, then the integral (2.8) also exists and these integrals are equal. The inverse statement does not generally hold; a corresponding example will be mentioned below.[22]

Let $L$ be a real Hilbert space, $\Phi$ be a functional in $L$, $E_1 \subset L$ be a subspace of $L$, and $E_2$ be the orthogonal complement of $E_1$. Evidently $\Phi$ can be written in the form of a functional of two variables as

$$\Phi(f) = \Phi(f_1, f_2), \quad f = f_1 + f_2, \quad f_i \in E_i.$$

We represent the integral of $\Phi$ in the form of a multiple integral

$$\int \Phi(f) \Pi \, df = \int \Phi(f_1, f_2) \Pi \, df_1 \Pi \, df_2.$$

Starting from the definitions of the continual integral, it is not difficult to show that if the multiple integral exists, the following two iterated integrals also exist and are equal to the multiple integral:

$$\int \Phi(f_1, f_2) \Pi \, df_1 \Pi \, df_2 = \int \left( \int \Phi(f_1, f_2) \Pi \, df_1 \right) \Pi \, df_2$$

$$= \int \left( \int \Phi(f_1, f_2) \Pi \, df_2 \right) \Pi \, df_1.$$

A similar formula holds for integrals of functionals in a complex Hilbert space with involution.

3. INTEGRATION BY PARTS. We prove the following auxiliary statement.

**Lemma 2.1.** *Let $\Phi$ be a differentiable functional in a real Hilbert space $L$ such that*

$$\lim_{\|f\| \to \infty} \Phi(f) = 0$$

*and there exists for some $h \in L$ the integral*

$$\int \left( \frac{\delta\Phi}{\delta f}, h \right) \Pi \, df.$$

---

[22] This is due to the fact that the integral (2.8) is defined by passing to the limit, not through an arbitrary sequence of *real* subspaces satisfying the condition (2.5), but through an arbitrary sequence of *complex* spaces satisfying this condition.

*Then*

$$\int \left( \frac{\delta \Phi}{\delta f}, h \right) \Pi \, df = 0. \tag{2.9}$$

Without loss of generality we may assume that $\|h\| = 1$.

We amplify the vector $h = h_1$ to an orthonormal basis $\{h_i\}$ in the space $L$. Denote by $L_n$ the space spanned by vectors $h_i$, $1 \le i \le n$. Let $f = x_1 h_1 + \cdots + x_n h_n \in L_n$ and $\Phi(f) = \Phi_n(x_1, ..., x_n)$. Evidently we have

$$\left( \frac{\delta \Phi}{\delta f}, h \right) = \frac{\partial \Phi_n}{\partial x_1}.$$

Further, it is clear that the sequence $L_n$ satisfies the condition (2.5). Therefore the integral (2.9) is the limit of finite-multiple integrals

$$I_n = \frac{1}{\pi^{n/2}} \int \frac{\partial \Phi_n}{\partial x_1} \, d^n x. \tag{2.10}$$

In view of the assumption about the functional $\Phi(f)$, the function $\Phi_n(x_1, ..., x_n)$ tends towards zero as $x_1^2 + \cdots + x_n^2 \to \infty$. Carrying out the integration with respect to $x_1$ in (2.10), we obtain $I_n = 0$.

We now prove the theorem on the integration by parts.

**Theorem 2.1.** *Let* $\Phi_1$, $\Phi_2$ *be differentiable functionals such that*

(1) $\Phi_1 \Phi_2 \to 0$ *for* $\|f\| \to \infty$.
(2) *There exist the integrals*

$$\int \Phi_1 \left( \frac{\delta \Phi_2}{\delta f}, h \right) \Pi \, df, \qquad \int \left( \frac{\delta \Phi_1}{\delta f}, h \right) \Phi_2 \Pi \, df.$$

*Then the following equality is valid:*

$$\int \Phi_1 \left( \frac{\delta \Phi_2}{\delta f}, h \right) \Pi \, df = - \int \left( \frac{\delta \Phi_1}{\delta f}, h \right) \Phi_2 \Pi \, df. \tag{2.11}$$

To prove the theorem we have to substitute in (2.9) the functional $\Phi_1 \Phi_2$ for $\Phi$ and make use of the formula

$$\frac{\delta}{\delta f}(\Phi_1 \Phi_2) = \frac{\delta \Phi_1}{\delta f} \Phi_2 + \Phi_1 \frac{\delta \Phi_2}{\delta f}.$$

We shall often write the formula of integration by parts in the form

$$\int \Phi_1 \frac{\delta \Phi_2}{\delta f} \Pi \, df = - \int \frac{\delta \Phi_1}{\delta f} \Phi_2 \Pi \, df \qquad (2.12)$$

instead of (2.11).

If $L$ is a complex space with involution, then a theorem similar to Theorem 2.1 is valid.

**Theorem 2.2.** *Let* $\Phi_1(f^*, f), \Phi_2(f^*, f)$ *be differentiable functionals such that*

(1) $\Phi_1 \Phi_2 \to 0$ *for* $\|f\| \to \infty$.

(2) *There exist the integrals*

$$\int \Phi_1 \frac{\delta \Phi_2}{\delta f} \Pi \, df \, df^*, \qquad \int \frac{\delta \Phi_1}{\delta f^*} \Phi_2 \Pi \, df \, df^*,$$

$$\int \frac{\delta \Phi_1}{\delta f} \Phi_2 \Pi \, df \, df^*, \qquad \int \Phi_1 \frac{\delta \Phi_2}{\delta f^*} \Pi \, df \, df^*.$$

*Then we have*

$$\int \frac{\delta \Phi_1}{\delta f} \Phi_2 \Pi \, df \, df^* = - \int \Phi_1 \frac{\delta \Phi_2}{\delta f} \Pi \, df \, df^*,$$

$$\int \frac{\delta \Phi_1}{\delta f^*} \Phi_2 \Pi \, df \, df^* = - \int \Phi_1 \frac{\delta \Phi_2}{\delta f^*} \Pi \, df \, df^*. \qquad (2.13)$$

The proof of this theorem is, in essence, not different from that of Theorem 2.1, so we shall omit it.

4. EXAMPLES. We calculate the Gauss integral. Let $A > 0$ be a symmetric operator in a real Hilbert space $L$. It is evident that

$$\int e^{-(Af, f)} \Pi \, df = (\det A)^{-1/2}; \qquad (2.14)$$

the determinant in the right member is the Fredholm determinant of the operator $A$. The integral (2.14) exists if and only if the operator $A - E$ is a trace-class operator (cf. the footnotes on p. 8).

As the second example we consider a similar integral in a complex Hilbert space with involution (cf. the Introduction, Subsection 3):

$$\int \exp\left[ -\tfrac{1}{2}(f \ \ f^*) \begin{pmatrix} A_{11} & A_{12} \\ A_{21} & A_{22} \end{pmatrix} \begin{pmatrix} f \\ f^* \end{pmatrix} \right] \Pi \, df \, df^* = \left[ \det \begin{pmatrix} A_{21} & A_{22} \\ A_{11} & A_{12} \end{pmatrix} \right]^{-1/2},$$

$$(2.15)$$

where $A_{ik} = A'_{ki}$. The determinant on the right is a regularized Fredholm determinant in the sense of the definition given in Subsection 3 of the Introduction.[23]

The integral (2.15) exists if $A_{21} - E$, $A_{12} - E$ are trace-class operators, $A_{11}$, $A_{22}$ are Hilbert-Schmidt operators,[24] and

$$\mathrm{Re}(f \ \ f^*) \begin{pmatrix} A_{11} & A_{12} \\ A_{21} & A_{22} \end{pmatrix} \begin{pmatrix} f \\ f^* \end{pmatrix} \geq \alpha(f, f);$$

$\alpha > 0$ is a certain real number. We note that the last condition is satisfied if $A_{12} = A_{21} = E$, $\|A_{11}\| < 1$, and $\|A_{22}\| < 1$. Formula (2.15) follows immediately from a similar formula for finite-multiple integrals.

We shall encounter the more general integral

$$\int \exp\left[ -\tfrac{1}{2}(f \ \ f^*) \begin{pmatrix} A_{11} & A_{12} \\ A_{21} & A_{22} \end{pmatrix} \begin{pmatrix} f \\ f^* \end{pmatrix} + (\varphi_1 \ \ \varphi_2) \begin{pmatrix} f \\ f^* \end{pmatrix} \right] \Pi \, df \, df^*$$

$$= \left[ \det \begin{pmatrix} A_{21} & A_{22} \\ A_{11} & A_{12} \end{pmatrix} \right]^{-1/2} \exp\left[ \tfrac{1}{2}(\varphi_1 \ \ \varphi_2) \begin{pmatrix} A_{11} & A_{12} \\ A_{21} & A_{22} \end{pmatrix}^{-1} \begin{pmatrix} \varphi_1 \\ \varphi_2 \end{pmatrix} \right]. \quad (2.16)$$

The calculation of (2.16) is reduced to (2.15) by singling out the complete square in the exponent. From (2.15) it follows, in particular, that

$$\int e^{-(f, f)} \Pi \, df \, df^* \equiv \int e^{-f^* f} \Pi \, df \, df^* = 1. \quad (2.17)$$

---

[23] The matrix $\mathscr{A} = \begin{pmatrix} A_{11} & A_{12} \\ A_{21} & A_{22} \end{pmatrix}$ obviously defines an operator in the space $\mathscr{E} = L \oplus L^*$, the direct sum of two copies of the space $L$.

[24] It should be noted that if $L$ is regarded as a real space and the corresponding definition of the integral is used, then (2.15) exists under more stringent restrictions on $A$; in that case it should be required that the operators $A_{11}$, $A_{22}$ be trace-class operators. Compare, in this respect, the remarks appended to the definition of the continual integral (Section 2.2) and to the definition of the determinant in the space with involution (Introduction, Subsection 3).

We consider the bounded homogeneous functional

$$\int A_{mn}(x_1,\ldots, x_m \mid y_1,\ldots, y_n)f^*(x_1) \cdots f^*(x_m)f(y_1) \cdots f(y_n)\, d^m x\, d^n y$$

and prove the equality

$$\int \left( \left( \int A_{mn}(x_1,\ldots, x_m \mid y_1,\ldots, y_n)f^*(x_1) \cdots f^*(x_m) \right. \right.$$

$$\left. \times f(y_1) \cdots f(y_n)d^m x\, d^n y \right) e^{-f^*f}\Pi\, df\, df^*$$

$$= \delta_{mn}n! \int A_{nn}(x_1,\ldots, x_n \mid x_1,\ldots, x_n)\, d^n x. \tag{2.18}$$

(The function $A$ is supposed to be symmetric with respect to $x_1, \ldots, x_m$ and $y_1,\ldots, y_n$, separately.) To verify this formula we note that

$$f^*(y_1) \cdots f^*(y_n)e^{-ff^*} = (-1)^n \frac{\delta^n}{\delta f(y_1) \cdots \delta f(y_n)} e^{-ff^*}. \tag{2.19}$$

Substituting this expression in the left side of (2.18) and then integrating by parts, we obtain the right side.

5. INNER PRODUCT IN THE STATE SPACE. In the preceding section we have shown that we can naturally put into one-to-one correspondence a functional $\Phi(a^*)$ with every vector $\hat{\Phi}$ in the state space. In the set $\mathscr{L}$ of functionals corresponding to the vectors, we introduce the inner product

$$(\Phi_1, \Phi_2) = (\hat{\Phi}_1, \hat{\Phi}_2). \tag{2.20}$$

The inner product (2.20) converts $\mathscr{L}$ into a Hilbert space. The functional Hilbert space thus obtained is a realization of the state space. In order that an arbitrary analytic functional

$$\Phi(a^*) = \sum \frac{1}{(n!)^{1/2}} \int K_n(x_1,\ldots, x_n)a^*(x_1) \cdots a^*(x_n)\, d^n x \tag{2.21}$$

belong to $\mathscr{L}$, it is evidently necessary and sufficient that the following inequality be satisfied:

$$\sum_n \int |K_n(x_1,\ldots, x_n)|^2\, d^n x < \infty. \tag{2.22}$$

The inner product (2.20) and the condition (2.22) can be expressed in the form of continual integrals.

**Theorem 2.3.**[25] (1) *The inner product (2.20) can be given by the formula*

$$(\Phi_1, \Phi_2) = \int \Phi_1(a^*)\overline{\Phi_2(a^*)}e^{-aa^*}\Pi \, da \, da^*. \qquad (2.23)$$

(2) *In order that an analytic functional $\Phi(a^*)$ correspond to a vector of the state space, it is necessary and sufficient that the following inequality be satisfied:*

$$\int |\Phi(a^*)|^2 e^{-a^*a}\Pi \, da^* \, da < \infty. \qquad (2.24)$$

Before proving the theorem it is to be noted that if we substitute in the right member of (2.23) the expressions for $\Phi_1$ and $\Phi_2$ in the form of the series (1.17), and then change the order of sum and integral and use formula (2.18), we readily obtain the inner product $(\hat{\Phi}_1, \hat{\Phi}_2)$. The change of order of the sum and integral is permissible whenever $\Phi_1$ and $\Phi_2$ are polynomial functionals. The content of the proposed proof of Theorem 2.3 amounts to showing that this interchange can be established in the general case. First, suppose that the number of degrees of freedom be finite and equal to $N$. Then

$$\Phi = \sum_n \frac{1}{(n!)^{1/2}} \sum_{1 \le p_k \le N} K_{p_1 \cdots p_n} a_{p_1}^* \cdots a_{p_n}^*,$$

$$\|\Phi\|^2 = \sum_n \sum_{1 \le p_k \le N} |K_{p_1 \cdots p_n}|^2.$$

We denote by $\Phi_M$ the partial sum of this series,

$$\Phi_M = \sum_{n=0}^{M} \frac{1}{(n!)^{1/2}} \sum_{1 \le p_k \le N} K_{p_1 \cdots p_n} a_{p_1}^* \cdots a_{p_n}^*.$$

Consider the integral

$$C(M, R) = \frac{1}{(2\pi i)^n} \int_{|a_k| < R} |\Phi_M(a^*)|^2 \exp\left(-\sum a_k a_k^*\right) d^n a \, d^n a^*.$$

It is evident that

$$\lim_{M \to \infty} \lim_{R \to \infty} C(M, R) = (\Phi, \Phi). \qquad (2.25)$$

[25] Cf. Bargmann [1] and the report by Berezin *et al.* [1], p. 535.

By carrying out the integration, we obtain for $C(M, R)$ the expression

$$C(M, R) = \sum_{n=0}^{M} \sum_{1 \le p_k \le N} |K_{p_1 \cdots p_n}|^2 \alpha(p_1, R) \cdots \alpha(p_n, R),$$

where

$$\alpha(p, R) = \frac{1}{p^n} \int_0^{R^2} e^{-s} s^p \, ds.$$

Hence it is seen that $C(M, R)$ is a monotonically increasing function of $M$ for fixed $R$ and it is a monotonically increasing function of $R$ for fixed $M$. Therefore, we can change the limits in (2.25):

$$\lim_{R \to \infty} \lim_{M \to \infty} C(M, R) = (\Phi, \Phi).$$

The limit on the left of this equality is evidently equal to the integral

$$\frac{1}{(2\pi i)^n} \int |\Phi(a^*)|^2 \exp(-\sum a_k a_k^*) \, d^n a \, d^n a^*.$$

Thus formula (2.23) is proved for the case $\Phi_1 = \Phi_2$. The extension of formula (2.23) to arbitrary $\Phi_1$, $\Phi_2$ is performed by standard arguments.

We pass to the general case. We realize the space $L$ as a space of sequences $\{a_k^*\}$. Then

$$\Phi_i = \sum_n \frac{1}{(n!)^{1/2}} \sum_p K^i_{p_1 \cdots p_n} a_{p_1}^* \cdots a_{p_n}^*, \quad \sum_n \sum_p |K^i_{p_1 \cdots p_n}|^2 < \infty \qquad (i = 1, 2)$$

and

$$(\Phi_1, \Phi_2) = \sum_n \sum_p K^1_{p_1 \cdots p_n} \overline{K^2_{p_1 \cdots p_n}}. \tag{2.26}$$

We consider the subspace $L_N \subset L$ consisting of the sequences $\{a_k^*\}$, $1 \le k \le N$, and the finite-dimensional approximation of the integral (2.23) connected with $L_N$. Let us denote the value of $\Phi_i$ on $L_N$ by $\Phi_i^N$. It is evident that

$$\Phi_i^N = \sum_n \frac{1}{(n!)^{1/2}} \sum_{1 \le p_k \le N} K^i_{p_1 \cdots p_n} a_{p_1}^* \cdots a_{p_n}^*.$$

Since Theorem 2.3 is proved for a finite number of degrees of freedom, the finite-dimensional approximation of the integral (2.23), connected with $L_N$, is equal to

$$(\Phi_1^N, \Phi_2^N) = \sum_n \sum_{1 \le p_k \le N} K^1_{p_1 \cdots p_n} \overline{K^2_{p_1 \cdots p_n}}. \tag{2.27}$$

The sum (2.27) is evidently an infinite partial sum of the series (2.26). Since the series (2.26) converges absolutely, it is the limit of (2.27) as $N \to \infty$. Thus $(\Phi_1, \Phi_2)$ is the limit of the finite-dimensional approximation of integral (2.27). The first assertion of the theorem is proved. The second assertion is proved in an analogous way.[26]

*Remark.* By the use of the result of Minlos [1], one can show that the integral (2.24) is an integral with respect to the Gaussian measure concentrated in an extension $\tilde{L}$ of the space $L$; $\tilde{L}$ is a Hilbert space obtained by supplementing $L$ by means of the inner product

$$(a_1, a_2)_1 = (Ka_1, Ka_2),$$

where $K$ is an arbitrary Hilbert-Schmidt operator which does not carry over any vector into the zero vector.

The functionals $\Phi(a^*)$ can be extended in a natural way to functionals in $\tilde{L}$.

In general, as far as bosons are concerned, all the continual integrals contained in the present book can be interpreted as integrals with respect to the Gaussian measure.

However, we shall not utilize this fact anywhere.

6. OPERATION OF AN OPERATOR ON A VECTOR. Let $\tilde{A}$ be a functional corresponding to the matrix form of a bounded operator $\hat{A}$, and $\Phi$ be a functional corresponding to a vector $\hat{\Phi}$. We find a functional $\hat{\Psi}$ corresponding to the vector $\hat{\Psi} = \hat{A}\hat{\Phi}$. Evidently the functional $\hat{\Psi}(a^*)$ is equal to [cf. (0.3), (0.6), (0.7)]

$$\hat{\Psi}(a^*) = \sum_{m,n} \frac{1}{(m!)^{1/2}} \int a^*(x_1) \cdots a^*(x_m)$$

$$\times A_{mn}(x_1, \ldots, x_m \mid y_1, \ldots, y_n) K_n(y_1, \ldots, y_n) d^m x \, d^n y.$$

In fixing the function $a^*$ this formula has the form

$$\hat{\Psi}(a^*) = (\hat{\Phi}, \hat{\mathfrak{A}}),$$

[26] It is evident that whatever the sequence of embedded subspaces $L_N$ satisfying the condition (2.5) may be, the realization of $L$ in the form of a space of sequences can be selected in such a way that $L_N$ consists of sequences of the form $(a_1^*, \ldots, a_N^*)$. Thus the sequence of subspaces $L_N$ considered in the proof is the most general one satisfying the condition (2.5).

where $\hat{\mathfrak{A}}$ is the vector, to which there corresponds the functional

$$\mathfrak{A}(a^*) = \sum_n \frac{1}{(n!)^{1/2}} \int \mathfrak{A}_n(y_1,\ldots,y_n) a^*(y_1) \cdots a^*(y_n)\, d^n y,$$

$$\mathfrak{A}_n(y_1,\ldots,y_n) = \sum_m \frac{1}{(m!)^{1/2}} \int a(x_1) \cdots a(x_m)$$

$$\times \bar{A}_{mn}(x_1,\ldots,x_m \mid y_1,\ldots,y_n) d^m x.$$

[From the boundedness of $\hat{A}$ it evidently follows that

$$\sum_n \int |\mathfrak{A}_n(y_1,\ldots,y_n)|^2 d^n y < \infty.]$$

Therefore, according to Theorem 2.3,

$$\hat{\Psi}(a^*) = \int \Phi(\alpha^*)\overline{\mathfrak{A}(\alpha^*)} e^{-\alpha\alpha^*}\Pi\, d\alpha^*\, d\alpha.$$

Substituting the value of $\mathfrak{A}$, we finally obtain

$$\Psi(a^*) = \int \tilde{A}(a^*, \alpha)\Phi(\alpha^*)e^{-\alpha\alpha^*}\Pi\, d\alpha^*\, d\alpha.) \qquad (2.28)$$

Passing, by means of formula (1.38), from the functional $\tilde{A}$ to the functional $A$ corresponding to the normal form of the operator $\hat{A}$, we get

$$\Psi(a^*) = \int A(a^*, \alpha)\Phi(\alpha^*)e^{-(\alpha^*-a^*)\alpha}\,\Pi\, d\alpha\, d\alpha^*. \qquad (2.29)$$

We substitute for $\tilde{A}$ and $\Phi$ in (2.28) the series corresponding to these functionals and change the order of sum and integral thus obtained. Carrying out the integration in each summand and using formula (2.18), we arrive at the right answer, as is easily seen. The interchange of sum and integral is allowable if $\Phi(a^*)$ is a polynomial functional. Thus the use of Theorem 2.3 is essentially the foundation of this interchange in the general case.

This remark applies also to the formula given below.

7. PRODUCT OF OPERATORS. Let $\hat{A}$ and $\hat{B}$ be bounded operators and let $\tilde{A}$ and $\tilde{B}$ be functionals corresponding to their matrix form. The

functional $\tilde{C}$ corresponding to the matrix form of the operator $\hat{C} = \hat{A}\hat{B}$ is equal to

$$\tilde{C}(a^*, a) = \int \tilde{A}(a^*, \alpha)\tilde{B}(\alpha^*, a)e^{-\alpha^*\alpha}\Pi \, d\alpha^* \, d\alpha. \qquad (2.30)$$

To prove (2.30) in the case when $\tilde{A}$ and $\tilde{B}$ are polynomial functionals, we have to permute sum and integral and then use formulas (2.18) and (0.4). In the general case the proof of (2.30) is reduced to Theorem 2.3 by means of a method similar to that which was used for the proof of formula (2.28). We shall not discuss these details.

From (2.30) and (1.38) It follows that the functionals $A$, $B$, $C$ corresponding to the normal form of the operators $\hat{A}$, $\hat{B}$, $\hat{C}$ are related by the formula

$$C(a^*, a) = \int A(a^*, \alpha)B(\alpha^*, a)e^{-(\alpha^* - a^*)(\alpha - a)}\Pi \, d\alpha^* \, d\alpha. \qquad (2.31)$$

8. TRACE OF AN OPERATOR. Let $\hat{A}$ and $\hat{B}$ be Hilbert-Schmidt operators and let $\|A_{mn}\|$, $\|B_{mn}\|$ be matrices of these operators. Evidently, we have

$$\text{Sp } \hat{A}\hat{B} = \sum_{m,n} \int A_{mn}(x_1,\ldots, x_m \,|\, y_1,\ldots, y_n)$$

$$\times \, B_{nm}(y_1,\ldots, y_n \,|\, x_1,\ldots, x_m) \, d^m x \, d^n y;$$

Sp $\hat{A}\hat{B}$, like the inner product $(\Phi_1, \Phi_2)$, can be calculated by means of the continual integral,

$$\text{Sp } \hat{A}\hat{B} = \int \tilde{A}(a^*, \alpha)\tilde{B}(\alpha^*, a)e^{-\alpha^*\alpha - a^*a}\Pi \, d\alpha^* \, d\alpha \, da^* \, da, \qquad (2.32)$$

where $\tilde{A}$ and $\tilde{B}$ are functionals corresponding to the matrix form of the operators $\hat{A}$ and $\hat{B}$. Formula (2.32) is proved in exactly the same way as (2.23), and so we shall omit the proof.

We replace the double integral (2.32) by the iterated integral:

$$\text{Sp } \hat{A}\hat{B} = \int e^{-a^*a} \left( \int \tilde{A}(a^*, \alpha)\tilde{B}(\alpha^*, a)e^{-\alpha^*\alpha}\Pi \, d\alpha^* \, d\alpha \right)\Pi \, da^* \, da.$$

We observe that the interior integral is the functional $\tilde{C}(a^*, a)$ corresponding to the matrix form of the operator $\hat{C} = \hat{A}\hat{B}$. Evidently $\tilde{C}$

is a trace-class operator. Moreover, it is well known that any trace-class operator is representable in the form of the product of two Hilbert-Schmidt operators.

Thus, if $\hat{C}$ is a trace-class operator and $\tilde{C}$ is the functional corresponding to its matrix form,

$$\mathrm{Sp}\ \hat{C} = \int \tilde{C}(a^*, a)e^{-a^*a}\Pi\ da^*\ da. \tag{2.33}$$

In terms of the functional $C(a^*, a)$ corresponding to the normal form of the operator $\hat{C}$, $\mathrm{Sp}\ \hat{C}$ can be written in the form

$$\mathrm{Sp}\ \hat{C} = \int C(a^*, a)\Pi\ da^*\ da. \tag{2.34}$$

## 3. Operations on Generating Functionals. Fermi Case

In this section we find the expression for a functional corresponding to a product of operators through functionals corresponding to factors, and solve some other problems for fermions. Since many formulas contain continual integrals on a Grassmann algebra, we formulate as preliminaries the basic notions needed in the sequel.

1. ANALYSIS ON A FINITE-DIMENSIONAL GRASSMANN ALGEBRA.[27] An algebra whose generators $x_1,..., x_n$ satisfy the relations

$$x_i x_k + x_k x_i \equiv \{x_i, x_k\} = 0 \tag{3.1}$$

is called a *Grassmann algebra with n generators*. In particular, $x_i^2 = 0$. The Grassmann algebra with $n$ generators will be denoted by $\mathscr{G}_n$. It follows from (3.1) that $\mathscr{G}_n$ as a linear space has the dimension $2^n$. It is convenient to consider as a basis in $\mathscr{G}_n$ the monomials

$$1, x_1,..., x_n, x_1 x_2,..., x_{n-1} x_n,..., x_1 \cdots x_n. \tag{3.2}$$

The monomial $x_{i_1} \cdots x_{i_p}$ will be referred to as a *monomial of degree p.*

---

[27] Cf. Berezin [2], and Vivier [1], where a well-developed differential calculus on the Grassmann algebra may be found.

Every element $f(x)$ of the algebra $\mathscr{G}_n$ is representable in the form of a linear combination of monomials:

$$f(x) = f_0 + \sum_k f_1(k)x_k + \sum_{k_i} f_2(k_1, k_2)x_{k_1}x_{k_2} + \cdots$$

$$+ \sum_{k_i} f_n(k_1, \ldots, k_n)x_{k_1} \cdots x_{k_n}. \tag{3.3}$$

An element of the form $\sum_{k_i} f_p(k_1, \ldots, k_p)x_{k_1} \cdots x_{k_p}$ will be called a *homogeneous element of degree p.*

The manner of writing the element $f$ in the form (3.3) is, in general, not unique. It is easy to prove that uniqueness is achieved if one takes as coefficients, not arbitrary, but antisymmetric functions, i.e., those which change sign with the permutation of any pair of arguments.

In the following, when an element $f$ is written in the form (3.3) and unless otherwise specified, it is assumed that the coefficients $f_p(k_1, \ldots, k_p)$ are antisymmetric.

It is possible to make the method of writing the element in the form (3.3) unique by other methods. To this end, for example, we may take as coefficients functions satisfying the condition $f_p(k_1, \ldots, k_p) = 0$, if $k_i \geq k_j$ for at least one pair of indices $i < j$. In this case the homogeneous element of degree $p$ is written in the form

$$\sum_{k_1 < k_2 < \cdots < k_p} f_p(k_1, \ldots, k_p)x_{k_1} \cdots x_{k_p}.$$

We consider the set $\mathscr{G}_n''$ of elements on $\mathscr{G}_n$ which are representable in the form of linear combinations of monomials of even degree:

$$f = f_0 + \sum_{k_i} f_2(k_1, k_2)x_{k_1}x_{k_2} + \cdots.$$

Elements of $\mathscr{G}_n''$ will be called *even.* Even elements are commutative with all elements of $\mathscr{G}_n$. The set $\mathscr{G}_n'$ of all elements that are linear combinations of odd degree will be called *odd.* Elements of $\mathscr{G}_n'$ have the form

$$f = \sum_k f_1(k)x_k + \sum_{k_i} f_3(k_1, k_2, k_3)x_{k_1}x_{k_2}x_{k_3} + \cdots$$

Evidently every element of $\mathscr{G}_n$ is uniquely represented in the form $f = f' + f''$, $f' \in \mathscr{G}_n'$, $f'' \in \mathscr{G}_n''$.

**A. Derivatives.** We define the left and right derivatives $(\partial/\partial x_k)f$ and $f(\partial/\partial x_k)$ of an element $f(x)$ of the algebra $\mathscr{G}_n$. Both derivatives are linear operators in $\mathscr{G}_n$, and hence it suffices to give them on the base elements (3.2). On the base elements the derivatives are given by the formulas

$$\frac{\partial}{\partial x_p} x_{i_1} \cdots x_{i_s} = \delta_{i_1 p} x_{i_2} \cdots x_{i_s}$$

$$- \delta_{i_2 p} x_{i_1} x_{i_3} \cdots x_{i_s} + \cdots + (-1)^{s-1} \delta_{i_s p} x_{i_1} \cdots x_{i_{s-1}},$$

$$x_{i_1} \cdots x_{i_s} \frac{\partial}{\partial x_p} = \delta_{i_s p} x_{i_1} \cdots x_{i_{s-1}} \tag{3.4}$$

$$- \delta_{i_{s-1} p} x_{i_1} \cdots x_{i_{s-2}} x_{i_s} + \cdots + (-1)^{s-1} \delta_{i_1 p} x_{i_2} \cdots x_{i_s}.$$

In other words, to calculate the left derivative of $x_{i_1} \cdots x_{i_s}$ by $x_p$, we have to permute $x_p$ to the first place in the monomial by using relations (3.1) and then drop it; to calculate the right derivative, we have to permute $x_p$ to the last place and drop it. If the monomial $x_{i_1} \cdots x_{i_s}$ does not contain $x_p$ at all, then both derivatives are equal to zero.

It is immediate from the definition of derivatives that the chain differentiation rule holds. We shall confine ourselves to the simplest cases.

(1) Let

$$x_k = \sum_p a_{kp} y_p, \qquad f(x) = f[x(y)].$$

Then

$$\frac{\partial}{\partial y_p} f[x(y)] = \sum_k \left[ \frac{\partial}{\partial x_k} f(x) \right]_{x=x(y)} a_{kp},$$

$$f[x(y)] \frac{\partial}{\partial y_p} = \sum_k \left[ f(x) \frac{\partial}{\partial x_k} \right]_{x=x(y)} a_{kp}. \tag{3.5}$$

(2) Let $t$ be a real parameter, and

$$x_k(t) = \sum_p a_{kp}(t) y_p.$$

Then

$$\frac{d}{dt} f[x(t)] = \sum_k \frac{dx_k}{dt} \frac{\partial}{\partial x_k} f = \sum_k \left( f \frac{\partial}{\partial x_k} \right) \frac{dx_k}{dt}. \tag{3.5'}$$

We also note formulas for the differentiation of a product. Let $f_1 \in \mathscr{G}_n''$ be an even element and $f_2$ be an arbitrary element of $\mathscr{G}_n$; then

$$\frac{\partial}{\partial x_p}(f_1 f_2) = \left(\frac{\partial}{\partial x_p} f_1\right) f_2 + f_1\left(\frac{\partial}{\partial x_p} f_2\right),$$

$$(f_2 f_1)\frac{\partial}{\partial x_p} = f_2\left(f_1 \frac{\partial}{\partial x_p}\right) + \left(f_2 \frac{\partial}{\partial x_p}\right) f_1.$$

(3.6)

If $f_1 \in \mathscr{G}_n'$ and $f_2$ is an arbitrary element, the formulas have the form

$$\frac{\partial}{\partial x_p}(f_1 f_2) = \left(\frac{\partial}{\partial x_p} f_1\right) f_2 - f_1\left(\frac{\partial}{\partial x_p} f_2\right),$$

$$(f_2 f_1)\frac{\partial}{\partial x_p} = f_2\left(f_1 \frac{\partial}{\partial x_p}\right) - \left(f_2 \frac{\partial}{\partial x_p}\right) f_1.$$

(3.7)

Let us turn our attention to the properties of second derivatives:

$$\frac{\partial}{\partial x_1}\left(\frac{\partial}{\partial x_2} f\right) = -\frac{\partial}{\partial x_2}\left(\frac{\partial}{\partial x_1} f\right),$$

$$\left(f\frac{\partial}{\partial x_1}\right)\frac{\partial}{\partial x_2} = -\left(f\frac{\partial}{\partial x_2}\right)\frac{\partial}{\partial x_1},$$

$$\left(\frac{\partial}{\partial x_1} f\right)\frac{\partial}{\partial x_2} = \frac{\partial}{\partial x_1}\left(f\frac{\partial}{\partial x_2}\right).$$

(3.8)

Like (3.5)–(3.7) these properties follow easily from the definition of the derivatives.

**B. Integral on a Grassmann Algebra.** We introduce the symbols $dx_1 \cdots dx_n$, subject to the commutation relations

$$\{dx_i, dx_k\} = \{x_k, dx_i\} = 0. \tag{3.9}$$

We define single integrals:

$$\int dx_i = 0, \qquad \int x_i \, dx_i = 1. \tag{3.10}$$

Multiple integrals will be understood as iterated integrals. Thus formulas (3.9) and (3.10) define the integral $\int f(x)\, dx_n \cdots dx_1$ for all monomials. The integral can be extended to arbitrary elements by linearity. The integral defined by formulas (3.9), (3.10) will be called the *integral on the Grassmann algebra* by the variables (or generators) $x_1,\ldots, x_n$.

From the definition of the integral it follows that for an arbitrary element $f(x)$ denoted by formula (3.3) we have

$$\int f(x)\, dx_n \cdots dx_1 = n!\, f_n(1,\ldots, n). \tag{3.11}$$

The integral on the finite-dimensional Grassmann algebra $\mathscr{G}_n$ has several properties similar to those of the ordinary integral. In particular, any linear functional on $\mathscr{G}_n$ is given by the formulas

$$F(f) = \int f(x) F_r(x)\, dx_n \cdots dx_1, \tag{3.12}$$

or

$$F(f) = \int F_l(x) f(x)\, dx_n \cdots dx_1, \tag{3.12'}$$

where $F_r$ and $F_l$ are fixed elements in $\mathscr{G}_n$.

A linear operator in $\mathscr{G}_n$ can be given by the formula

$$(Tf)(x) = \int f(y_1,\ldots, y_n) K_r(y_1,\ldots, y_n \,|\, x_1,\ldots, x_n)\, dy_n \cdots dy_1, \tag{3.13}$$

or

$$(Tf)(x) = \int K_l(x_1,\ldots, x_n \,|\, y_1,\ldots, y_n) f(y_1,\ldots, y_n)\, dy_n \cdots dy_1, \tag{3.13'}$$

where $K_r$ and $K_l$ are elements of the algebra $\mathscr{G}_{2n}$, and $x_i$, $y_k$ are generators in $\mathscr{G}_{2n}$.

To prove formula (3.12) it suffices to verify that the equality $\int f(x) F(x)\, dx_n \cdots dx_1 = 0$ for any $f \in \mathscr{G}_n$ is possible only if $F = 0$. In fact, the space of linear functionals on $\mathscr{G}_n$ has the dimension $2^n$. Under the condition stated above, the space of functionals represented in the form $\int f(x) F(x)\, dx_n \cdots dx_1$ has the same dimension. To verify that the equality $\int f(x) F(x)$

$dx_n \cdots dx_1 = 0$, for all $f$, implies $F = 0$, it is necessary to represent $F$ in the form (3.3) and to take as $f$ all base elements successively. Similarly one can establish that any functional is representable in the form (3.12′).

For the proof of formula (3.13) we note that linear operators in $\mathscr{G}_n$ form a space of dimension $2^{2n}$. The algebra $\mathscr{G}_{2n}$ has the same dimension. Therefore it suffices to verify that the equality $\int f(y)K(y\,|\,x)\,dy_n \cdots dy_1 = 0$, for all $f$, implies $K(y\,|\,x) = 0$. We observe that any element of the algebra $\mathscr{G}_{2n}$ with generators $x_1,\ldots,x_n$, $y_1,\ldots,y_n$ may be represented in the form $\mathscr{F} = \sum_{i,k} a_{ik} f_i(x) g_k(y)$. Hence, if $\int f(y)K(y\,|\,x)\,dy_n \cdots dy_1 = 0$, then the linear functional on $\mathscr{G}_{2n}$ defined by the equality

$$F(\mathscr{F}) = \int \mathscr{F}(x\,|\,y)K(y\,|\,x)\,dy_n \cdots dy_1\,dx_n \cdots dx_1$$

is equal to zero. As we know, this is possible only if $K(y\,|\,x) = 0$.

Similarly, we can establish that any operator is representable in the form (3.13′).

As in ordinary analysis, formulas for integration by parts on the Grassmann algebra are true:

$$\int f(x)\left(\frac{\partial}{\partial x_p} g(x)\right) dx_n \cdots dx_1 = \int \left(f(x)\frac{\partial}{\partial x_p}\right) g(x)\,dx_n \cdots dx_1, \quad (3.14)$$

$$\int f(x)\left(g(x)\frac{\partial}{\partial x_{p'}}\right) dx_n \cdots dx_1 = (-1)^{n+1} \int \left(\frac{\partial}{\partial x_p} f(x)\right) g(x)\,dx_n \cdots dx_1. \tag{3.14′}$$

For the proof it is sufficient to consider arbitrary monomials as $f$ and $g$.

Formulas (3.14) and (3.14′) must often be applied in the cases when the integration is not carried out over the whole Grassmann algebra, but over part. It turns out that in such cases formula (3.14) remains valid, but formula (3.14′) can be shown to be invalid.

Consider as an example the "Fourier transformation"

$$\varphi(y) = \int f(x)\exp(\sum x_k y_k)\,dx_n \cdots dx_1.$$

Here $x_k$, $y_k$ are generators of the algebra $\mathscr{G}_{2n}$. Multiplying $\varphi(y)$ from the right by $y_p$ and applying (3.14), we have

$$\varphi(y)y_p = (-1)^n \int f(x) \exp(\sum x_k y_k) y_p \, dx_n \cdots dx_1$$

$$= (-1)^n \int f(x) \left[ \frac{\partial}{\partial x_p} \exp(\sum x_k y_k) \right] dx_n \cdots dx_1$$

$$= (-1)^n \int \left[ f(x) \frac{\partial}{\partial x_p} \right] \exp(\sum x_k y_k) \, dx_n \cdots dx_1.$$

On the other hand, by making use of formula (3.14′), we obtain

$$\varphi(y)y_p = (-1)^{n+1} \int f(x) \left[ \exp(\sum x_k y_k) \frac{\partial}{\partial x_p} \right] dx_n \cdots dx_1$$

$$= \int \left[ \frac{\partial}{\partial x_p} f(x) \right] \exp(\sum x_k y_k) \, dx_n \cdots dx_1.$$

Thus, if

$$(-1)^n \left[ f(x) \frac{\partial}{\partial x_p} \right] \neq \frac{\partial}{\partial x_p} f(x),$$

the answer given by formula (3.14′) is not correct!

It is not difficult, however, to show that formula (3.14′) remains valid if the functions $f$, $g$ depend on the generators over which an even-multiple integration (of parameters) is not carried out.

Here we still note that the differentiation operator anticommutes with differentials:

$$\varphi(y) \frac{\partial}{\partial y_p} = (-1)^n \int f(x) \left[ \exp(\sum x_k y_k) \frac{\partial}{\partial y_p} \right] dx_n \cdots dx_1$$

$$= (-1)^n \int f(x)x_p \exp(\sum x_k y_k) \, dx_n \cdots dx_1.$$

For integrals on a Grassmann algebra the formula for the change of variables also holds. We confine ourselves to the simplest case, when the substitution is linear:

$$x_i = \sum_k a_{ik} y_k, \qquad dx_i = \sum_k \tilde{a}_{ik} \, dy_k;$$

$\|\tilde{a}_{ik}\|$ is the matrix inverse to $\|a_{ik}\|$. For such a change of variables the following formula holds:

$$\int f(x)dx_n \cdots dx_1 = \det \|\tilde{a}_{ik}\| \int f[x(y)] \, dy_n \cdots dy_1 \qquad (3.15)$$

We note that in distinction to the ordinary rule for changing variables, independent variables and differentials are transformed by means of mutually inverse matrices.

Formula (3.15) is a consequence of the obvious equalities

$$x_1 \cdots x_n = \det \|a_{ik}\| y_1 \cdots y_n,$$

$$dx_n \cdots dx_1 = \det \|\tilde{a}_{ik}\| dy_n \cdots dy_1.$$

In closing this subsection we calculate the "Gauss integral"

$$I = \int \exp\left(\sum a_{ik} x_i x_k\right) dx_n \cdots dx_1, \qquad a_{ik} = -a_{ki},$$

First, let $\|a_{ik}\|$ be a real matrix. We make use of the fact that by a proper orthogonal transformation $\|s_{ik}\|$, the matrix $\|a_{ik}\|$ can be brought to the form

$$\begin{pmatrix} 0 & \lambda_1 & 0 & 0 & 0 & \cdots \\ -\lambda_1 & 0 & 0 & 0 & 0 & \cdots \\ 0 & 0 & 0 & \lambda_2 & 0 & \cdots \\ 0 & 0 & -\lambda_2 & 0 & 0 & \cdots \\ \cdots\cdots\cdots\cdots\cdots\cdots\cdots \end{pmatrix}.$$

Let us, in the integral, carry out the substitution

$$x_i = \sum s_{ik} y_k.$$

According to formula (3.15) we obtain

$$I = \int \exp[2(\lambda_1 y_1 y_2 + \lambda_2 y_3 y_4 + \cdots + \lambda_{n/2} y_{n-1} y_n)] \, dy_n \cdots dy_1$$

for even $n$ and

$$I = \int \exp[2(\lambda_1 y_1 y_2 + \cdots + \lambda_{(n-1)/2} y_{n-2} y_{n-1})] \, dy_n \cdots dy_1$$

for odd $n$. ($\det \|s_{ik}\| = 1$ since $\|s_{ik}\|$ is a proper orthogonal matrix.)

Using formula (3.11) we find that

$$I = 2^{n/2} \lambda_1 \cdots \lambda_n = \det(\|2a_{ik}\|)^{1/2}$$

for even $n$, whereas $I = 0$ for odd $n$. Since det $\|a_{ik}\| = 0$ for odd $n$, these cases can be unified.

As a result we obtain

$$\int \exp\left(\sum a_{ik}x_ix_k\right) dx_n \cdots dx_1 = (\det \|2a_{ik}\|)^{1/2}. \qquad (3.16)$$

The root on the right of this equality is defined in such a way that it is positive for positive values of det $\|2a_{ik}\|$.

Formula (3.16) is valid not only for real matrices but also for complex matrices. To extend it to complex matrices $\|a_{ik}\|$, we note that there is a monomial of $a_{ik}$ in the left member of (3.16), and consequently the right member is also a monomial. If both monomials are equal for real values of the arguments, then these are also equal for complex values of the arguments.[28]

2. CLIFFORD ALGEBRA. An algebra $K_n$ with generators $k_1,\ldots, k_n$ is called a *Clifford* or *spinor algebra*, if it satisfies the relations

$$k_ik_j + k_jk_i \equiv \{k_i, k_j\} = 0 \qquad \text{for} \quad i \neq j,$$

$$k_i^2 = 1.$$

With each Grassmann algebra $\mathcal{G}_n$ there is closely connected a Clifford algebra $K_{2n}$ with a duplicated number of generators.

We consider in $\mathcal{G}_n$ the generator $\hat{x}_k$ of left multiplication by $x_k$ and $\partial/\partial x_k$, left differentiation by $x_k$. It is not difficult to verify that these operators satisfy the relations

$$\left\{\hat{x}_k, \frac{\partial}{\partial x_j}\right\} = \delta_{kj}.$$

We now form operators $Q_k = \hat{x}_k + (\partial/\partial x_k)$ and $P_k = (1/i)[\hat{x}_k - (\partial/\partial x_k)]$. It is easy to see that these operators satisfy the relations

$$\{P_i, Q_j\} = 0 \qquad \{P_i, P_j\} = \{Q_i, Q_j\} = 2\delta_{ij}. \qquad (3.17)$$

---

[28] The square root of the determinant of a skew-symmetric matrix is called the *Pfaffian*. It is well known that this is a monomial of the matrix elements (cf., for example, Weyl's book [1]). The proof we have obtained as a consequence of formula (3.16) is, in essence, a modification of the reasoning given in this book.

Thus the operators $P_i$, $Q_j$ are generators of the Clifford algebra $K_{2n}$.
It is natural to introduce in the algebra $\mathscr{G}_n$ the inner product

$$(f_1, f_2) = \int \exp\left(-\sum y_k x_k\right) f_1(x) \overline{f_2'(y)} \, dy_n \, dx_n \cdots dy_1 \, dx_1, \quad (3.18)$$

where $f \to f'$ is a linear transformation in $\mathscr{G}_n$ given by the formula
$(y_{i_1}, \ldots, y_{i_k})' = y_{i_k}, \ldots, y_{i_1}$. Without effort we can verify that this inner
product is positive definite, $\hat{x}_k$ and $\partial/\partial x_k$ are adjoint to each other in
the sense of this inner product, and $P_i$ and $Q_j$ are self-adjoint. By the
same formula we have used to express $P_i$ and $Q_j$ in terms of the operators
of left multiplication and differentiation, we can construct the operators
$\tilde{P}_i$ and $\tilde{Q}_j$ from the operators of right multiplication and differentiation.
Then it can be shown that for any $i, j$,

$$P_i \tilde{P}_j - \tilde{P}_j P_i \equiv [P_i, \tilde{P}_j] = 0, \qquad Q_i \tilde{Q}_j - \tilde{Q}_j Q_i \equiv [Q_i, \tilde{Q}_j] = 0. \quad (3.19)$$

We shall verify the second of these equalities:

$$Q_i \tilde{Q}_j f = \left(x_i + \frac{\partial}{\partial x_i}\right)\left[f\left(x_j + \frac{\partial}{\partial x_j}\right)\right]$$

$$= x_i(fx_j) + \frac{\partial}{\partial x_i}\left(f\frac{\partial}{\partial x_j}\right) + x_i\left(f\frac{\partial}{\partial x_j}\right) + \frac{\partial}{\partial x_i}(fx_j).$$

By virtue of the associative law for multiplication we have $x_i(fx_j) = (x_i f)x_j$. In addition, according to (3.8), we also have $(\partial/\partial x_i)[f(\partial/\partial x_j)] = [(\partial/\partial x_i)f](\partial/\partial x_j)$. Therefore,

$$[Q_i, \tilde{Q}_j]f = x_i\left(f\frac{\partial}{\partial x_j}\right) + \frac{\partial}{\partial x_i}(fx_j) - (x_i f)\frac{\partial}{\partial x_j} - \left(\frac{\partial}{\partial x_i}f\right)x_j.$$

Evidently for $i \neq j$,

$$x_i\left(f\frac{\partial}{\partial x_j}\right) = (x_i f)\frac{\partial}{\partial x_j}, \qquad \frac{\partial}{\partial x_i}(fx_j) = \left(\frac{\partial}{\partial x_i}f\right)x_j.$$

Hence $[Q_i, \tilde{Q}_j] = 0$ for $i \neq j$. We now represent $f$ in the form $f = f' + f''$,
where $f''$ and $f'$ are even and odd elements, respectively, of $\mathscr{G}_n$, and
consider the expression in the brackets for $i = j$.

Using formulas (3.6) and (3.7), we have

$$\frac{\partial}{\partial x_i}(fx_i) = \frac{\partial}{\partial x_i}(f'x_i + f''x_i)$$

$$= \left(\frac{\partial}{\partial x_i}f'\right)x_i - f' + \left(\frac{\partial}{\partial x_i}f''\right)x_i + f'' = \left(\frac{\partial}{\partial x_i}f\right)x_i + f'' - f',$$

$$(x_if)\frac{\partial}{\partial x_i} = (x_if' + x_if'')\frac{\partial}{\partial x_i}$$

$$= x_i\left(f'\frac{\partial}{\partial x_i}\right) - f' + x_i\left(f''\frac{\partial}{\partial x_i}\right) + f'' = x_i\left(f\frac{\partial}{\partial x_i}\right) + f'' - f'.$$

Substituting these equalities in the expressions for $[Q_i, \tilde{Q}_i]$ we find that $[Q_i, \tilde{Q}_i] = 0$. Thus $[Q_i, \tilde{Q}_j] = 0$ for all $i, j$. Analogously it can be established that $[P_i, \tilde{P}_j] = 0$. The assertion just proved remains true for $n = \infty$. By means of this we can establish that in the case $n = \infty$ the ring generated by $P_i$, and also the ring generated by $Q_i$ is a factor of type $\mathrm{II}_1$ (cf. also p. 86). The operators $P_i$ and $Q_j$ are to some extent similar to the coordinate and momentum operators for the Bose system with $n$ degrees of freedom.

We recall that the Bose system with $n$ degrees of freedom can be described in terms of the Hilbert space of analytic functions of $n$ variables $f(z_1,\ldots, z_n)$ provided with the inner product

$$(f_1, f_2) = \frac{1}{(2\pi i)^n} \int \exp(-\sum_k z_k\bar{z}_k)f_1(z)\overline{f_2(z)}\, dz_1\, d\bar{z}_1 \cdots dz_n\, d\bar{z}_n.$$

Coordinate and momentum operators are given by the formulas

$$Q_kf = \frac{1}{\sqrt{2}}\left(z_k + \frac{\partial}{\partial z_k}\right)f, \qquad P_kf = \frac{1}{i\sqrt{2}}\left(z_k - \frac{\partial}{\partial z_k}\right)f.$$

3. GRASSMANN ALGEBRA WITH AN INFINITE NUMBER OF GENERATORS. The Grassmann algebra with an infinite number of generators is the direct sum of a countable number of topological linear spaces. We shall, in this connection, give the definition of the direct sum of topological spaces.

Let $E^0, E^1,\ldots, E^n,\ldots$ be a sequence of linear topological spaces which are not necessarily complete. Elements of the space $E^n$ will be denoted by $f_n$. The linear space $E$ is called the *direct sum of the spaces $E^n$* if it consists of formal sums

$$f = f_0 + f_1 + \cdots + f_n + \cdots$$

with the usual rules for linear combination satisfying the condition: If

$$f = f_0 + f_1 + \cdots + f_n + \cdots \in E,$$

then

$$\tilde{f} = k_0 f_0 + k_1 f_1 + \cdots + k_n f_n + \cdots \in E,$$

where $k_i$ are arbitrary complex numbers.

We note that this property implies that elements of the form $f = f_n$, $f_n \in E^n$, belong to $E$. Thus the space $E^n$ turns out to be embedded in $E$.

It will be said that the sequence of elements $f(k) = f_0(k) + f_1(k) + \cdots + f_n(k) + \cdots$ *converges* to $f = f_0 + f_1 + \cdots + f_n + \cdots$ if $f_n(k) \to f_n$ for $k \to \infty$ in the sense of the topology of the space $E^n$.[29]

A direct sum of the spaces $E^n$ is referred to as the *Grassmann algebra* $\mathscr{G}$ if it has the following properties:

(1) $E^0$ is a one-dimensional space with a fixed base element $f_0$.

(2) For any $f \in E^p$, $g \in E^q$, there is defined the product $fg \in E^{p+q}$ such that

(2a) if $f = \alpha f_0 \in E^0$, $\alpha$ being a complex number, then $fg = \alpha g$;

(2b) $fg = (-1)^{pq} gf$;

(2c) if $f_1, \ldots, f_n, \ldots$, are linearly independent elements of $E^1$, then $f_{i_1} \cdots f_{i_p}$, $i_1 < i_2 < \cdots < i_p$, are linearly independent elements of $E^p$;

(2d) finite linear combinations of elements of the form $fg$, $f \in E^p$, $g \in E^q$, form a dense set in $E^{p+q}$.

(3) The space $\mathscr{G}$ is closed relative to the multiplication, which is defined as follows. If

$$f = f_0 + f_1 + \cdots + f_n + \cdots, \qquad f_n \in E^n,$$

$$g = g_0 + g_1 + \cdots + g_n + \cdots, \qquad g_n \in E^n,$$

then

$$fg = h = h_0 + h_1 + \cdots + h_n + \cdots,$$

where

$$h_n = \sum_{k=0}^{n} f_k g_{n-k}. \tag{3.20}$$

[29] For the idea of a union of topological spaces which is close to the notion of a direct sum, cf. the book by Gel'fand and Silov [1].

Evidently, if $E^1$ is a space of finite dimension $N$, then $\mathscr{G}$ is a Grassmann algebra with $N$ generators which may be served by base elements of $E^1$. Therefore, if $E^1$ is infinite-dimensional, it is natural to call $\mathscr{G}$ a *Grassmann algebra with an infinite number of generators*. If $f \in E^n \subset \mathscr{G}$, then $f$ will be called a homogeneous element of degree $n$.

We denote by $\mathscr{G}' \subset \mathscr{G}$ the subspace consisting of linear combinations of homogeneous elements of odd degree and by $\mathscr{G}'' \subset \mathscr{G}$ the space consisting of linear combinations of homogeneous elements of even degree. From (3.20) it follows that elements of $\mathscr{G}''$ are commutative with all elements of the algebra $\mathscr{G}$.

Elements of $\mathscr{G}'$ and $\mathscr{G}''$ will be called *odd* and *even*, respectively. Evidently, every element $f$ is uniquely represented in the form of the sum of even and odd elements:

$$f = f' + f'', \qquad f' \in \mathscr{G}', \qquad f'' \in \mathscr{G}''. \tag{3.21}$$

Finally we define a normed Grassmann algebra.

A Grassmann algebra $\mathscr{G}$ is said to be *normed* if there exists in it a norm satisfying the conditions

(1) $\|fg\| \leq \|f\| \, \|g\|, \qquad \|f + g\| \leq \|f\| + \|g\|$.

An algebra $\mathscr{G}$ is called a *complete normed* algebra if, besides (1), it satisfies the conditions
(2) $\mathscr{G}$ is a complete normed space.
(3) The spaces $E^n$ are closed subspaces of $\mathscr{G}$.

4. GRASSMANN ALGEBRA WITH AN INNER PRODUCT. GENERATORS. We consider a Grassmann algebra $\mathscr{G}$ whose subspaces $E^n$ have the following supplementary properties:

(1) In each space $E^n$ we can single out a linear manifold $\tilde{E}^n$ dense in the sense of the topology of $E^n$, which is a linear topological space with its own topology.

(2) For any $f_0 \in E^n$ and $f \in \tilde{E}^n$, there is defined an inner product $(f, f_0)$ which gives a continuous linear functional on $\tilde{E}^n$.

(3) The topology of the space $E^n$ is the topology of the space conjugate to $\tilde{E}^n$.

(4) If $f \in \tilde{E}^n$, then $(f, f) \geq 0$ for which $(f, f) = 0$ only if $f = 0$.

(5) The completion of $\tilde{E}^n$ by the inner product belongs to $E^n$. This completion is denoted by $H^n$. $H^n$ is evidently a Hilbert space.[30]

(6) If $f_1, f_2, ..., f_n, ...$ is an orthonormal basis in $H^1$, then $\{f_{i_1} \cdots f_{i_n}\}$, $i_1 < i_2 < \cdots < i_n$, is an orthonormal basis in $H_n$.

A Grassmann algebra having these properties will be called a *Grassmann algebra with an inner product*.

Let $M$ be some set with measure $dx$. We consider the space $L_2(M)$ of square-integrable functions on $M$. Let us denote by $\alpha$ an isometric mapping of the space $L_2(M)$ onto $H^1$:

$$\varphi(x) \to \alpha(\varphi) \in H^1, \qquad (\alpha(\varphi), \alpha(\varphi)) = \int |\varphi(x)|^2 \, dx.$$

In view of its linearity, the mapping $\alpha(\varphi)$ may be conveniently written in the symbolic form

$$\alpha(\varphi) = \int \alpha(x)\varphi(x) \, dx. \tag{3.22}$$

If $M$ consists of a countable set of points $x_n$, each of which has measure unity, then $\alpha(x_n) = \alpha_n$, $\varphi(x_n) = \varphi_n$, and the integral in (3.22) is converted into the sum

$$\alpha(\varphi) = \sum_n \alpha_n \varphi_n.$$

Evidently in this case $\{\alpha_n\}$ is an orthonormal basis in $H^1$:

$$(\alpha_n, \alpha_{n'}) = \delta_{nn'}.$$

In the general case the symbols $\alpha(x)$ are not elements of $H^1$. However, these can be regarded as generalized elements in $H^1$.[31]

---

[30] A triple of spaces $E^n \supset H^n \supset \tilde{E}^n$ satisfying conditions (1)–(5) are frequently encountered in the theory of generalized functions (cf., for example, the book by Gel'fand and Vilenkin [1]).

[31] We consider in $L_2(M)$ the commutative ring of operators involving multiplication by bounded real functions. To this ring there corresponds the commutative ring $\mathfrak{A}$ of self-adjoint operators in $H^1$. It is not difficult to verify that $\alpha(x)$ are generalized eigenfunctions common to all operators of the ring $\mathfrak{A}$. (The notion of a generalized eigenfunction is found in Gel'fand and Kostyučenko [1] or Gel'fand and Vilenkin [1].)

The condition that the mapping $\alpha(\varphi)$ is isometric can be written in terms of $\alpha(x)$ in the form

$$(\alpha(x), \alpha(y)) = \delta(x, y),$$

where $\delta(x, y)$ is Dirac's $\delta$ function on $M$:

$$\int \delta(x, y)\varphi(y) \, dy = \varphi(x).$$

We shall refer later to the set of all generalized elements $\alpha(x)$ as the *generalized orthonormal basis* in $H^1$.

We denote by $\tilde{E}^1(M) \subset L_2(M)$ the set of all functions that correspond to elements of $\tilde{E}^1$ under the mapping $\alpha$. This space will be called the *space of basic functions*. From property (2) of the inner product it follows evidently that each element $f_0 \in \tilde{E}^1(M)$ defines in $\tilde{E}^1(M)$ a continuous functional $F_0(f)$ by virtue of the formula $F_0(f) = (f, f_0) = \int f(x)\bar{f}_0(x) \, dx$. This circumstance allows us to introduce into $\tilde{E}^1(M)$ the topology of the space of functionals on $\tilde{E}^1(M)$. The completion of $\tilde{E}^1(M)$ by this topology is denoted by $\tilde{E}^{1\prime}(M)$. Evidently, $\tilde{E}^{1\prime}(M)$ is the space of all continuous functionals on $\tilde{E}^1(M)$. The space $\tilde{E}^{1\prime}(M)$ will be called the *space of generalized functions* on $M$.

In the space $\tilde{E}^1$ we can also introduce the topology of the space of functionals on $\tilde{E}^1$. The completion of $\tilde{E}^1$ by this topology is denoted by $\tilde{E}^{1\prime}$. Since $\tilde{E}^{1\prime}$ is the space of *all* continuous functionals on $\tilde{E}^1$, it follows from condition (2) that $E^1 \subset \tilde{E}^{1\prime}$.

We now remark that the mapping $\alpha\colon \tilde{E}^1(M) \to \tilde{E}^1$ can be extended by continuity to the mapping $\alpha\colon \tilde{E}^{1\prime}(M) \to \tilde{E}^{1\prime}$. We shall write this mapping in the form (3.22), as before. The set of elements of $\tilde{E}^{1\prime}(M)$ corresponding to elements of $E^1$ under the mapping $\alpha$ is denoted by $E^1(M)$.

Summarizing the above results, we obtain that each element of the space $E^1$ is represented in the form

$$f = \int \alpha(x)\varphi(x) \, dx, \tag{3.22'}$$

where $\varphi(x) \in \tilde{E}^1(M) \subset L_2(M)$ is a basic function if $f \in \tilde{E}^1$, $\varphi(x) \in L_2(M)$ if $f$ is an arbitrary element of $H^1$, and $\varphi(x) \in E^1(M)$ is in general a generalized function if $f$ is an arbitrary element of $E^1$.

We consider elements

$$f_1 = \int \alpha(x)\varphi_1(x) \, dx \in E^1$$

and

$$f_2 = \int \alpha(x)\varphi_2(x) \, dx \in E^1.$$

and form their product,

$$f_1 f_2 = \int \alpha(x)\varphi_1(x) \, dx \int \alpha(x)\varphi_2(x) \, dx.$$

We define the product $\alpha(x)\alpha(y)$ of generalized elements $\alpha(x)$, $\alpha(y)$ by putting

$$f_1 f_2 = \int \alpha(x)\varphi_1(x) \, dx \int \alpha(y)\varphi_2(y) \, dy$$

$$= \int \alpha(x)\alpha(y)\varphi_1(x)\varphi_2(y) \, dx \, dy. \qquad (3.23)$$

According to the definition of the Grassmann algebra,

$$f_1 f_2 = -f_2 f_1, \qquad f_1(f_2 f_3) = (f_1 f_2)f_3.$$

Evidently these equalities are equivalent to the relations

$$\alpha(x)\alpha(y) = -\alpha(y)\alpha(x),$$
$$\alpha(x)(\alpha(y)\alpha(z)) = (\alpha(x)\alpha(y))\alpha(z) \qquad (3.24)$$

Now let $f \in E^n$. According to the definition of the Grassmann algebra [cf. Subsection 3, property (2d)] elements of the form

$$f_N = \sum_{\text{(finite sum)}} f_{k_1} \cdots f_{k_n}, \qquad f_k \in E^1$$

are dense in $E^n$.

Expressing $f_k$ in terms of $\varphi(x)$ by formula (3.22') we obtain

$$f_N = \int \alpha(x_1) \cdots \alpha(x_n) \sum \varphi_{k_1}(x_1) \cdots \varphi_{k_n}(x_n) \, d^n x,$$

or

$$f_N = \int \alpha(x_1) \cdots \alpha(x_n)\varphi_N(x_1, \ldots, x_n) \, d^n x. \qquad (3.25)$$

From the multiplication law (3.24) for $\alpha(x)$ it follows that the function $\varphi_N(x_1,\ldots, x_n)$ can be taken as antisymmetric. In the following, whenever the element $f_N$ is written in the form (3.25) and unless otherwise specified, $\varphi_N(x_1,\ldots, x_n)$ signifies an antisymmetric function.

We introduce in the space of antisymmetric functions $\varphi_N(x_1,\ldots, x_n)$ a topology induced by that of the space $E^n$. The completion of the space of functions $\varphi_N$ by this topology gives the space $E'^n(M)$ of generalized antisymmetric functions of $n$ variables on $M$.

Let a sequence $f_N$ converge in the topology of $E^n$ to an element $f$. Then the sequence $\varphi_N$ converges in the topology of $E'^n(M)$ to a generalized function $\varphi$. Passing to the limit, we find that every element $f \in E^n$ is representable in the form

$$f = \int \alpha(x_1) \cdots \alpha(x_n) \varphi(x_1,\ldots, x_n)\, d^n x, \tag{3.25'}$$

where $\varphi(x_1,\ldots, x_n)$ is, generally speaking, a generalized function. We denote the space of generalized functions corresponding to an element of $E^n$ by $E^n(M)$.

We finally note that it follows from property (6) of the inner product that if $f \in H^n$, then $\varphi(x_1,\ldots, x_n)$ is a square-integrable function of $n$ variables.

The space of antisymmetric square-integrable functions of $n$ variables is denoted by $H^n(M)$. The space of functions $\varphi(x_1,\ldots, x_n)$ which correspond to elements of $\tilde{E}^n$ is denoted by $\tilde{E}^n(M)$ and is called the *space of basic functions*. Like the space $\tilde{E}^1(M)$, the space $\tilde{E}^n(M)$ can be closed in the topology of the space conjugate to $\tilde{E}^n(M)$. Evidently the space thus obtained coincides with the space of generalized functions $E'^n(M)$ introduced above.

According to the definition of the Grassmann algebra $\mathscr{G}$, every element of $\mathscr{G}$ may be represented in the form

$$f = f_0 + f_1 + \cdots + f_n + \cdots, \qquad f_n \in E^n.$$

By writing $f_n$ in the form (3.25'), we obtain for an arbitrary element $f \in \mathscr{G}$ the representation

$$f = f(\alpha) = \sum_{n=0}^{\infty} \int \varphi(x_1,\ldots, x_n)\alpha(x_1) \cdots \alpha(x_n)\, d^n x, \tag{3.26}$$

where $\varphi(x_1,\ldots, x_n)$ is an antisymmetric function of $n$ variables and is in general a generalized function.

We shall refer later to the generalized elements $\alpha(x)$ as the *generators of the algebra* $\mathscr{G}$. For arbitrary algebras they play a role similar to that of generators in finite-dimensional algebras.

We remark that formula (3.26) recalls in form the manner of writing the analytic functional. In this connection the elements $f = f(\alpha)$ of the Grassmann algebra with an inner product will sometimes be called *functionals of functions with anticommuting values.*

We consider a subspace $L$ in $E^1$. The subalgebra of $\mathscr{G}$ generated by elements of $L$ is denoted $\mathscr{G}_L$. Evidently $\mathscr{G}_L$ is a Grassmann algebra. If the space $L$ is finite-dimensional, then $\mathscr{G}_L$ is an algebra with a finite number of generators which are served by base elements of $L$.

Let $L$ be an $n$-dimensional subspace of $H^1$. We consider in $H^1$ an orthonormal basis $\{\alpha_k\}$ such that

$$\alpha_1,\ldots, \alpha_n \in L. \tag{3.27}$$

Let $F$ be an arbitrary element of $\mathscr{G}$. According to formula (3.26) it may be represented in the form

$$F = F(\alpha) = \sum_p \sum_k F(k_1,\ldots, k_p)\alpha_{k_1} \cdots \alpha_{k_p}.$$

Let us now consider the element $F_L(\alpha)$:

$$F_L(\alpha) = \sum_p \sum_{k_s \leq n} F(k_1,\ldots, k_p)\alpha_{k_1} \cdots \alpha_{k_p}. \tag{3.28}$$

Evidently $F_L(\alpha)$ belongs to $\mathscr{G}_L$. We shall call $F_L(\alpha)$ the *value of the element* $F(\alpha)$ on the subspace $L$. Although the element $F_L(\alpha)$ has been represented in terms of the basis $\{\alpha_k\}$, it is independent of the basis; it is readily seen that elements $F_L$ defined by any basis satisfying the condition (3.27) coincide.

Analogously one can define the value of $F$ on the infinite-dimensional subspace $L \subset H^1$.

5. GRASSMANN ALGEBRA WITH INVOLUTION. Let $\mathscr{G}$ be a Grassmann algebra with an inner product, in which there is defined a one-to-one mapping onto itself $f \leftrightarrow f^*$ satisfying the following conditions:

(1) $(f^*)^* = f$.

(2) $(f_1 f_2)^* = f_2^* f_1^*$.

(3) $(\alpha f)^* = \bar{\alpha} f^*$     ($\alpha$ is a complex number).

(4) If the inner product is defined for $f$, $g$, then it is defined also for $f^*$, $g^*$ and $(f^*, g^*) = (g, f)$.

(5) The space $E^1$ is decomposed into the direct sum of subspaces: $E^1 = F + F^*$, and moreover $F \cap H^1$ is orthogonal to $F^* \cap H^1$.

The mapping $f^*$ satisfying these conditions is called the *involution* in $\mathcal{G}$. Elements $f \in \mathcal{G}$ and $f^* \in \mathcal{G}$ and subspaces $\mathcal{L} \subset \mathcal{G}$ and $\mathcal{L}^* \subset \mathcal{G}$ will be called *adjoint to each other*.

We consider the space $E^{pq}$ consisting of linear combinations of elements of the form $f^*_{k_1} \cdots f^*_{k_p} f_{l_1} \cdots f_{l_q}$, where $f_l, f_k \in F$. Evidently, the space $E^n$ is decomposed into the direct sum $E = \sum_{p+q=n} E^{pq}$, and moreover the spaces $H^{pq} = H_n \cap E^{pq}$ are orthogonal to each other. It is clear that the spaces $E^{pq}$ and $E^{qp}$ are adjoint to each other.

Decomposition of the space $E^1$ into the direct sum of adjoint spaces $F$ and $F^*$ is not unique. However, as far as the algebra with involution is concerned, we may always assume that this decomposition is fixed. We consider in the space $F$ a generalized orthonormal basis $\alpha(x)$. In the space $F^*$ we introduce an adjoint basis by setting, by definition, $f^* = \int \alpha^*(x) \bar{\varphi}(x)\, dx$ for $f = \int \alpha(x) \varphi(x)\, dx$. The union of these bases is evidently a basis in $E^1$. Like every basis in $E^1$, $\{\alpha, \alpha^*\}$ is a system of generators of the algebra $\mathcal{G}$. The generators $\alpha$, $\alpha^*$ will later be called *involutive*. In terms of the generators $\alpha(x)$, $\alpha^*(x)$ elements of $\mathcal{G}$ are naturally written in the form

$$f = \sum_{m,n} \int \varphi_{mn}(x_1, \ldots, x_m \mid y_1, \ldots, y_n)$$

$$\times\ \alpha^*(x_1) \cdots a^*(x_m) \alpha(y_1) \cdots \alpha(y_n)\, d^m x\, d^n y. \tag{3.29}$$

Evidently individual terms in this sum are elements of the subspaces $E^{mn}$. It is easy to see that if $f$ is of the form (3.29), then $f^*$ is of the form

$$f^* = \sum_{m,n} \int \bar{\varphi}_{mn}(x_1, \ldots, x_m \mid y_1, \ldots, y_n)$$

$$\times\ \alpha^*(y_n) \cdots \alpha^*(y_1) \alpha(x_m) \cdots \alpha(x_1)\, d^m x\, d^n y. \tag{3.30}$$

Unless otherwise stated, we shall suppose the functions $\varphi_{mn}$ to be antisymmetric with respect to $x_1, \ldots, x_m$ and $y_1, \ldots, y_n$, separately.

6. VARIATIONAL DERIVATIVES. Let $\mathscr{G}$ be a Grassmann algebra with inner product, and let $\alpha(x)$, $x \in M$, be a system of generators of $\mathscr{G}$. We define the left and right derivatives by $\alpha(x)$ of an element $f \in \mathscr{G}$. The left and right derivatives of the element $f$ will be denoted by $[\delta/\delta\alpha(x)]f$ and $f[\delta/\delta\alpha(x)]$, respectively. Both derivatives are linear operators in $\mathscr{G}$, so it is sufficient to give them on homogeneous elements. It is even more convenient to give derivatives first on products of generators:

$$\frac{\delta}{\delta\alpha(x)}\alpha(x_1) \cdots \alpha(x_n) = \delta(x, x_1)\alpha(x_2) \cdots \alpha(x_n)$$
$$- \delta(x, x_2)\alpha(x_1)\alpha(x_3) \cdots \alpha(x_n) + \cdots$$
$$+ (-1)^{n-1}\delta(x, x_n)\alpha(x_1) \cdots \alpha(x_{n-1}),$$

$$\alpha(x_1) \cdots \alpha(x_n)\frac{\delta}{\delta\alpha(x)} = \delta(x, x_n)\alpha(x_1) \cdots \alpha(x_{n-1})$$
$$- \delta(x, x_{n-1})\alpha(x_1) \cdots \alpha(x_{n-2})\alpha(x_n) + \cdots$$
$$+ (-1)^{n-1}\delta(x, x_1)\alpha(x_2) \cdots \alpha(x_n);$$

$$(3.31)$$

$\delta(x, x_k)$ in these formulas signifies Dirac's $\delta$ function on $M$:

$$\int \delta(x, y)f(y)\, dy = f(x).$$

The generators themselves, generally speaking, are not necessarily elements of the algebra $\mathscr{G}$. Furthermore, the derivatives of their products do not necessarily belong to $\mathscr{G}$. However, the derivatives of the products of generators have clear meanings as generalized functions: differentiating formally under the integral sign and applying formulas (3.31), we find that if

$$f = \int \varphi(x_1,\ldots, x_n)\alpha(x_1) \cdots \alpha(x_n)\, d^n x,$$

then

$$\frac{\delta}{\delta\alpha(x)}f = n\int \varphi(x, x_2,\ldots, x_n)\alpha(x_2) \cdots \alpha(x_n)\, d^{n-1}x,$$

$$f\frac{\delta}{\delta\alpha(x)} = n\int \varphi(x_1,\ldots, x_{n-1}, x)\alpha(x_1) \cdots \alpha(x_{n-1})\, d^{n-1}x.$$

$$(3.32)$$

[In deriving formula (3.32) from (3.31) we have used the fact that $\varphi(x_1,\ldots, x_n)$ is an antisymmetric function.]

The derivatives $[\delta/\delta\alpha(x)]f$ and $f[\delta/\delta\alpha(x)]$ of the element $f$, also, do not necessarily belong to $\mathscr{G}$.

It is a natural attempt to regard them as generalized functions, i.e., to consider, instead of $[\delta/\delta\alpha(x)]f$ and $f[\delta/\delta\alpha(x)]$,

$$\int \varphi(x)\, \frac{\delta}{\delta\alpha(x)} f\, dx \qquad (3.33)$$

or, correspondingly,

$$\int \varphi(x) f\, \frac{\delta}{\delta\alpha(x)}\, dx, \qquad (3.33')$$

where $\varphi(x)$ belongs to some set of basic functions. We examine this possibility.

Suppose that there exists a certain function $\varphi \in E^1(M)$ for which $\int \varphi(x)\, [\delta/\delta\alpha(x)]f\, dx \in \mathscr{G}$. In this case the element $f$ will be called *left-differentiable* for the function $\varphi$. Analogously we define an element which is *right-differentiable* for $\varphi$.

Suppose that $\int \varphi(x)\, [\delta/\delta\alpha(x)]f\, dx$ does not belong to $\mathscr{G}$ for all functions $\varphi(x) \in E^1(M)$ except for $\varphi(x) \equiv 0$. In this case it is said that the element $f$ is *left-nondifferentiable*. Analogously we define an element which is *right-nondifferentiable*.

It can be shown that if an element $f$ is left-differentiable for some function $\varphi$, then it is right-differentiable for $\varphi$, and vice versa. Therefore elements which are left-nondifferentiable are right-nondifferentiable, and vice versa.

If an element $f$ is differentiable for all functions $\varphi$ belonging to some set $D \subset E^1(M)$, then we call it *D-differentiable*.

We shall verify that if an element $f$ is left-differentiable for $\varphi$, then it is also right-differentiable for $\varphi$. First, let $f$ be a homogeneous element of degree $k$,

$$f = \int \varphi(x_1,\ldots, x_k)\alpha(x_1) \cdots \alpha(x_k)\, d^kx.$$

From formula (3.32) it evidently follows that $\int \varphi(x)[\delta/\delta\alpha(x)] f \, dx = (-1)^{k+1} \int \varphi(x) f [\delta/\delta\alpha(x)] \, dx$. Therefore, both integrals simultaneously belong to $\mathcal{G}$ or not.

Now let $f$ be an arbitrary element of $\mathcal{G}$ and let $I_l = \int \varphi(x)[\delta/\delta\alpha(x)] f \, dx \in \mathcal{G}$. We divide $I_l$ into the sum of even and odd terms $I_l = u' + u''$. By definition of the algebra $\mathcal{G}$ we have $u' \in \mathcal{G}$ and $u'' \in \mathcal{G}$. On the other hand, from what has been stated above, it is clear that $I_r = \int \varphi(x) f [\delta/\delta\alpha(x)] \, dx = u' - u''$. Therefore, $I_r \in \mathcal{G}$. In exactly the same way it is confirmed that if $I_r \in \mathcal{G}$, then $I_l \in \mathcal{G}$.

We note in conclusion that the following property follows from the definition of the variational derivatives. We consider an algebra $\mathcal{G}$ with generators $\alpha(x)$, $\beta(x)$. Let $F(\alpha) \in \mathcal{G}$. If $F(\alpha + \beta)$ is expanded in a power series in terms of $\beta$, then the left and right derivatives of $F$ are obtained as coefficients of the first-order terms in $\beta$:

$$F(\alpha + \beta) = F(\alpha) + \int \beta(x) \frac{\delta}{\delta\alpha(x)} F(\alpha) \, dx + \cdots$$

$$= F(\alpha) + \int \left( F \frac{\delta}{\delta\alpha(x)} \right) \beta(x) \, dx + \cdots \qquad (3.34)$$

This property may be used for the definition of variational derivatives.[32]

7. CHANGE OF VARIABLES FOR DIFFERENTIATION. Let $\alpha(x)$, $x \in M_\alpha$, and $\beta(y)$, $y \in M_\beta$, be two systems of generators of the algebra $\mathcal{G}$.

Suppose that an element $f \in H^1$ can be written in terms of the bases $\alpha(x)$ and $\beta(y)$ as follows:

$$f = \int \alpha(x)\varphi_\alpha(x) \, dx = \int \beta(y)\varphi_\beta(y) \, dy. \qquad (3.35)$$

Thus a linear correspondence between the spaces $H^1(M_\alpha)$ and $H^1(M_\beta)$ is provided. Evidently, this correspondence is an isomorphism. The isomorphism thus obtained will be written in the form

$$\varphi_\alpha(x) = \int K(x, y)\varphi_\beta(y) \, dy. \qquad (3.36)$$

[32] Compare with the definition of variational derivatives for bosons (Section 2.1).

The kernel $K(x, y)$ defined by this equation may be interpreted as a generalized function on a certain space of basic functions of $x$, $y$. However, we do not need the functional nature of $K(x, y)$ at all, so we shall not discuss it further.

By the use of (3.36), formula (3.35) can be rewritten in the form

$$\int \alpha(x)K(x, y)\varphi_\beta(y)\, dy\, dx = \int \beta(y)\varphi_\beta(y)\, dy.$$

The formula obtained can be written in symbolic form as

$$\int \alpha(x)K(x, y)\, dx = \beta(y).$$

Thus the kernel $K(x, y)$ is an analog of the matrix transferring the system of generators from $\alpha(x)$ to $\beta(y)$.

Now let $f \in \mathscr{G}$. The following formulas of changing variables for differentiation hold:

$$\frac{\delta}{\delta\alpha(x)} f = \int K(x, y) \frac{\delta}{\delta\beta(y)} f\, dy,$$

$$f\frac{\delta}{\delta\alpha(x)} = \int K(x, y) f \frac{\delta}{\delta\beta(y)}\, dy. \tag{3.37}$$

It is easy to prove formulas (3.37) directly. We note an important special case of these formulas. Let $M$ consist of a countable set of points, each of which has measure equal to unity. Then $\alpha(x) = \alpha_n$ is an orthonormal basis in $H^1$ in the usual sense of the word. Formulas (3.37) in this case take the form

$$\frac{\delta}{\delta\alpha_n} f = \int K_n(y) \frac{\delta}{\delta\beta(y)} f\, dy,$$

$$f\frac{\delta}{\delta\alpha_n} = \int K_n(y) f \frac{\delta}{\delta\beta(y)}\, dy. \tag{3.37'}$$

The functions $K_n(y)$ appearing on the right of (3.37') evidently form an orthonormal basis in $L_2(M_\beta)$. We observe that the right members of formulas (3.37'), apart from the notations, coincide with expressions (3.33) and (3.33') considered in the preceding subsection.

8. CONTINUAL INTEGRAL.[33] Let $\mathscr{G}$ be a Grassmann algebra with involution, and $E^1 = F + F^*$ be the decomposition of the space $E^1$ appearing in the definition of the algebra with involution.

We consider in the space $F$ a system of successively embedded finite-dimensional subspaces $F_n$ of dimension $2n$ such that the closure of their sum coincides with $F$: $\overline{\cup F_n} = F$. Denote by $\mathscr{G}_{Ln}$ the subalgebra of $\mathscr{G}$ generated by the subspace $L_n = F_n + F_n^*$. We introduce in $F_n$ an orthonormal basis $\alpha_1, \ldots, \alpha_{2n}$ in an arbitrary way and in $F_n^*$ a basis consisting of adjoint elements $\alpha_1^*, \ldots, \alpha_{2n}^*$. Now let $f(\alpha^*, \alpha)$ be an arbitrary element of $\mathscr{G}$. We denote the value of $f$ on $\mathscr{G}_{Ln}$ by $f_n(\alpha^*, \alpha)$. Let us consider the integral

$$I_n(f_n) = \int f_n(\alpha^*, \alpha)\, d\alpha_{2n}^*\, d\alpha_{2n} \cdots d\alpha_1^*\, d\alpha_1. \tag{3.38}$$

We shall show that the integral (3.38) does not depend on the choice of an orthonormal basis in $F_n$. In fact, let $\{\beta_k\}$ be another orthonormal basis in $F_n$, and $\{\beta_k^*\}$ the corresponding basis in $F_n^*$. Then $\beta_k$ is expressed by $\alpha_k$ with the aid of a unitary matrix: $\beta_k = \sum_s u_{ks}\alpha_s$. Evidently $\beta_k^*$ is expressed by $\alpha_k^*$ with the aid of the complex-conjugate matrix: $\beta_k^* = \sum_s \bar{u}_{ks}\alpha_s^*$. By the use of formula (3.15) we find that

$$\int f_n(\beta^*, \beta)\, d\beta_{2n}^*\, d\beta_{2n} \cdots d\beta_1^*\, d\beta_1$$
$$= \det(u^{-1}\bar{u}^{-1}) \int f_n(\alpha^*, \alpha)\, d\alpha_{2n}^*\, d\alpha_{2n} \cdots d\alpha_1^*\, d\alpha_1.$$

Since $u = \|u_{sk}\|$ is a unitary matrix, $\det(u^{-1}\bar{u}^{-1}) = 1$. Thus the equality of the integrals is proved.

*Definition.* If the limit $I(f) = \lim_{n \to \infty} I_n(f_n)$ exists independent of the choice of the system of subspaces $F_n$ (only provided that they are countable and the closure of their sum coincides with $F$), then this limit is called the *continual integral of the functional f on the algebra $\mathscr{G}$*. The continual integral in the Grassmann algebra will sometimes be called the *Fermi continual integral*. We denote it, just like the ordinary continual integral, by

$$I(f) = \int f(\alpha^*, \alpha)\Pi\, d\alpha^*\, d\alpha. \tag{3.39}$$

---

[33] Cf. Berezin [2]. The continual integral for fermions in an implicit form has been encountered earlier in the physics papers by Salam and Matthews [1] and Halatnikov [1].

If confusion should occur, we shall ascribe the superscript $F$ to the integral of (3.39):

$$I(f) = \int^F f(\alpha^*, \alpha)\Pi \, d\alpha^* \, d\alpha. \tag{3.40}$$

9. INTEGRATION BY PARTS. Let $\mathscr{G}$ be an algebra with involution, $E^1 = F + F^*$ be the decomposition of $E^1$ into the sum of adjoint spaces, and $\alpha(x)$, $x \in M$, be a generalized orthonormal basis in $F$.

Let us consider two $D$-differentiable elements $f_1, f_2 \in \mathscr{G}$ and the integral

$$\int f_1 \left( \frac{\delta}{\delta\alpha(x)} f_2 \right) \Pi \, d\alpha^* \, d\alpha. \tag{3.41}$$

This integral has a clear meaning as a generalized function on $D$:

$$\int \varphi(x) \left( \int f_1 \left( \frac{\delta}{\delta\alpha(x)} f_2 \right) \Pi \, d\alpha^* \, d\alpha \right) dx = \int f_1 \left( \int \frac{\delta}{\delta\alpha(x)} f_2 \varphi(x) \, dx \right) \Pi \, d\alpha^* \, d\alpha.$$

A similar meaning is possessed by seven integrals obtained from (3.41) by replacing $\alpha$ by $\alpha^*$, the left derivative by the right derivative, and $f_1$ by $f_2$. Then the following formulas for integration by parts are valid:

$$\int f_1 \left( \frac{\delta}{\delta\alpha(x)} f_2 \right) \Pi \, d\alpha^* \, d\alpha = \int \left( f_1 \frac{\delta}{\delta\alpha(x)} \right) f_2 \Pi \, d\alpha^* \, d\alpha,$$

$$\int f_1 \left( f_2 \frac{\delta}{\delta\alpha(x)} \right) \Pi \, d\alpha^* \, d\alpha = - \int \left( \frac{\delta}{\delta\alpha(x)} f_1 \right) f_2 \Pi \, d\alpha^* \, d\alpha,$$

$$\int f_1 \left( \frac{\delta}{\delta\alpha^*(x)} f_2 \right) \Pi \, d\alpha^* \, d\alpha = \int \left( f_1 \frac{\delta}{\delta\alpha^*(x)} \right) f_2 \Pi \, d\alpha^* \, d\alpha, \tag{3.42}$$

$$\int f_1 \left( f_2 \frac{\delta}{\delta\alpha^*(x)} \right) \Pi \, d\alpha^* \, d\alpha = - \int \left( \frac{\delta}{\delta\alpha^*(x)} f_1 \right) f_2 \Pi \, d\alpha^* \, d\alpha.$$

In the case when the integration is not carried out over the whole algebra, the first and third of these formulas remain valid. In order that the second and fourth formulas should still hold, it is sufficient that the functionals $f_1$ and $f_2$ should depend on the generators over which an even-multiple integration is not carried out. [For more details on this point, see p. 55, where similar formulas (3.14) and (3.14') are discussed.]

Here it is assumed that all integrals in the formulas really exist. We shall prove the second of them. Let $\varphi \in D$ with $\|\varphi\| = 1$. We amplify $\varphi(x)$ to an orthonormal basis $\{\varphi_k(x)\}$ $(\varphi_1 = \varphi)$ in $E^1(M)$ and construct a system of generators in $\mathscr{G}$,

$$\varphi_k = \int \alpha(x)\varphi_k(x)\, dx, \qquad \varphi_k{}^* = \int \varphi_k{}^*(x)\alpha^*(x)\, dx.$$

The element $f$ can be written in terms of generators $\varphi_k$. Evidently in that case

$$\int \varphi_1(x) \frac{\delta}{\delta\alpha(x)} f(\alpha^*, \alpha)\, dx = \frac{\delta}{\delta\varphi_1} f(\varphi^*, \varphi).$$

Therefore, it suffices to prove the equality

$$\int f_1\left(f_2 \frac{\delta}{\delta\varphi_1}\right)\Pi\, d\varphi^*\, d\varphi = -\int \left(\frac{\delta}{\delta\varphi_1} f_1\right) f_2\Pi\, d\varphi^*\, d\varphi. \qquad (3.43)$$

To prove (3.43) we use the definition of the continual integral. Let us construct the subspaces $F_p$ having $\{\varphi_1,\ldots, \varphi_{2p}\}$ as a basis. Evidently $F_p$ form a system of successively embedded subspaces and the closure of their sum coincides with $F$. We denote by $\mathscr{G}_p$ the algebra with generators $\varphi_1,\ldots, \varphi_{2p}, \varphi_1{}^*,\ldots, \varphi_{2p}^*$ and by $f_{1p}, f_{2p}$ the values of $f_1, f_2$ on $\mathscr{G}_p$.

From formulas (3.14′) for $n = 4p$ it follows that

$$\int f_{1p}\left(f_{2p} \frac{\delta}{\delta\varphi_1}\right) d\varphi_{2p}^*\, d\varphi_{2p} \cdots d\varphi_1{}^*\, d\varphi_1$$

$$= -\int \left(\frac{\delta}{\delta\varphi_1} f_{1p}\right) f_{2p}\, d\varphi_{2p}^*\, d\varphi_{2p} \cdots d\varphi_1{}^*\, d\varphi_1. \qquad (3.44)$$

In view of the definition of the continual integral the limit of the left member of (3.44) is equal to that of (3.43), and the limit of the right member of (3.44) is equal to that of (3.43). Thus formula (3.43), and with this the second of formulas (3.42), are proved. The remaining formulas of (3.42) are proved analogously. Formulas (3.42) play in the analysis on Grassmann algebra a role similar to that which is played by the usual formulas for integration by parts.

10. EXAMPLES. Let $\mathcal{G}$ be an algebra with involution, $E^1 = F + F^*$, and $\alpha(x)$ be a generalized orthonormal basis in $F$. Let us consider in $E^1$ an operator $A$. It is naturally given by the matrix

$$A = \begin{pmatrix} A_{11}(x, x') & A_{12}(x, x') \\ A_{21}(x, x') & A_{22}(x, x') \end{pmatrix}, \qquad A_{ik}(x, x') = - A_{ki}(x', x).$$

By means of the operator $A$ we construct an element $f(\alpha^*, \alpha)$ of the space $E^2$ which is equal to

$$f(\alpha^*, \alpha) = \int [\alpha(x)A_{11}(x, x')\alpha(x')$$
$$+ 2\alpha(x)A_{12}(x, x')\alpha^*(x') + \alpha^*(x)A_{22}(x, x')\alpha^*(x')] \, dx \, dx'.$$

The element $f(\alpha^*, \alpha)$ plays a role analogous to that of the quadratic form for bosons. We agree for brevity to write $f(\alpha^*, \alpha)$, in analogy with the Bose case, in the form

$$f = \alpha A_{11}\alpha + 2\alpha A_{12}\alpha^* + \alpha^* A_{22}\alpha^* \qquad (3.45)$$

or in the form

$$f = (\alpha \quad \alpha^*)\begin{pmatrix} A_{11} & A_{12} \\ A_{21} & A_{22} \end{pmatrix}\begin{pmatrix} \alpha \\ \alpha^* \end{pmatrix}, \qquad A_{ij} = - A'_{ji}. \qquad (3.46)$$

In particular, $f = 2\alpha\alpha^*$ if $A_{12} = E$, $A_{11} = A_{22} = 0$. We calculate the Gauss integral $\int \exp(\frac{1}{2}f(\alpha^*, \alpha))\Pi \, d\alpha^* \, d\alpha$. Using formula (3.16) and the definition of the continual integral, we find

$$\int \exp\left[\tfrac{1}{2}(\alpha \quad \alpha^*)\begin{pmatrix} A_{11} & A_{12} \\ A_{21} & A_{22} \end{pmatrix}\begin{pmatrix} \alpha \\ \alpha^* \end{pmatrix}\right]\Pi \, d\alpha^* \, d\alpha = \left[\det\begin{pmatrix} A_{11} & A_{12} \\ A_{21} & A_{22} \end{pmatrix}\right]^{1/2}.$$
$$(3.47)$$

The determinant in the right member of (3.47) is a generalized Fredholm determinant (cf. Introduction, Subsection 3), and the $\frac{1}{2}$ in the exponent means the branch of the square root which is positive for real positive values of the argument. It is not difficult to see that such a definition of the square root in (3.47) is unique.[34]

---

[34] In fact, the square root of a determinant of a finite-dimensional skew-symmetric matrix is a polynomial in its elements. Consequently, in the finite-dimensional approximation of the integral (3.47), the above rule leads to a unique answer (cf. p. 57).

From (3.47) it follows in particular that

$$\int e^{-\alpha^*\alpha} \Pi \, d\alpha^* \, d\alpha = 1. \tag{3.48}$$

Let us calculate the variational derivatives of $\exp(\tfrac{1}{2}f(\alpha^*, \alpha))$:

$$\frac{\delta}{\delta\alpha(x)} \exp\left[\tfrac{1}{2}(\alpha \quad \alpha^*)A\binom{\alpha}{\alpha^*}\right] = (A_{11}\alpha + A_{12}\alpha^*) \exp\left[\tfrac{1}{2}(\alpha \quad \alpha^*)A\binom{\alpha}{\alpha^*}\right],$$

$$\frac{\delta}{\delta\alpha^*(x)} \exp\left[\tfrac{1}{2}(\alpha \quad \alpha^*)A\binom{\alpha}{\alpha^*}\right] = (A_{21}\alpha + A_{22}\alpha^*) \exp\left[\tfrac{1}{2}(\alpha \quad \alpha^*)A\binom{\alpha}{\alpha^*}\right],$$

$$\exp\left[\tfrac{1}{2}(\alpha \quad \alpha^*)A\binom{\alpha}{\alpha^*}\right]\frac{\delta}{\delta\alpha} = (\alpha A_{11} + \alpha^* A_{21}) \exp\left[\tfrac{1}{2}(\alpha \quad \alpha^*)A\binom{\alpha}{\alpha^*}\right],$$

$$\exp\left[\tfrac{1}{2}(\alpha \quad \alpha^*)A\binom{\alpha}{\alpha^*}\right]\frac{\delta}{\delta\alpha^*} = (\alpha A_{12} + \alpha^* A_{22}) \exp\left[\tfrac{1}{2}(\alpha \quad \alpha^*)A\binom{\alpha}{\alpha^*}\right]. \tag{3.49}$$

To obtain formula (3.49) it is more convenient to apply formula (3.34) than to use directly the definition of variational derivatives.

As the next example we consider the integrals

$$\int \alpha(x_1) \cdots \alpha(x_m)\alpha^*(y_n) \cdots \alpha^*(y_1) \exp\left[-\int \alpha^*(x)\alpha(x) \, dx\right]\Pi \, d\alpha^* \, d\alpha$$

$$= \delta_{mn} \sum_i \pm \delta(x_1 - y_{i_1}) \cdots \delta(x_m - y_{i_m}), \tag{3.50}$$

$$\int \alpha^*(x_1) \cdots \alpha^*(x_m)\alpha(y_n) \cdots \alpha(y_1) \exp\left[-\int \alpha(x)\alpha^*(x) \, dx\right]\Pi \, d\alpha \, d\alpha^*$$

$$= \delta_{mn} \sum_i \pm \delta(x_1 - y_{i_1}) \cdots \delta(x_m - y_{i_m}). \tag{3.50'}$$

In these formulas the plus or minus sign is to be taken according as the permutation $i_1, \ldots, i_m$ is even or odd.

Formula (3.50) is proved by integration by parts:

$$\alpha^*(y_n) \cdots \alpha^*(y_1) \exp\left[-\int \alpha^*(x)\alpha(x) \, dx\right]$$

$$= \frac{\delta}{\delta\alpha(y_n)} \cdots \frac{\delta}{\delta\alpha(y_1)} \exp\left[-\int \alpha^*(x)\alpha(x) \, dx\right].$$

Substituting this identity in the left member of (3.50) and integrating by parts, we obtain the right member. Formula (3.50′) is proved similarly. From (3.50) there follows a consequence which will be used frequently in the sequel:

$$\int \left( \int F(x_1,\ldots, x_m \mid y_1,\ldots, y_n) \alpha(x_1) \cdots \alpha(x_m) \right.$$

$$\left. \times \alpha^*(y_n) \cdots \alpha^*(y_1)\, d^m x\, d^n y \right) \exp\left[ -\int \alpha^*(x)\alpha(x)\, dx \right] \Pi\, d\alpha^*\, d\alpha$$

$$= \delta_{mn} n! \int F(x_1,\ldots, x_n \mid x_1,\ldots, x_n)\, d^n x. \tag{3.51}$$

In this formula $F(x_1,\ldots, x_m \mid y_1,\ldots, y_n)$ is supposed to be a function anti-symmetric with respect to $x_1,\ldots, x_m$ and $y_1,\ldots, y_n$, separately.

We note that formula (3.51) coincides in form with the corresponding formula for bosons [cf. (2.18)].

11. ALGEBRA OF FUNCTIONALS CORRESPONDING TO VECTORS AND OPERATORS. In Section 1.7 we have assigned functionals of functions with anticommuting values which are formal series to the matrix form of every bounded operator, to the normal form of every bounded operator, and to every vector. We shall show that all these functionals are elements of a certain Grassmann algebra $\mathscr{G}$. We begin with functionals corresponding to the matrix form of operators. We denote these functionals by $\tilde{A}(a^*, a)$ and recall that the functionals $\tilde{A}$ have the form

$$\tilde{A}(a^*, a) = \sum_{p,q} \frac{1}{(p!q!)^{1/2}} \int A_{pq}(x_1,\ldots, x_p \mid y_1,\ldots, y_q)$$

$$\times a^*(x_1) \cdots a^*(x_p) a(y_q) \cdots a(y_1)\, d^p x\, d^q y, \tag{3.52}$$

where $A_{pq}(x_1,\ldots, x_p \mid y_1,\ldots, y_q)$ is a matrix element of the operator $\hat{A}$, and moreover $A_{pq}(x \mid y)$ is the kernel of a bounded operator from the Hilbert space $H^q$ of square-integrable functions of $q$ variables to the Hilbert space $H^p$ of square-integrable functions of $p$ variables. The symbols $a(x)$, $a^*(x)$ satisfy the relations

$$\{a(x), a(y)\} = \{a^*(x), a^*(y)\} = \{a(x), a^*(y)\} = 0. \tag{3.53}$$

We consider the set $\mathscr{G}$ of all functionals having the form

$$F(a^*, a) = \sum_{p,q} \frac{1}{(p!q!)^{1/2}} \int F_{pq}(x_1, \ldots, x_p \,|\, y_1, \ldots, y_q)$$

$$\times a^*(x_1) \cdots a^*(x_p)a(y_q) \cdots a(y_1) \, d^p x \, d^q y, \qquad (3.54)$$

where $F_{pq}(x \,|\, y)$ is the kernel of a bounded operator from $H^q$ to $H^p$. Concerning all series $F(a^*, a)$, we do not assume that these correspond to the matrix form of one operator or another.

We can introduce naturally into $\mathscr{G}$ operations of linear combination and multiplication, the latter being defined by formula (3.53). It is not difficult to verify that $\mathscr{G}$ is a Grassmann algebra, in which the role of the spaces $E^n$ is played by the set of functionals of the form

$$F(a^*, a) = \sum_{p+q=n} \frac{1}{(p!q!)^{1/2}} \int F_{pq}(x_1, \ldots, x_p \,|\, y_1, \ldots, y_q)$$

$$\times a^*(x_1) \cdots a^*(x_p)a(y_q) \cdots a(y_1) \, d^p x \, d^q y. \qquad (3.55)$$

We shall verify that $\mathscr{G}$ is closed relative to the operations of linear combination and multiplication. The closed property relative to the linear combination is evident, since it is reducible to the linear combination of $F_{pq}$, but the linear combination of bounded operators is again a bounded operator.

The closed property relative to multiplication is proved in the following way. Let $F_1 \in \mathscr{G}$, $F_2 \in \mathscr{G}$, $\Phi = F_1 F_2$ be functionals, and $F^1_{pq}(x_1, \ldots, x_p | y_1, \ldots, y_q)$, $F^2_{pq}(x_1, \ldots, x_p | y_1, \ldots, y_q)$, $\Phi_{pq}(x_1, \ldots, x_p | y_1, \ldots, y_q)$ be functions entering into the expansion of these functionals into the series of the form (3.54). Carrying out the multiplication of the series, we find that

$$\Phi_{pq}(x_1, \ldots, x_p \,|\, y_1, \ldots, y_q)$$

$$= \sum_{p'+p''=p,\, q'+q''=q} \left( \frac{p!q!}{p'!\, q'!\, p''!\, q''!} \right)^{1/2} F^1_{\{p'q'}(x_1, \ldots, x_{p'} \,|\, y_1, \ldots, y_{q'})$$

$$\times F^2_{p''q''\}}(x_{p'+1}, \cdots, x_p \,|\, y_{q'+1}, \cdots y_q). \qquad (3.56)$$

The symbol $\{ \ \}$ denotes antisymmetrization with respect to $x_1, \ldots, x_p$ and $y_1, \ldots, y_q$, separately.

We shall show that the operator $F_{pq}$ with the kernel

$$F_{pq}(x_1,\ldots, x_p \,|\, y_1,\ldots, y_q)$$

$$= F^1_{p'q'}(x_1,\ldots, x_{p'} \,|\, y_1,\ldots, y_{q'}) F^2_{p''q''}(x_{p'+1},\ldots, x_p \,|\, y_{q'+1},\ldots, y_q)$$

is bounded. For brevity we introduce the notations

$$\xi_1 = (x_1,\ldots, x_{p'}), \qquad \xi_2 = (x_{p'+1},\ldots, x_p),$$

$$\eta_1 = (y_1,\ldots, y_{q'}), \qquad \eta_2 = (y_{q'+1},\ldots, y_q),$$

$$F^1_{p'q'}(\xi_1, \eta_1) = F_1(\xi_1, \eta_1), \qquad F^2_{p''q''}(\xi_2, \eta_2) = F_2(\xi_2, \eta_2).$$

In view of the isomorphism of the Hilbert spaces, we may assume without loss of generality that the variables $\xi_i$, $\eta_i$ run through one and the same set $\mathfrak{M}$ with a measure; the spaces $H^{p'}$, $H^{p''}$, $H^{q'}$, $H^{q''}$ coincide with each other and form the space $H$ of square-integrable functions on $\mathfrak{M}$. We consider the Hilbert space $H_2$ of square-integrable functions $K$ on $\mathfrak{M}$ of two variables. It should be verified that the operator $F$ in $H_2$ with the kernel $F(\xi_1, \xi_2 \,|\, \eta_1, \eta_2) = F(\xi_1, \eta_1)F(\xi_2, \eta_2)$ is bounded.

We shall interpret $H_2$ as a space of Hilbert-Schmidt operators in $H$ with $(K_1, K_2) = \mathrm{Sp}\, K_1 K_2^*$. In such a case we have

$$\int F(\xi_1, \xi_2 \,|\, \eta_1, \eta_2) K(\eta_1, \eta_2)\, d\eta_1\, d\eta_2 = F_1 K F_2, \qquad K \in H_2$$

Using a well-known inequality we obtain

$$\mathrm{Sp}(F_1 K F_2 F_2^* K^* F_1^*) \le \|F_1 F_1^*\| \mathrm{Sp}(K F_2 F_2^* K^*)$$

$$= \|F_1 F_1^*\| \mathrm{Sp}(K^* K F_2 F_2^*)$$

$$\le \|F_1 F_1^*\| \, \|F_2 F_2^*\| \mathrm{Sp}\, K^* K.$$

Thus $\|F\| \le \|F_1\| \, \|F_2\|$. (It is not difficult to show that indeed $\|F\| = \|F_1\| \, \|F_2\|$.)

From the boundedness of the operator $F = F_{pq}$ there follows in an obvious way the boundedness of the operator $\Phi_{pq}$ with the kernel (3.56), and hence the closed property of $\mathscr{G}$ relative to the multiplication. The remaining items of the definition of the Grassmann algebra are proved more easily.

We consider in the space $E^n$ of functionals of the form (3.55) the set $\tilde{E}^n$ of generating functionals for trace-class operators. Let $F_1 \in \tilde{E}^n$,

$F_2 \in E^n$, and $\hat{F}_1$ and $\hat{F}_2$ be corresponding operators. We introduce in $E^n$ an inner product by setting

$$(F_1, F_2) = \operatorname{Sp} \hat{F}_1 \hat{F}_2^* \tag{3.57}$$

($\hat{F}_2^*$ is the operator adjoint to $\hat{F}_2$). Finally, we introduce in $\mathscr{G}$ an involution by setting, when $F$ is given by the series (3.55),

$$F^*(a^*, a) = \sum_{p,q} \frac{1}{(p!\,q!)^{1/2}} \int \overline{F_{pq}(x_1,\ldots, x_p \mid y_1,\ldots, y_q)}$$

$$\times a^*(y_1) \cdots a^*(y_q) a(x_p) \cdots a(x_1)\, d^p x\, d^q y. \tag{3.58}$$

(Evidently, if the functional $F$ corresponds to the operator $\hat{F}$, then the functional $F^*$ corresponds to $\hat{F}^*$.)

It is easy to verify that the inner product (3.57) and the involution (3.58) convert $\mathscr{G}$ into an algebra with an inner product and involution in the sense of the definition given in Subsections 5 and 6. The symbols $a(x)$, $a^*(x)$ are the system of involutive generators in the sense of the definition given in Subsection 6.

The proof of these assertions is very simple, so we shall not dwell on it.

Thus it has been proved that generating functionals for the matrix form of bounded operators are elements of the Grassmann algebra $\mathscr{G}$ with an inner product and involution.

Now let $A(a^*, a)$ and $\tilde{A}(a^*, a)$ be functionals corresponding to an operator $\hat{A}$ in its normal and matrix forms, respectively. According to formula (1.38) we have

$$A(a^*, a) = \tilde{A}(a^*, a) \exp\left[-\int a^*(x)a(x)\, dx\right].$$

It is not difficult to verify directly that $\exp\left[-\int a^*(x)a(x)\, dx\right]$ is a functional corresponding to the matrix form of a bounded operator. Therefore $\exp\left[-\int a^*(x)a(x)\, dx\right] \in \mathscr{G}$. Thus $A(a^*, a) \in \mathscr{G}$.

The algebra $\mathscr{G}$ contains elements of the form

$$\Phi(a^*) = \sum_n \frac{1}{(n!)^{1/2}} \int \Phi_n(x_1,\ldots, x_n) a^*(x_1) \cdots a^*(x_n)\, d^n x, \tag{3.59}$$

$$\sum_n \int |\Phi_n|^2\, d^n x < \infty.$$

The elements $\Phi(a^*)$ will be identified with generating functionals for vectors of the state space (cf. Section 1.7).

Thus all three types of functionals in which we are interested, that is, the functionals $\tilde{A}(a^*, a)$ and $A(a^*, a)$ corresponding to operators and the functionals $\Phi(a^*)$ corresponding to vectors, are shown to be elements of one and the same Grassmann algebra $\mathscr{G}$.

In closing this subsection we show that the algebra $\mathscr{G}$ has the sub-algebra $\mathscr{G}_1$ which is a normed Grassmann algebra and still contains the functionals $\tilde{A}(a^*, a)$, $A(a^*, a)$, and $\Phi(a^*)$.

To this end we take in the space $L_2(M)$ an orthonormal basis $\{f_k(x)\}$. We consider the set $\mathscr{G}_1$ of functionals $F$ of the form (3.54) having the property

$$\left| \int F_{pq}(x_1,\ldots, x_p \mid y_1,\ldots, y_q) f_{k_1}(x_1) \cdots f_{k_p}(x_p) \right.$$
$$\left. \times \overline{f_{l_1}(y_1)} \cdots \overline{f_{l_q}(y_q)}\, d^p x\, d^q y \right| \le c. \quad (3.60)$$

Let us denote by $F_{pq}(k_1,\ldots, k_p \mid l_1,\ldots, l_q)$ the expression under the modulus sign in the left member.

It is easy to see that functionals corresponding to the matrix form of bounded operators belong to $\mathscr{G}_1$. In fact, if $\tilde{A}(a^*, a)$ is a functional corresponding to an operator $\hat{A}$, then $A_{pq}(k_1,\ldots, k_p \mid l_1,\ldots, l_q)$ is a matrix element of the operator $\hat{A}$ in the orthonormal basis. Therefore we have

$$|A_{pq}(k_1,\ldots, k_p \mid l_1,\ldots, l_q)| \le \|\hat{A}\|. \quad (3.61)$$

We introduce a norm in the space of functionals $F(a^*, a)$ by setting

$$\|F\| = \sup_{\sum_k |\alpha_k| = 1} \sum_{p,q} \sum_{k,l} \frac{1}{(p!\,q!)^{1/2}} |F_{pq}(k_1,\ldots, k_p \mid l_1,\ldots, l_q)|$$
$$\times |\alpha_{k_1}| \cdots |\alpha_{k_p}| |\alpha_{l_1}| \cdots |\alpha_{l_q}|.$$

Using the inequality (3.60) we find

$$\sum_{p,q} \sum_{k,l} \frac{1}{(p!\,q!)^{1/2}} |F_{pq}(k_1,\ldots, k_p \mid l_1,\ldots, l_q)| |\alpha_{k_1}| \cdots |\alpha_{k_p}| |\alpha_{l_1}| \cdots |\alpha_{l_q}|$$
$$\le c \sum_p \frac{1}{(p!)^{1/2}} \left( \sum_k |\alpha_k| \right)^p \sum_q \frac{1}{(q!)^{1/2}} \left( \sum_l |\alpha_l| \right)^q = c U^2 \left( \sum_k |\alpha_k| \right),$$

where $U(z) = \sum (n!)^{-1/2} z^n$. In particular, if $F = \tilde{A}(a^*, a)$ is the functional corresponding to the matrix form of the operator $\hat{A}$, then, as is seen from (3.61),

$$\|F\| = \|\tilde{A}\| \le \|\hat{A}\| U^2(1).$$

We shall show that the norm introduced above satisfies the condition

$$\|F_1 F_2\| \le \|F_1\| \, \|F_2\|. \tag{3.62}$$

We denote by $F_0$ the product of functionals $F_0 = F_1 F_2$ and by $F_{pq}^i(x_1,..., x_p | y_1,..., y_q)$ the coefficients of the expansions of the functionals $F_i$, $i = 0, 1, 2$, into the series (3.54). Further, let

$$F_{pq}^i(k_1,..., k_p | l_1,..., l_q) = \int F_{pq}^i(x_1,..., x_p | y_1,..., y_q)$$

$$\times f_{k_1}(x_1) \cdots f_{k_p}(x_p) \overline{f_{l_1}}(y_1) \cdots \overline{f_{l_q}}(y_q) \, d^p x \, d^q y.$$

It is easy to see that

$$F_{pq}^0(k_1,..., k_p | l_1,..., l_q) = \sum_{p'+p''=p, q'+q''=q} \left( \frac{p! q!}{p'! p''! q'! q''!} \right)^{1/2}$$

$$\times F_{\{p'q'}^1(k_1,..., k_{p'} | l_1,..., l_{q'}) F_{p''q''\}}^2(k_{p'+1},..., k_p | l_{q'+1},..., l_q). \tag{3.63}$$

(The symbol $\{ \ \}$ denotes antisymmetrization with respect to $k_1,..., k_p$ and $l_1,..., l_q$, separately.)

We obtain from (3.63), taking account of $\sum |\alpha_k| = 1$,

$$\sum_{p,q,k,l} (p! q!)^{-1/2} |F_{pq}^0(k_1,..., k_p | l_1,..., l_q)| \, |\alpha_{k_1}| \cdots |\alpha_{l_q}|$$

$$\le \sum_{p',p'',q',q'',k,l} (p'! p''! q'! q''!)^{-1/2} |F_{p'q'}^1(k_1,..., k_{p'} | l_1,..., l_{q'})|$$

$$\times |F_{p''q''}^2(k_{p'+1},..., k_p | l_{q'+1},..., l_q)| \, |\alpha_{k_1}| \cdots |\alpha_{l_q}|$$

$$= \sum_{p',q',k,l} (p'! q'!)^{-1/2} |F_{p'q'}^1(k_1,..., k_{p'} | l_1,..., l_{q'})|$$

$$\times |\alpha_{k_1}| \cdots |\alpha_{k_{p'}}| \, |\alpha_{l_1}| \cdots |\alpha_{l_{q'}}|$$

$$\times \sum_{p'',q'',k,l} (p''! q''!)^{-1/2} |F_{p''q''}^2(k_1,..., k_{p''} | l_1,..., l_{q''})|$$

$$\times |\alpha_{k_{p'+1}}| \cdots |\alpha_{k_{p''}}| \, |\alpha_{l_{q'+1}}| \cdots |\alpha_{l_{q''}}| \le \|F^1\| \, \|F^2\|.$$

Thus the property (3.62) of the norm is verified and so it is proved that $\mathscr{G}_1$ is a normed algebra.

By completing $\mathscr{G}_1$ by the norm introduced above, we obtain a complete normed algebra.

That the functionals $A(a^*, a)$ and $\Phi(a^*)$ belong to the algebra $\mathscr{G}_1$ is proved in the same way as is the similar fact in the fundamental text.

The assertion proved in this part of the present subsection is an analog of Theorem 1.3 proved in Section 1.9.

12. INNER PRODUCT IN THE STATE SPACE. Let $\hat{\Phi}_1, \hat{\Phi}_2$ be vectors of the state space, and let $\Phi_1(a^*)$ and $\Phi_2(a^*)$, functionals corresponding to them, be elements of the algebra $\mathscr{G}$. We introduce in the set $\mathscr{L}$ of functionals corresponding to state vectors an inner product by the formula

$$(\Phi_1, \Phi_2) = (\hat{\Phi}_1, \hat{\Phi}_2). \tag{3.64}$$

The inner product (3.64) converts $\mathscr{L}$ into a Hilbert space serving as a realization of the state space.

We have

**Theorem 3.1.** (1) *The inner product* (3.64) *can be given by the formula*

$$(\Phi_1, \Phi_2) = \int \Phi_1(a^*)\Phi_2^*(a)e^{-aa^*}\Pi \, da \, da^* \tag{3.65}$$

*or*

$$(\Phi_1, \Phi_2) = \int \Phi_2^*(a)\Phi_1(a^*)e^{-a^*a}\Pi \, da^* \, da, \tag{3.66}$$

*where* $\Phi_2^*(a)$ *is the element adjoint to* $\Phi_2(a^*)$ *[cf.* (3.30)*].*

(2) *In order that the functional* $\Phi$ *should belong to the space* $\mathscr{L}$, *it is necessary and sufficient that it should satisfy the inequality*

$$\int \Phi(a^*)\Phi^*(a)e^{-aa^*}\Pi \, da \, da^* < \infty \tag{3.65'}$$

*or*

$$\int \Phi^*(a)\Phi(a^*)e^{-a^*a}\Pi \, da^* \, da < \infty. \tag{3.66'}$$

In formulas (3.65)–(3.66') and in what follows we use the simplified notation $a^*a = \int a^*(x)a(x) \, dx$ (cf. p. 75).

Formula (3.65) is proved by means of (3.50′), and formula (3.66) by means of (3.50). The proof of this theorem differs from that of the similar theorem for bosons (Theorem 2.1) only in the simplification connected with the fact that the space $\mathscr{H}_F$ for the case of a finite number of degrees of freedom is finite-dimensional. Therefore we shall omit the proof.

Formulas (3.67)–(3.72) given below are easily proved for the case when the functionals entering these formulas are polynomials. The proof in the general case requires the aid of Theorem 3.1. We shall not carry out these proofs, since they repeat word by word the proof of similar formulas for bosons.

We point out that all the formulas of the operational calculus (3.65) –(3.74), except the formula for the trace (3.72), coincide in form with similar formulas for bosons.

13. OPERATION OF AN OPERATOR ON A VECTOR. Let $\hat{\Psi} = \hat{A}\hat{\Phi}$, $\Phi(a^*)$, $\Psi(a^*)$ be functionals corresponding to vectors $\hat{\Phi}$, $\hat{\Psi}$, let $\tilde{A}(a^*, a)$ be a functional corresponding to the matrix form of the operator $\hat{A}$, and $A(a^*, a)$ be a functional corresponding to its normal form. We find the expression of $\Psi$ in terms of $\Phi$ and $\tilde{A}$. Combining formula (0.1) in the Introduction and formula (3.50), we find

$$\Psi(a^*) = \int \tilde{A}(a^*, \alpha)\Phi(\alpha^*)e^{-\alpha^*\alpha}\Pi \, d\alpha^* \, d\alpha. \qquad (3.67)$$

By using the connection between the functionals $\tilde{A}(a^*, a)$ and $A(a^*, a)$ [formula (1.38)], we express $\Psi$ in terms of $\Phi$ and $A$ as follows:

$$\Psi(a^*) = \int A(a^*, \alpha)\Phi(\alpha^*)e^{-(\alpha^* - a^*)\alpha}\Pi \, d\alpha^* \, d\alpha. \qquad (3.68)$$

14. PRODUCT OF OPERATORS. Let us express the functional corresponding to the operator $\hat{C} = \hat{A}\hat{B}$ in terms of functionals corresponding to $\hat{A}$ and $\hat{B}$. We begin with functionals $\tilde{A}$, $\tilde{B}$, $\tilde{C}$ corresponding to the matrix form of the operators. Combining formula (0.2) in the Introduction and (3.50) we find

$$\tilde{C}(a^*, a) = \int \tilde{A}(a^*, \alpha)\tilde{B}(\alpha^*, a)e^{-\alpha^*\alpha}\Pi \, d\alpha^* \, d\alpha. \qquad (3.69)$$

Passing from the functionals $\tilde{A}$, $\tilde{B}$, $\tilde{C}$ to $A$, $B$, $C$ by formula (1.38) we obtain

$$C(a^*, a) = \int A(a^*, \alpha)B(\alpha^*, a)e^{-(\alpha^* - a^*)(\alpha - a)}\Pi \, d\alpha^* \, d\alpha. \qquad (3.70)$$

15. TRACE OF AN OPERATOR. Let $\tilde{A}(a^*, a)$ be functional corresponding to the matrix form of a trace-class operator $\hat{A}$. As in the Bose case, we find by the aid of formula (3.50′) the expression for the trace of $\hat{A}$,

$$\text{Sp } \hat{A} = \int \tilde{A}(a^*, a)e^{-aa^*}\Pi \, da \, da^*. \qquad (3.71)$$

Passing from the functional $\tilde{A}$ to the functional $A$ by formula (1.37) we obtain

$$\text{Sp } \hat{A} = \int A(a^*, a)e^{-2aa^*}\Pi \, da \, da^*. \qquad (3.72)$$

16. ANOTHER DEFINITION OF THE TRACE. We change the definition of the trace by setting

$$\text{Sp}_1 \, A = \int A\left(\frac{a^*}{\sqrt{2}}, \frac{a}{\sqrt{2}}\right)e^{-aa^*}\Pi \, da \, da^*. \qquad (3.73)$$

Let, as usual, $a = a(x)$, $a^* = a^*(x)$. By use of the rule for changing variables, it is not difficult to verify that in the case when $x$ runs through a finite set consisting of $n$ elements, and consequently the operator $\hat{A}$ is a linear operator in $2^n$-dimensional space, the traces defined by formulas (3.72) and (3.73) are connected by the relation

$$\text{Sp}_1 \, \hat{A} = \frac{1}{2^n} \text{Sp } \hat{A}. \qquad (3.74)$$

Of course, such a connection cannot remain valid in the infinite-dimensional case. In this case it can be shown that the traces (3.72) and (3.73) are defined for different classes of operators: (3.72) for trace-class operators, (3.73) for the ring consisting of operators of the form

$$\hat{A} = \sum_{m,n} A_{mn}(x_1,\ldots, x_m \,|\, y_1,\ldots, y_n)\hat{a}^*(x_1) \cdots \hat{a}^*(x_m)$$

$$\times \hat{a}(y_1) \cdots \hat{a}(y_n) \, d^m x \, d^n y. \qquad (3.75)$$

(The sum in the right member is finite.) Operators (3.75) form a ring $\mathcal{A}$ including the identity operator $E$, for which evidently $\mathrm{Sp}_1 E = 1$. The trace (3.73) has the fundamental properties of the usual trace: It is a linear function on elements of $\mathcal{A}$ and $\mathrm{Sp}\,\hat{A}_1\hat{A}_2 = \mathrm{Sp}\,\hat{A}_2\hat{A}_1$.

We consider the operators

$$\hat{q}(x) = \hat{a}(x) + \hat{a}^*(x) \qquad \text{and} \qquad \hat{p}(x) = \frac{1}{i}(\hat{a}^*(x) - \hat{a}(x)).$$

The ring of operators of the form

$$\hat{A} = \sum_{k=0}^{N} \int A_k(x_1,\ldots, x_k)\hat{p}(x_1) \cdots \hat{p}(x_k)\, d^k x \tag{3.76}$$

is denoted by $\tilde{\mathcal{P}}$, and the ring of operators of the form

$$\hat{A} = \sum_{k=0}^{N} \int A_k(x_1,\ldots, x_k)\hat{q}(x_1) \cdots \hat{q}(x_k)\, d^k x \tag{3.77}$$

is denoted by $\tilde{\mathcal{Q}}$. The functions $A(x_1,\ldots, x_k)$ are square-integrable in both cases.

Evidently $\tilde{\mathcal{P}} \subset \mathcal{A}$ and $\tilde{\mathcal{Q}} \subset \mathcal{A}$. Therefore the trace (3.73) is defined for elements of $\tilde{\mathcal{P}}$, as well as for elements of $\tilde{\mathcal{Q}}$. The weak closure of the rings $\tilde{\mathcal{P}}$ and $\tilde{\mathcal{Q}}$ are denoted by $\mathcal{P}$ and $\mathcal{Q}$, respectively.

It can be shown that the trace (3.73) is extended by continuity to $\mathcal{P}$ and $\mathcal{Q}$. The rings $\mathcal{P}$ and $\mathcal{Q}$ are shown to be factors of type $\mathrm{II}_1$ (in this connection, cf. also Section 3.2). It is not difficult to verify that if $\hat{A}$ is of the form (3.76) or (3.77), then $\mathrm{Sp}_1\,\hat{A} = A_0$.

The assertions formulated in this subsection are a rephrasing of von Neumann's results [2]. See also Berezin [5].

## Chapter II

## Linear Canonical Transformations

Every unitary transformation $\hat{U}$ in the state space induces an automorphism in the algebra of operators: $\hat{A} \rightarrow \hat{U}\hat{A}\hat{U}^{-1}$. In particular, if $\hat{a}^*(f)$, $\hat{a}(f)$ are creation and annihilation operators, the operators $\hat{b}^*(f) = \hat{U}\hat{a}^*(f)\hat{U}^{-1}$, $\hat{b}(f) = \hat{U}\hat{a}(f)\hat{U}^{-1}$ satisfy the same commutation relations as the operators $\hat{a}^*(f)$, $\hat{a}(f)$. The correspondence arising in this way between the operators $\hat{a}$, $\hat{a}^*$ and $\hat{b}$, $\hat{b}^*$ is called a *proper canonical transformation*.

In a broader sense any system of operators $\hat{b}(f)$, $\hat{b}^*(f)$ satisfying the same commutation relations as $\hat{a}(f)$, $\hat{a}^*(f)$ is called a *canonical transformation*. A canonical transformation is said to be *linear* if the operators $\hat{b}(f)$, $\hat{b}^*(f)$ are expressed linearly in terms of the annihilation and creation operators $\hat{a}(f)$, $\hat{a}^*(f)$. Without effort one can prove that every canonical transformation is proper if the number of degrees of freedom is finite.[1] It is a characteristic feature of the case of an infinite number of degrees of freedom that there are improper canonical transformations. Improper canonical transformations appear frequently in the quantum field theory. Their role therein is distinctly visible in an example of Thirring's model, which will be considered in Section 9.

In the present chapter linear canonical transformations are studied: for bosons in Section 4, and for fermions in Section 5. Criteria are established that a linear canonical transformation is proper; then in that case the unitary operator $\hat{U}$ realizing this canonical transformation is restored in the state space.

Formulas for the canonical transformation of operators are established at the end of Section 4 and in Section 5.

[1] Cf. Theorem 1.4 and the footnote on p. 21.

Finally, it is noted that canonical transformations in quantum mechanics, just like those in ordinary mechanics, may be useful for reducing a certain operator to the simplest canonical form. However, although the description of all (not only linear) canonical transformations is well known for ordinary mechanics, such a problem has not yet been solved in quantum mechanics.

## 4. Bose Case

1. DEFINITIONS. Let $L$ be a Hilbert space with involution, and $\hat{a}^*(\varphi)$ and $\hat{a}(\varphi)$, $\varphi \in L$, be creation and annihilation operators satisfying the Bose commutation relations

$$[\hat{a}(\varphi_1), \hat{a}^*(\varphi_2)] = \varphi_1\varphi_2 = (\varphi_1, \varphi_2^*),$$

$$[\hat{a}(\varphi_1), \hat{a}(\varphi_2)] = [\hat{a}^*(\varphi_1), \hat{a}^*(\varphi_2)] = 0. \tag{4.1}$$

Consider in $L$ a dense set $D$ invariant relative to the involution. Let $\Phi$ and $\Psi$ be operators, defined in $D$ and possessing their adjoints defined on a common dense domain $D_1$ which is also invariant relative to the involution. Further, let $f$ be a functional in $D_1$. It is convenient to assume that the space $D_1'$ of functionals in $D_1$ is an extension of the space $L: D_1' \supset L \supset D_1$. The involution in $L$ is extended in a natural way to the space $D_1'$. The value of a functional $f \in D_1'$ on an element $\varphi \in D_1$ will be denoted by $(\varphi, f^*)$ or $\varphi f$. If $f \in L$, then $(\varphi, f)$ is the inner product of $\varphi$ and $f$, and $\varphi f = (\varphi, f^*)$ is the corresponding bilinear form.

We form operators $\hat{b}(\varphi)$, $\hat{b}^*(\varphi)$ $(\varphi \in D_1)$:

$$\hat{b}(\varphi) = \hat{a}(\varphi\Phi) + \hat{a}^*(\varphi\Psi) + \varphi f,$$

$$\hat{b}^*(\varphi) = \hat{a}(\varphi\overline{\Psi}) + \hat{a}^*(\varphi\overline{\Phi}) + \varphi f^*. \tag{4.2}$$

If equations (4.2) are solvable with respect to $\hat{a}(\varphi)$ and $\hat{a}^*(\varphi)$, and the operators $\hat{b}(\varphi)$ and $\hat{b}^*(\varphi)$ satisfy the commutation relations

$$[\hat{b}(\varphi_1), \hat{b}^*(\varphi_2)] = \varphi_1\varphi_2,$$

$$[\hat{b}(\varphi_1), \hat{b}(\varphi_2)] = [\hat{b}^*(\varphi_1), \hat{b}^*(\varphi_2)] = 0, \tag{4.1'}$$

then formula (4.2) determining the connection between $\hat{a}(\varphi)$, $\hat{a}^*(\varphi)$ and $\hat{b}(\varphi)$, $\hat{b}^*(\varphi)$ is called an *inhomogeneous linear canonical transformation*.

If the functional $f$ is equal to zero, then the transformation (4.2) is called a *homogeneous linear canonical transformation.*

The operators $\Phi$ and $\Psi$ providing the transformation (4.2) are not arbitrary. There are relations between them to be determined in the next subsection.

If the space $L$ can be realized in concordance with involution by means of square-integrable functions on a certain set provided with a measure, then the operators $\Phi$, $\Psi$, $\overline{\Phi}$, and $\overline{\Psi}$ are given by kernels $\Phi(x, y)$, $\Psi(x, y)$, $\overline{\Phi}(x, y)$, and $\overline{\Psi}(x, y)$, respectively. The functional $f$ is then given by a function $f(x)$. The functions $f(x)$, $\Phi(x, y)$, $\Psi(x, y)$ are, in general, generalized functions.[2] The operators $\hat{a}(\varphi)$, $\hat{a}^*(\varphi)$, $\hat{b}(\varphi)$, $\hat{b}^*(\varphi)$ are generated by operator-generalized functions $\hat{a}(x)$, $\hat{a}^*(x)$, $\hat{b}(x)$, $\hat{b}^*(x)$: $\hat{a}(\varphi) = \int \varphi(x)\hat{a}(x)\,dx$, etc. Evidently formulas (4.2) may be transcribed in the form

$$\hat{b}(x) = \int \Phi(x, y)\hat{a}(y)\,dy + \int \Psi(x, y)\hat{a}^*(y)\,dy + f(x),$$

$$\hat{b}^*(x) = \int \overline{\Psi}(x, y)\hat{a}(y)\,dy + \int \overline{\Phi}(x, y)\hat{a}^*(y)\,dy + f^*(x).$$

$$(4.3)$$

Let us consider the case when the space $L$ has a finite dimension $N$.

It has been noted in Section 1 (cf. p. 21) that in this case all irreducible representations of the commutation relations are unitary equivalent. It follows easily from this that the operators $\hat{a}(\varphi)$, $\hat{a}^*(\varphi)$ and $\hat{b}(\varphi)$, $\hat{b}^*(\varphi)$ are connected by the relation

$$\hat{b}(\varphi) = \hat{U}\hat{a}(\varphi)\hat{U}^{-1}, \qquad \hat{b}^*(\varphi) = \hat{U}\hat{a}^*(\varphi)\hat{U}^{-1}, \qquad (4.4)$$

where $\hat{U}$ is a unitary operator in $\mathcal{H}_B$. [The irreducibility of the set of operators $\hat{a}(\varphi)$, $\hat{a}^*(\varphi)$ implies easily that the operator $\hat{U}$ is determined uniquely by relation (4.4) up to a factor.] In the general case when $L$ is infinite-dimensional, there are two possibilities: Either the unitary operator $\hat{U}$ satisfying the conditions (4.4) does exist as in the finite-dimensional case, or else such an operator does not exist.

In the former case the canonical transformation will be called *proper,* and in the latter *improper.*[3]

---

[2] Cf. footnote 4 on p. 3.

[3] It is not difficult to show (cf. p. 93) that if there exists a certain operator defined on the vacuum vector and satisfying relation (4.4), then this operator differs from a unitary operator only by a factor.

2. Relations between the Operators $\Phi$ and $\Psi$. Putting $\hat{b}(\varphi)$ and $\hat{b}^*(\varphi)$ from (4.2) into (4.1′) and using formulas (4.1), we find the relations between operators $\Phi$ and $\Psi$:

$$\Phi\Psi' - \Psi\Phi' = 0, \qquad \overline{\Phi}\Psi^* - \overline{\Psi}\Phi^* = 0,$$
$$\Phi\Phi^* - \Psi\Psi^* = E, \qquad \overline{\Phi}\Phi' - \overline{\Psi}\Psi' = E. \tag{4.5}$$

The expressions in the left members have the meaning of Hermitian forms on the set $D_1$ on which the operators $\Phi^*$, $\Psi^*$ are defined; for example, $(\Phi\Psi'f, g) = (\Psi'f, \Phi^*g)$ for $f, g \in D_1$.

We consider the matrix $\mathscr{A}$ consisting of the operators $\Phi, \Psi, \overline{\Phi}, \overline{\Psi}$:

$$\mathscr{A} = \begin{pmatrix} \Phi & \Psi \\ \overline{\Psi} & \overline{\Phi} \end{pmatrix}. \tag{4.6}$$

The matrix $\mathscr{A}$ will be called the *matrix of a canonical transformation*. It is readily seen that the conditions (4.5) are equivalent to the following:

$$\begin{pmatrix} \Phi & \Psi \\ \overline{\Psi} & \overline{\Phi} \end{pmatrix} \begin{pmatrix} \Phi^* & -\Psi' \\ -\Psi^* & \Phi' \end{pmatrix} = \begin{pmatrix} E & 0 \\ 0 & E \end{pmatrix}.$$

Thus the matrix $\mathscr{A}$ has a right inverse. By definition the canonical transformation is reversible. This means that the matrix $\mathscr{A}$ has a left inverse. Since the left inverse of an operator is equal to its right inverse (if both exist), the matrix $\mathscr{A}$ thus has the two-sided inverse equal to

$$\mathscr{A}^{-1} = \begin{pmatrix} \Phi^* & -\Psi' \\ -\Psi^* & \Phi' \end{pmatrix}. \tag{4.7}$$

It is easy to see that there corresponds to the product of canonical transformations the product of their respective matrices. By using the circumstance that the matrix of a canonical transformation has an inverse, it is not difficult to verify that inhomogeneous linear canonical transformations form a group. Homogeneous transformations evidently form a subgroup of this group.

By the use of the fact that $\mathscr{A}^{-1}\mathscr{A} = E$ we obtain, in addition to (4.5), the relations

$$\Phi'\overline{\Psi} - \Psi^*\Phi = 0, \qquad \Phi^*\Psi - \Psi'\overline{\Phi} = 0,$$
$$\Phi^*\Phi - \Psi'\overline{\Psi} = E, \qquad \Phi'\overline{\Phi} - \Psi^*\Psi = E. \tag{4.8}$$

The expressions in the left member have the meaning of Hermitian forms on the dense set $D$ on which the operators $\Phi$, $\Psi$ are defined; for example, $(\Phi'\bar{\Psi}f, g) = (\bar{\Psi}f, \bar{\Phi}g)$ for $f, g \in D$.

We note two important properties of the canonical transformations which arise from the relations (4.5) and (4.8).

(1) The operator $\Phi$ has the bounded inverse. In fact, it follows from (4.5) and (4.8) that $\Phi\Phi^* = E + \Psi\Psi^*$ and $\Phi^*\Phi = E + \Psi'\bar{\Psi}$. Thus $\Phi^*\Phi$ and $\Phi\Phi^*$ have bounded inverses. Hence it follows that $\Phi = U(\Phi\Phi^*)^{1/2}$, where $U$ is a unitary operator, and accordingly that there also exists the bounded operator $\Phi^{-1} = (\Phi^*\Phi)^{-1/2}U^{-1}$.

(2) The matrix $\left(\begin{smallmatrix} \Phi & \Psi \\ \bar{\Psi} & \bar{\Phi} \end{smallmatrix}\right)$ of the canonical transformation can be represented in the form

$$\begin{pmatrix} \Phi & \Psi \\ \bar{\Psi} & \bar{\Phi} \end{pmatrix} = \begin{pmatrix} U & 0 \\ 0 & \bar{U} \end{pmatrix}\begin{pmatrix} \Phi_1 & \Psi_1 \\ \bar{\Psi}_1 & \bar{\Phi}_1 \end{pmatrix}, \tag{4.9}$$

where $U$ is a unitary operator and $\Phi_1 = (\Phi^*\Phi)^{1/2}$ is an Hermitian positive-definite operator. Each one of the factors on the right is the matrix of a canonical transformation. Property (2) follows from the first in an obvious way.

In closing this subsection we shall make some further remarks.

Consider the matrix $I = \left(\begin{smallmatrix} 0 & E \\ -E & 0 \end{smallmatrix}\right)$. It is not difficult to verify that the conditions (4.5) and (4.8) are equivalent to the conditions

$$\mathscr{A}I\mathscr{A}' = I, \qquad \mathscr{A}'I\mathscr{A} = I, \tag{4.10}$$

where $\mathscr{A}'$ is the transposed matrix of $\mathscr{A}$: $\mathscr{A}' = \left(\begin{smallmatrix} \Phi' & \Psi^* \\ \Psi' & \Phi^* \end{smallmatrix}\right)$.

Consider the matrix $U = \frac{1}{\sqrt{2}}\left(\begin{smallmatrix} E & E \\ -iE & iE \end{smallmatrix}\right)$. We denote by $\mathscr{B}$ the matrix

$$\mathscr{B} = U\mathscr{A}U^{-1}, \tag{4.11}$$

where $\mathscr{A}$ is the matrix of a canonical transformation. By carrying out the matrix multiplication, we obtain

$$\mathscr{B} = \begin{pmatrix} A & B \\ C & D \end{pmatrix}, \qquad \begin{array}{ll} A = \operatorname{Re}(\Phi + \Psi), & B = -\operatorname{Im}(\Phi - \Psi), \\ C = \operatorname{Im}(\Phi + \Psi), & D = \operatorname{Re}(\Phi - \Psi). \end{array} \tag{4.12}$$

It is not difficult to verify that the matrix $\mathscr{B}$, as before, satisfies the condition (4.10), and moreover the set of matrices $\mathscr{B}$ of the form (4.11) coincides with the set of all real matrices that satisfy the condition

$(4.10).^4$ Multiplying $(4.10)$ from the right by $I$, and because of $I^2 = -E$, we find that the matrix $\mathscr{B}^{-1}$ has the form

$$\mathscr{B}^{-1} = -UI\mathscr{A}'IU^{-1} = \begin{pmatrix} D' & -B' \\ -C' & A' \end{pmatrix}. \tag{4.13}$$

3. PROPER CANONICAL TRANSFORMATIONS. In this subsection we shall find criteria that a canonical transformation given by operators $\Phi$, $\Psi$ and functional $f$ should be proper.[5]

**Theorem 4.1.** *The canonical transformation*

$$\hat{b}(\varphi) = \hat{a}(\varphi\Phi) + \hat{a}^*(\varphi\Psi) + \varphi f,$$

$$\hat{b}^*(\varphi) = \hat{a}(\varphi\overline{\Psi}) + \hat{a}^*(\varphi\overline{\Phi}) + \varphi f^* \tag{4.14}$$

*is proper if and only if*
(1) $\Psi$ *is a Hilbert-Schmidt operator,*
(2) $f \in L$.

Before entering into the proof we observe that $\Phi\Phi^* = E + \Psi\Psi^*$ by $(4.5)$. If the canonical transformation is proper, then $\Psi\Psi^*$ is a trace-class operator, and accordingly the operator $\Phi\Phi^*$ has the Fredholm determinant.

The proof of Theorem 4.1 is based on the following lemma.

**Lemma 4.1.** *In order that the canonical transformation be proper, it is necessary and sufficient that there should exist in the state space a vector $\hat{F}_0$ satisfying the conditions*

$$\hat{b}(\varphi)\hat{F}_0 = 0 \tag{4.15}$$

*for every $\varphi \in L$ for which the operator $\hat{b}(\varphi)$ is defined.*

The vector $\hat{F}_0$ will be referred to as the *vacuum relative to $\hat{b}(\varphi)$*.

---

[4] Finite-dimensional matrices satisfying the conditions $(4.10)$ are said to be *symplectic*. They form a group called a *symplectic group*. In analogy with the finite-dimensional case, the group of operators satisfying the conditions $(4.10)$ is naturally called the *infinite-dimensional symplectic group*.

[5] Cf. Friedrichs' book [1].

We consider the subspace $\tilde{\mathcal{H}} \subset \mathcal{H}_B$ consisting of vectors of the form

$$\hat{\Phi} = \sum_n (n!)^{-1/2} \int K_n(x_1,\ldots, x_n)\hat{b}^*(x_1) \cdots \hat{b}^*(x_n)\, d^n x \hat{F}_0. \quad (4.16)$$

According to Theorem 1.4 there exists a one-to-one isometric mapping $\hat{U}$ from $\tilde{\mathcal{H}}$ onto $\mathcal{H}_B$ such that $\hat{U}\hat{a}(\varphi)\hat{U}^{-1} = \hat{b}(\varphi)$. We shall show that $\tilde{\mathcal{H}} = \mathcal{H}_B$. In fact, $\tilde{\mathcal{H}}$ is invariant with respect to $\hat{b}(\varphi)$ and $\hat{b}^*(\varphi)$. As we know, the operators $\hat{a}(\varphi)$, $\hat{a}^*(\varphi)$ are expressed linearly by $\hat{b}(\varphi)$, $\hat{b}^*(\varphi)$. Consequently, the space $\tilde{\mathcal{H}}$ is invariant with respect to $\hat{a}(\varphi)$, $\hat{a}^*(\varphi)$. By (3) of Theorem 1.4 we have $\tilde{\mathcal{H}} = \mathcal{H}_B$. Hence, in turn, it evidently follows that $\hat{U}$ is a unitary operator in $\mathcal{H}_B$.

*Remark.* The lemma implies that if $\hat{U}_1$ is an arbitrary operator which satisfies the condition (4.4) and is defined on the vacuum, then $\hat{U}_1$ differs from a unitary operator only by a factor. In fact, let us consider the vector $\hat{F}_0 = \hat{U}_1\hat{\Phi}_0$, where $\hat{\Phi}_0$ is the vacuum vector. Evidently, the vector $\hat{F}_0$ satisfies the equations $\hat{b}(\varphi)\hat{F}_0 = 0$. Hence it follows from the lemma that $\hat{b}(\varphi) = \hat{U}\hat{a}(\varphi)\hat{U}^{-1}$, where $\hat{U}$ is a unitary operator. It is clear that the operator $\hat{U}^{-1}\hat{U}_1$ is commutative with $\hat{a}(\varphi)$, $\hat{a}^*(\varphi)$ and defined on the vacuum vector. Therefore, according to Theorem 1.4, $\hat{U}^{-1}\hat{U}_1 = \lambda E$ or $\hat{U}_1 = \lambda\hat{U}$ (cf. footnote 3 on p. 89).

We proceed to the proof of the theorem. Let

$$\hat{F}_0 = \sum_n (n!)^{-1/2} \int K_n(x_1,\ldots, x_n)\hat{a}^*(x_1) \cdots \hat{a}^*(x_n)\, d^n x\, \hat{\Phi}_0 \quad (4.17)$$

be a vector satisfying the condition (4.15). Putting the expression of $\hat{b}(\varphi)$ into the left member of (4.15), we obtain for determining the functions $K_n$ the system of equations

$$\int \Phi(x, y)K_{n+1}(y, x_1,\ldots, x_n)\, dy$$

$$= -\frac{1}{[n(n + 1)]^{1/2}}\, (\Psi(x, x_1)K_{n-1}(x_2,\ldots, x_n) + \cdots$$

$$+ \Psi(x, x_n)K_{n-1}(x_1,\ldots, x_{n-1})) - \frac{1}{(n + 1)^{1/2}} f(x)K_n(x_1,\ldots, x_n).$$

Since the operator $\Phi$ has a bounded inverse, these equations can be solved with respect to $K_{n+1}$:

$$K_{n+1}(x, x_1, \ldots, x_n)$$

$$= -\frac{1}{[n(n+1)]^{1/2}} \, (C(x, x_1)K_{n-1}(x_2, \ldots, x_n) +$$

$$+ C(x, x_n)K_{n-1}(x_1, \ldots, x_{n-1}))$$

$$- \frac{1}{(n+1)^{1/2}} \, g(x)K_n(x_1, \ldots, x_n), \tag{4.18}$$

where $C(x, y)$ signifies the kernel of the operator $C = \Phi^{-1}\Psi$ and $g(x) = (\Phi^{-1}f)(x)$. It can be seen from (4.18) that $\hat{F}_0 \neq 0$ only when $K_0 \neq 0$. Putting $n = 0$ in (4.18) we obtain

$$K_1(x) = -K_0 g(x).$$

Consequently, $g(x)$ is a square-integrable function. Putting $n = 1$ we obtain

$$K_2(x, x_1) = -2^{-1/2}K_0 C(x, x_1) - 2^{-1/2}g(x)K_1(x_1).$$

Hence it follows that $C(x, x_1)$ is a square-integrable function, and as a consequence $C = \Phi^{-1}\Psi$ is a Hilbert-Schmidt operator.

We shall now show that the operator $\Phi$ is bounded. To this end we make use of the identity

$$(\Phi^*\Phi)^{-1} = E - \Phi^{-1}\Psi\overline{\Phi}^{-1}\overline{\Psi}, \tag{4.19}$$

which follows easily from (4.5).

According to the above proof, $\Phi^{-1}\Psi$ is a Hilbert-Schmidt operator. Evidently, the operator $\overline{\Phi}^{-1}\overline{\Psi}$ is also a Hilbert-Schmidt operator. Therefore the operator $\Phi^*\Phi = (E - \Phi^{-1}\Psi\overline{\Phi}^{-1}\overline{\Psi})^{-1}$ is bounded, because by definition of the canonical transformation the inner product $(\Phi^*\Phi f, g)$ exists on an everywhere-dense set. Consequently, the operator $\Phi$ also is bounded.

Returning to the operator $\Psi$ and the functional $f$, we obtain from this that $\Psi = \Phi C$ is a Hilbert-Schmidt operator, since $C$ is a Hilbert-Schmidt operator, and that $f = \Phi g \in L$, since $g \in L$. The necessity proof is thus finished.

To prove the sufficiency we construct the functional corresponding to the vector $\hat{F}_0$. According to (1.20), the condition $\hat{b}(x)\hat{F}_0 = 0$ is equivalent to the equation for the functional $F_0$,

$$\left\{ \int \left( \Phi(x, y) \frac{\delta}{\delta a^*(y)} + \Psi(x, y)a^*(y) \right) dy + f(x) \right\} F_0 = 0. \quad (4.20)$$

From (4.20) we find that

$$F_0 = c \exp(-\tfrac{1}{2}a^*\Phi^{-1}\Psi a^* - a^*\Phi^{-1}f). \quad (4.21)$$

In order that the functional $F_0$ correspond to a vector of the state space, it is necessary and sufficient that the inequality

$$I = \int F_0(a^*)\overline{F_0(a^*)}\, e^{-a^*a}\Pi\, da^*\, da < \infty \quad (4.22)$$

be satisfied (cf. Theorem 2.3).

We write out the integral (4.22) in detail:

$$I = |c|^2 \int \exp[-\tfrac{1}{2}(a^*\Phi^{-1}\Psi a^* + a\overline{\Phi}^{-1}\overline{\Psi}a)$$
$$- a^*\Phi^{-1}f - a\overline{\Phi}^{-1}f^* - a^*a]\Pi\, da^*\, da. \quad (4.23)$$

We make use of formula (2.16) to calculate the integral (4.23). Since $\Phi^{-1}\Psi$ is a Hilbert-Schmidt operator, this formula is certainly applicable if the inequality $\|\Phi^{-1}\Psi\| < 1$ is satisfied. Using formula (4.19) and the identity $\Phi\Psi' = \Psi\Phi'$ we find that $\Phi^{-1}\Psi(\Phi^{-1}\Psi)^* = E - (\Phi^*\Phi)^{-1}$. Therefore, eigenvalues $\rho_i$ and $\lambda_i$ of the operators $\Phi^{-1}\Psi(\Phi^{-1}\Psi)^*$ and $(\Phi^*\Phi)^{-1}$ are connected by the relation $0 \le \rho_i = 1 - \lambda_i$. Since the operator $(\Phi^*\Phi)^{-1}$ is nonnegative and has the bounded inverse, we have $\lambda_i > 0$. In addition $\rho_i \to 0$ as $i \to \infty$. Therefore, $\rho_i < \alpha < 1$ for all $i$, and accordingly $\|\Phi^{-1}\Psi(\Phi^{-1}\Psi)^*\| < 1$ and $\|\Phi^{-1}\Psi\| < 1$. Thus formula (2.16) can be utilized to calculate the integral (4.23).

By applying this formula we obtain

$$I = |c|^2 \left[ \det \begin{pmatrix} E & \overline{\Phi}^{-1}\overline{\Psi} \\ \Phi^{-1}\Psi & E \end{pmatrix} \right]^{-1/2}$$
$$\times \exp\left[ \tfrac{1}{2}(\varphi \quad \varphi^*) \begin{pmatrix} \Phi^{-1}\Psi & E \\ E & \overline{\Phi}^{-1}\overline{\Psi} \end{pmatrix}^{-1} \begin{pmatrix} \varphi \\ \varphi^* \end{pmatrix} \right], \quad (4.24)$$

where $\varphi = \Phi^{-1}f$. We denote by $A$ the matrix under the symbol of the determinant. Since $\Phi^{-1}\Psi$ is a Hilbert-Schmidt operator, det $A$ exists. To verify that det $A \neq 0$, we transform it into the form

$$\det A = \det(E - \Phi^{-1}\Psi\overline{\Phi}^{-1}\overline{\Psi}) = \det(\Phi^*\Phi)^{-1}$$

[cf. (4.19)]. Thus det $A > 0$, and accordingly $I < \infty$ and $F_0$ is a functional corresponding to a vector of the state space. The theorem is completely proved.

Along with the proof of the theorem we have obtained the expression for the transformed vacuum vector $\hat{F}_0$. Since, evidently, $I = (\hat{F}_0, \hat{F}_0)$, we can determine $c$ by starting from (4.24) and the condition $(F_0, F_0) = 1$. Before writing down the expression to be obtained we reduce, with the help of (4.7), the operator in the exponent of (4.24) to a more convenient form:

$$\begin{pmatrix} \Phi^{-1}\Psi & E \\ E & \overline{\Phi}^{-1}\overline{\Psi} \end{pmatrix}^{-1}$$

$$= \left[ \begin{pmatrix} \Phi^{-1} & 0 \\ 0 & \overline{\Phi}^{-1} \end{pmatrix} \begin{pmatrix} \Phi & \Psi \\ \overline{\Psi} & \overline{\Phi} \end{pmatrix} \begin{pmatrix} 0 & E \\ E & 0 \end{pmatrix} \right]^{-1}$$

$$= \begin{pmatrix} 0 & E \\ E & 0 \end{pmatrix} \begin{pmatrix} \Phi^* & -\Psi' \\ -\overline{\Psi}^* & \overline{\Phi}' \end{pmatrix} \begin{pmatrix} \Phi & 0 \\ 0 & \overline{\Phi} \end{pmatrix} = \begin{pmatrix} -\overline{\Psi}^* & \overline{\Phi}' \\ \Phi^* & -\Psi' \end{pmatrix} \begin{pmatrix} \Phi & 0 \\ 0 & \overline{\Phi} \end{pmatrix}.$$

By recalling that $\varphi = \Phi^{-1}f$, we obtain

$$(\varphi \quad \varphi^*) \begin{pmatrix} \Phi^{-1}\Psi & E \\ E & \overline{\Phi}^{-1}\overline{\Psi} \end{pmatrix}^{-1} \begin{pmatrix} \varphi \\ \varphi^* \end{pmatrix}$$

$$= (f \quad f^*) \begin{pmatrix} -\Phi'^{-1}\Psi^* & E \\ E & -\overline{\Phi}^{*-1}\overline{\Psi}' \end{pmatrix} \begin{pmatrix} f \\ f^* \end{pmatrix}.$$

Thus we have finally[6]

$$c = \frac{\theta}{(\det \Phi\Phi^*)^{1/4}} \exp\left[ \tfrac{1}{4}(f \quad f^*) \begin{pmatrix} \Phi'^{-1}\Psi^* & -E \\ -E & \overline{\Phi}^{*-1}\overline{\Psi}' \end{pmatrix} \begin{pmatrix} f \\ f^* \end{pmatrix} \right], \quad (4.25)$$

where $\theta$ is an arbitrary complex number such that $|\theta| = 1$.

---

[6] The expression for the transformed vacuum vector is found in Friedrichs' book [1]. However, as functionals are not used in that book, formulas therein differ in form from (4.21), (4.25) and are highly unwieldy.

4. DETERMINANT OF THE MATRIX OF A PROPER CANONICAL TRANS-
FORMATION. It is well known that the determinant of a symplectic
matrix of $n$th degree is equal to unity. A similar fact remains valid in
the infinite-dimensional case.

We shall prove the following theorem.

**Theorem 4.2.** *Let* $\mathscr{A} = \begin{pmatrix} \Phi & \Psi \\ \bar{\Psi} & \bar{\Phi} \end{pmatrix}$ *be the matrix of a proper canonical
transformation such that* $\Phi$ *is an Hermitian positive-definite operator.
Then the matrix* $\mathscr{A}$ *has a determinant and* det $\mathscr{A} = 1$.

Let us recall that by the determinant of $\mathscr{A}$ is meant the limit[7]
$\lim_{n \to \infty} \det \begin{pmatrix} P_n & 0 \\ 0 & P_n \end{pmatrix} \mathscr{A} \begin{pmatrix} P_n & 0 \\ 0 & P_n \end{pmatrix}$, where $P_n$ is a monotonically increasing
sequence of projection operators onto finite-dimensional spaces, which
converges strongly to the identity operator.

We observe first of all that relations (4.5) and the Hermiticity of $\Phi$
imply that $\Phi^2 = E + \Psi\Psi^*$. Then it follows from Theorem 4.1 that $\Psi\Psi^*$
is a trace-class operator. Therefore the operator $\Phi$ has a discrete
spectrum and its eigenvalues are of the form $\lambda_n = (1 + \alpha_n)^{1/2} = 1 + \sigma_n$,
where $\alpha_n > 0$ is an eigenvalue of the operator $\Psi\Psi^*$ and $\sigma_n = \alpha_n/[1 + (1 + \alpha_n)]$. Since $\sum_n \alpha_n < \infty$, we have also that $\sum_n \sigma_n < \infty$. Thus
the operator $\Phi$ can be represented in the form $\Phi = E + \Sigma$, where $\Sigma$ is
a trace-class operator. As we have noted in the Introduction, Subsection
3, it follows from this that the operator $\mathscr{A}$ has a regularized Fredholm
determinant. We carry out the formal transformations:

$$\det \mathscr{A} = \det\begin{pmatrix} \Phi & \Psi \\ \bar{\Psi} & \bar{\Phi} \end{pmatrix} = \det\left[ \begin{pmatrix} \Phi & 0 \\ 0 & \bar{\Phi} \end{pmatrix} \begin{pmatrix} E & \Phi^{-1}\Psi \\ \bar{\Phi}^{-1}\bar{\Psi} & E \end{pmatrix} \right]$$

$$= \det \Phi \det \bar{\Phi} \det\begin{pmatrix} E & \Phi^{-1}\Psi \\ \bar{\Phi}^{-1}\bar{\Psi} & E \end{pmatrix}$$

$$= \det \Phi \det \Phi^* \det\begin{pmatrix} E & \Phi^{-1}\Psi \\ 0 & E - \bar{\Phi}^{-1}\bar{\Psi}\Phi^{-1}\Psi \end{pmatrix}$$

$$= \det \Phi\Phi^* \det(E - \bar{\Phi}^{-1}\bar{\Psi}\Phi^{-1}\Psi).$$

It is a very simple task to pursue these transformations, and so we shall
disregard it. It is to be remarked that as a result we have obtained the

----

[7] Cf. Introduction, Subsection 3.

product of determinants which are Fredholm determinants in the usual sense.

Furthermore, by using relations (4.5), we shall transform the operator $E - \overline{\Phi}^{-1}\overline{\Psi}\Phi^{-1}\Psi$:

$$E - \overline{\Phi}^{-1}\overline{\Psi}\Phi^{-1}\Psi = E - \Phi^{-1}\overline{\Psi}\Psi'\Phi'^{-1}$$

$$= E - \overline{\Phi}^{-1}(\overline{\Phi}\Phi' - E)\Phi'^{-1} = \overline{\Phi}^{-1}\Phi'^{-1}.$$

Thus we have

$$\det(E - \overline{\Phi}^{-1}\overline{\Psi}\Phi^{-1}\Psi) = \det \overline{\Phi}^{-1}\Phi'^{-1} = \det(\Phi\Phi^*)^{-1},$$

and hence $\det \mathscr{A} = 1$, as was required to be proved.

In conclusion we observe that the assertion of the theorem remains valid when the operator $\Phi$ can be represented in the form $\Phi = U\Phi_0$, where $\Phi_0$ is an Hermitian positive-definite operator and $U$ is a unitary operator such that $E - U$ is a trace-class operator.

5. CONSTRUCTION OF THE OPERATOR $\hat{U}$. Suppose that operators $\Phi$, $\Psi$ and a vector $f$ provide a proper canonical transformation. By definition this means that there exists a unitary operator $\hat{U}$ satisfying the condition (4.4). In Section 1 we have assigned functionals to every bounded operator: a functional corresponding to the matrix form of the operator and a functional corresponding to its normal form. In this subsection we shall find these functionals for the operator $\hat{U}$.

**Theorem 4.3.** *The functional $\tilde{U}(a^*, a)$, the generating functional for the matrix form of the operator $\hat{U}$, has the form*

$$\tilde{U}(a^*, a) = c \exp\left[ \tfrac{1}{2}(a \quad a^*)\begin{pmatrix} \Psi\Phi^{-1} & \Phi'^{-1} \\ \Phi^{-1} & -\Phi^{-1}\Psi \end{pmatrix}\begin{pmatrix} a \\ a^* \end{pmatrix} \right.$$

$$\left. + a(f^* - \Psi\Phi^{-1}f) - a^*\Phi^{-1}f \right], \tag{4.26}$$

$$c = c(f^*, f) = \frac{\theta}{(\det \Phi\Phi^*)^{1/4}} \exp\left[ \tfrac{1}{4}(f \quad f^*)\begin{pmatrix} \Phi'^{-1}\Psi^* & -E \\ -E & \Phi^{*-1}\Psi' \end{pmatrix}\begin{pmatrix} f \\ f^* \end{pmatrix} \right]. \tag{4.26'}$$

*where* $|\theta| = 1$. *The functional* $U(a^*, a)$, *the generating functional for the normal form of the operator* $\hat{U}$, *has the form*

$$U(a^*, a) = \tilde{U}(a^*, a)e^{-a^*a}. \tag{4.27}$$

Formula (4.27) is a consequence of the general formula (1.38). We shall calculate the functional $\tilde{U}(a^*, a)$ corresponding to the matrix form of the operator $\hat{U}$. Consider the identity

$$\hat{b}(x)\hat{U} = \hat{U}\hat{a}(x), \qquad \hat{b}^*(x)\hat{U} = \hat{U}\hat{a}^*(x), \tag{4.28}$$

which follows from (4.4). We put $\hat{b}(x)$, $\hat{b}^*(x)$ from (4.3) into (4.28) and pass to the functionals. According to (1.22) we obtain from (4.28),

$$\int \Phi(x, y) \frac{\delta}{\delta a^*(y)} \, dy \tilde{U} + \int \Psi(x, y) a^*(y) \, dy \tilde{U} + f(x)\tilde{U} = \tilde{U}a(x),$$

$$\tag{4.29}$$

$$\int \Psi(x, y) \frac{\delta}{\delta a^*(y)} \, dy \tilde{U} + \int \bar{\Phi}(x, y) a^*(y) \, dy \tilde{U} + f^*(x)\tilde{U} = \frac{\delta}{\delta a(x)} \tilde{U}.$$

Identities (4.29) are to be regarded as the equations to define the functional $\tilde{U}(a^*, a)$.

Before solving equations (4.29) we observe that they have a unique solution, up to a factor, which is a functional corresponding to the matrix form of an operator whose domain of definition contains the vacuum vector $\hat{\Phi}_0$. Let, in fact, $\tilde{U}_1$ be a solution of (4.29) corresponding to an operator $\hat{U}_1$ defined on $\hat{\Phi}_0$. Since (4.29) is equivalent to (4.28), $\hat{U}_1$, like $\hat{U}$, satisfies identities (4.28). Hence it follows easily that the operator $\hat{A} = \hat{U}^{-1}\hat{U}_1$ is commutative with $\hat{a}(x)$, $\hat{a}^*(x)$ and defined on $\hat{\Phi}_0$. Therefore, by Theorem 1.4, $\hat{A} = \lambda E$, and accordingly $\hat{U}_1 = \lambda\hat{U}$ and $\tilde{U}_1 = \lambda\tilde{U}$.

We assume

$$\tilde{U} = c \exp\left[ \tfrac{1}{2}(a \quad a^*)\begin{pmatrix} A_{11} & A_{12} \\ A_{21} & A_{22} \end{pmatrix}\begin{pmatrix} a \\ a^* \end{pmatrix} + a\varphi_1 + a^*\varphi_2 \right], \qquad A_{ik} = A'_{ki}.$$

$$\tag{4.30}$$

Substituting (4.30) into (4.29) and reducing by $\tilde{U}$, we obtain

$$\int \Phi(x, y')A_{22}(y', y)a^*(y)\, dy\, dy'$$

$$+ \int \Phi(x, y')A_{21}(y', y)a(y)\, dy\, dy' + \int \Psi(x, y)a^*(y)\, dy$$

$$+ \int \Phi(x, y)\varphi_2(y)\, dy + f(x) = a(x),$$

$$\int \Psi(x, y')A_{22}(y', y)a^*(y)\, dy\, dy' + \int \Psi(x, y')A_{21}(y', y)a(y)\, dy\, dy'$$

$$+ \int \overline{\Phi}(x, y)a^*(y)\, dy + \int \overline{\Psi}(x, y)\varphi_2(y)\, dy + f^*(x)$$

$$= \int A_{12}(x, y)a^*(y)\, dy + \int A_{11}(x, y)a(y)\, dy + \varphi_1(x),$$

where $A_{ik}(x, y)$ are kernels of the operators $A_{ik}$.

We equate the coefficients for $a(x)$ and $a^*(x)$. As a result we obtain the following equations for the operators $A_{ik}$ and the vector $(\varphi_1 \quad \varphi_2)$:

$$\Phi A_{22} + \Psi = 0, \qquad \overline{\Psi}A_{22} + \overline{\Phi} = A_{12}, \qquad \Phi\varphi_2 + f = 0,$$

$$\Phi A_{21} = E, \qquad \overline{\Psi}A_{21} = A_{11}, \qquad \overline{\Psi}\varphi_2 + f^* = \varphi_1.$$

We obtain from the third column

$$\varphi_2 = -\Phi^{-1}f, \qquad \varphi_1 = -\overline{\Psi}\Phi^{-1}f + f^*. \tag{4.31}$$

From the equations of the first column we find

$$A_{22} = -\Phi^{-1}\Psi, \qquad A_{21} = \Phi^{-1}. \tag{4.32}$$

From the second equation of the second column we find

$$A_{11} = \overline{\Psi}\Phi^{-1}. \tag{4.32'}$$

We shall verify that the first equation of the second column which is left unused does not contradict the values of $A_{ik}$ already found. For this purpose we make use of the last relation of (4.8). Further, $\Psi^*\Psi = \Psi^*\Phi\Phi^{-1}\Psi$. By using the first relation of (4.8) we have $\Psi^*\Phi = \Phi'\overline{\Psi}$. Thus

$$E = \Phi'\overline{\Phi} - \Phi'\overline{\Psi}\Phi^{-1}\Psi.$$

Multiplying the above equality from the left by $\Phi'^{-1}$, we finally obtain

$$\Phi'^{-1} = \overline{\Phi} - \overline{\Psi}\Phi^{-1}\Psi.$$

The same equality is obtained if one substitutes $A_{21}$ and $A_{22}$ from (4.32) into the first equation of the second column and takes account of $A_{12} = A'_{21}$.

We denote by $\|u_{ik}\|$ the matrix whose generating functional is $\tilde{U}(a^*, a)$. We shall show that $\|u_{ik}\|$ is the matrix of some operator whose domain of definition contains the vacuum vector $\hat{\Phi}_0$. We denote by $\hat{F}_0$ a vector obtained from $\hat{\Phi}_0$ by applying the matrix $\|u_{ik}\|$, and by $F_0(a^*)$ its corresponding functional. From $(2.28)$[8] it is found that

$$F_0(a^*) = \int \tilde{U}(a^*, \alpha)e^{-\alpha^*\alpha} \prod d\alpha^* \, d\alpha$$

$$= c \int \exp[\tfrac{1}{2}(\alpha\overline{\Psi}\Phi^{-1}\alpha - a^*\Phi^{-1}\Psi a^* + 2\alpha\Phi'^{-1}a^*)$$

$$+ \alpha(f^* - \overline{\Psi}\Phi^{-1}f) - a^*\Phi^{-1}f - \alpha^*\alpha]\prod d\alpha \, d\alpha^*$$

$$= c \exp(-\tfrac{1}{2}a^*\Phi^{-1}\Psi a^* - a^*\Phi^{-1}f)$$

$$\times \int \exp[\tfrac{1}{2}(\alpha\overline{\Psi}\Phi^{-1}\alpha + 2\alpha\Phi'^{-1}a^*)$$

$$+ \alpha(f^* - \overline{\Psi}\Phi^{-1}f) - \alpha^*\alpha]\prod d\alpha^* \, d\alpha.$$

We shall show that the last integral is equal to unity. To this end we shall first of all confirm the applicability of formula (2.16). Since $\overline{\Psi}\Phi^{-1}$ is a Hilbert-Schmidt operator, it is sufficient to show that $\|\overline{\Psi}\Phi^{-1}\| < 1$. This is proved in exactly the same way as in the case of the similar inequality $\|\Phi^{-1}\Psi\| < 1$ on p. 95. Here we must use the identity derived from (4.5) and (4.8):

$$\overline{\Psi}\Phi^{-1}(\overline{\Psi}\Phi^{-1})^* = E - (\overline{\Phi}\Phi')^{-1}.$$

By applying formula (2.16) it is found that

[8] Strictly speaking, the application of formula (2.28) requires verification, since it has been derived under the assumption that the functional $\tilde{U}$ corresponds to a bounded operator. This verification is not complicated and we shall omit it.

$$\int \exp[\tfrac{1}{2}(\alpha\Psi\Phi^{-1}\alpha + 2\alpha\Phi'^{-1}a^*) + \alpha(f^* - \Psi\Phi^{-1}f) - \alpha^*\alpha]\Pi\, d\alpha^*\, d\alpha$$

$$= \det\begin{pmatrix} E & \Psi\Phi^{-1} \\ 0 & E \end{pmatrix} = 1.$$

Thus we have obtained an expression for $F_0$ which is identical with (4.21). Consequently, the functional $F_0$ corresponds to a vector in the state space, which means that there corresponds to the functional $U$ an operator $\hat{U}$ whose domain of definition contains the vacuum vector $\hat{\Phi}_0$. In order that the operator $\hat{U}$ should be unitary, one should evidently determine the constant $c$ from the condition $(F_0, F_0) = 1$. The corresponding calculation has been carried out in Subsection 4. The theorem is proved.

In the sequel we shall need the expression for the transformed Poisson vector $\hat{P}_\sigma$. We recall that the corresponding functional is equal to $P_\sigma(a^*) = \exp[a^*\sigma - \tfrac{1}{2}(\sigma, \sigma)]$. The functional corresponding to the transformed vector is denoted by $\mathscr{P}_\sigma(a^*)$. The calculation of the functional $\mathscr{P}_\sigma(a^*)$ is hardly different from that of $F_0(a^*)$, which has been carried out in this subsection. We mention the final answer

$$\mathscr{P}_\sigma(a^*) = c(f^* - \sigma^*, f - \sigma)\exp[-\tfrac{1}{2}a^*\Phi^{-1}\Psi a^* - a^*\Phi^{-1}(f - \sigma)], \quad (4.33)$$

where $c(f^*, f)$ is defined by formula (4.26′).

Formula (4.26) associates with every proper canonical transformation $g$ a one-parameter (parameter $\theta$) family of operators in the space $\mathscr{H}_B$: $g \to \theta\hat{U}_g$. In that case, evidently, the following condition is satisfied: If

$$g_1 \to \theta\hat{U}_{g_1}, \quad g_2 \to \theta\hat{U}_{g_2}, \quad \text{then} \quad g_1 g_2 \to \theta\hat{U}_{g_1}\hat{U}_{g_2}.$$

Such a kind of correspondence, in which a family of operators, differing by factors, corresponds to every element of a group, and the product of operators corresponds to the product of elements of the group, is called a *projective representation of the group*.

A question arises as to whether it is impossible to choose $\theta$ in such a way that the nonuniqueness of the correspondence $g \to \theta\hat{U}_g$ should be removed or at least diminished. This can be achieved if one considers not all proper canonical transformations, but only a subgroup $G$ of the group of homogeneous transformations into which there enter transformations whose matrix $\begin{pmatrix} \Phi & \Psi \\ \Psi & \Phi \end{pmatrix}$ has the property $\Phi = E + K$, where $K$ is a trace-class operator. For transformations from $G$ the factor $c$ in formula (4.26) can be taken equal to

$$c = (\det \Phi)^{-1/2}.$$

For such a choice of the constant $c$ there remains the nonuniqueness in the sign: two transformations $\pm \hat{U}_g$ correspond to every $g$ of the group $G: g \to \pm U_g$. By making use of the formula for multiplication of operators (2.30) or (2.31), we find that if

$$g_1 \to \pm \hat{U}_{g_1}, \quad g_2 \to \pm \hat{U}_{g_2}, \quad \text{then} \quad g_1 g_2 \to \pm \hat{U}_{g_1} \hat{U}_{g_2}.$$

This last nonuniqueness cannot be removed. In fact, in order to single out a unique branch of the function $\sqrt{z}$, one should make a cut in the complex plane joining $0$ and $\infty$. But there is a family of transformations $g(t)$ such that $\det \Phi(t)$, $0 \le t \le 2\pi$, goes around the origin of coordinates and hence intersects the cut, however the latter may be drawn. On the other hand, it is also impossible to replace the function $c(g) = (\det \Phi)^{-1/2}$ by another function $c_1(g)$ for which the representation might become unique; we choose a unique branch of $\sqrt{z}$ by making a cut along the negative real axis and putting $\sqrt{1} = 1$. By making use of this branch we define $c(g) = (\det \Phi)^{-1/2}$ uniquely in the neighborhood of the identity of the group $G$, satisfying the condition $|\arg \det \Phi| < \pi$. In this neighborhood the function $\alpha(g) = c_1(g)c^{-1}(g)$ satisfies the condition $\alpha(g_1 g_2) = \alpha(g_1)\alpha(g_2)$. There is, however, only one function satisfying this condition: $\alpha(g) \equiv 1.$[9]

Thus, for $c(g) = (\det \Phi)^{-1/2}$ the representation of the group $G$ by means of the operators $\hat{U}_g$ is two-valued. The construction of this representation duplicates the construction of the spinor representation of the orthogonal group (cf. Section 5.5). Therefore, it is natural to call it the spinor representation of the group $G$. In the case of a finite number of degrees of freedom, the group $G$ is isomorphic to the group of real symplectic matrices (cf. Section 4.2). In this way there arises the spinor representation of the group of real symplectic matrices.

6. CANONICAL TRANSFORMATIONS OF OPERATORS.[10] Let $\hat{U}$ be a unitary operator which gives a linear canonical transformation $\hat{b}(\varphi) = \hat{U}\hat{a}(\varphi)\hat{U}^{-1} = \hat{a}(\varphi\Phi) + \hat{a}^*(\varphi'I') + \varphi f$. We consider an arbitrary operator

---

[9] This is connected with the fact that the group $G$ does not have a normal divisor (except for the group itself) with a one-dimensional or null-dimensional factor group.

[10] Cf. Berezin [2].

$\hat{A}$ representable in the normal form and the operator $\hat{B} = \hat{U}\hat{A}\hat{U}^{-1}$, which is also assumed to be representable in the normal form. We shall express the generating functional $B(a^*, a)$ for the normal form of the operator $\hat{B}$ in terms of the analogous functional $A(a^*, a)$ corresponding to the operator $\hat{A}$.

First let the canonical transformation be of the form

$$\hat{b}(\varphi) = \hat{a}(\varphi\Phi), \qquad \hat{b}^*(\varphi) = \hat{a}^*(\varphi\overline{\Phi}). \tag{4.34}$$

Relations (4.5) tell us that in this case $\Phi$ is a unitary operator. It is readily seen that if the canonical transformation is of the form (4.34), then the functional $B(a^*, a)$ is equal to

$$B(a^*, a) = A(\overline{\Phi}a^*, \Phi a). \tag{4.35}$$

Thus, in this case, the transformation of functionals comprises a change of variables.

We now recall [cf. (4.9)] that every canonical transformation can be factorized into the product of a transformation of the form (4.34) and the transformation

$$\hat{b}(\varphi) = \hat{a}(\varphi\Phi) + \hat{a}^*(\varphi\Psi) + \varphi f,$$

$$\hat{b}^*(\varphi) = \hat{a}(\varphi\overline{\Psi}) + \hat{a}^*(\varphi\overline{\Phi}) + \varphi f^*,$$

where $\Phi$ is an Hermitian positive-definite operator. Thus we have a great interest in the case when the canonical transformation is given by the operators $\Phi$, $\Psi$ and a vector $f$, in which $\Phi$ is an Hermitian positive-definite operator.

Before formulating a fundamental theorem, we prove a lemma.

**Lemma 4.2.** *Let $A = \|a_{ik}\|$ be a symmetric $(n \times n)$ matrix. There exists a unitary symmetric $(n \times n)$ matrix $U = \|u_{ik}\|$ such that $UAU$ is a real symmetric nonnegative matrix which is equal to $UAU = U(AA^*)^{1/2}U^{-1}$.*

The matrix $A$ is representable in the form $A = (AA^*)^{1/2}V = BV$, where $V$ is a unitary matrix. We shall show that $V' = V$. From the symmetry of $A$ there follows the identity $BV = V'B'$. Hence $B' = V'^{-1}BV = V'^{-1}VV^{-1}BV = WC$, where $C = V^{-1}BV$ is an Hermitian positive-definite matrix and $W = V'^{-1}V$ is a unitary matrix. Now it is observed that $B'$, similar to $B$, is an Hermitian nonnegative matrix.

From the uniqueness of the representation of an arbitrary matrix in the form $WC$, where $W$ is unitary and $C$ Hermitian nonnegative, it therefore follows that $W = E$, and accordingly $V' = V$.

As is well known, every symmetric unitary matrix has its square root, which is again a symmetric unitary matrix. Therefore there exists a symmetric unitary matrix $U$ such that $V = U^{-2}$. Evidently, $U$ is the desired matrix.

We denote by $P_n$ the projection operator onto an $n$-dimensional space belonging to the spectral family of the operator $\Phi$. Further, let $\alpha$ be a positive-definite operator and $S$ a unitary operator defined by the equality $\Psi = \alpha S$. From relations (4.5) and (4.8), because of $\Phi = \Phi^*$, we have

$$\Phi^2 - \alpha^2 = E, \qquad \Phi^2 - S'\alpha'\bar{\alpha}\bar{S} = E.$$

Hence $\alpha^2 = S'\alpha'\bar{\alpha}\bar{S}$ and $\bar{\alpha}^2 = S^{-1}\alpha^2 S$. The same relation should be satisfied for projection operators belonging to the spectral decomposition of $\alpha^2$, since these operators are real functions of $\alpha^2$. We now observe that the relation $\Phi^2 - \alpha^2 = E$ implies that the families of projection operators belonging to the spectral decomposition of $\Phi$ and $\alpha^2$ coincide. Thus the operators $P_n$ satisfy the relation

$$\bar{P}_n = S^{-1}P_n S, \qquad S\bar{P}_n = P_n S.$$

Multiplying both sides of the latter equality from the left by $\alpha$ and using the commutability of $\alpha$ and $P_n$, we obtain

$$\Psi\bar{P}_n = P_n\Psi, \tag{4.36}$$

and, passing to the complex-conjugate operators,

$$\bar{\Psi}P_n = \bar{P}_n\bar{\Psi}. \tag{4.36'}$$

We consider the operator $A_n = P_n'\Phi\Psi^{-1}P_n$. The operator $A_n$ induces in the space $L_n = P_n L$ a bilinear form[11]: $\xi\Phi\Psi^{-1}\eta = \xi A_n\eta$ for $\xi, \eta \in L_n$. We choose in the space $L_n$ an orthonormal basis $\{\xi_k\}$. The matrix of the bilinear form $\xi A_n\eta$, written in the basis $\{\xi_k\}$, is denoted by $\mathscr{A}_n$. It is found by applying the lemma proved above that there exists a unitary symmetric matrix $U_n$ such that $U_n\mathscr{A}_n U_n$ is a real positive-definite matrix.

We shall show that all eigenvalues of the matrix $U_n\mathscr{A}_n U_n$ are greater than unity. Since $U_n\mathscr{A}_n U_n = U_n(\mathscr{A}_n\mathscr{A}_n^*)^{1/2}U_n^{-1}$, it suffices to examine

---

[11] It follows from relations (4.8) that the bilinear form $\xi\bar{\Phi}\Psi^{-1}\eta$ is symmetric.

the matrix $\mathscr{A}_n\mathscr{A}_n{}^*$. Evidently $\mathscr{A}_n\mathscr{A}_n{}^*$ is the matrix of the operator $A_nA_n{}^*$, which is the value on the space $L_n$ of the operator

$$A_nA_n{}^* = P_n{}'\overline{\Phi}\Psi^{-1}P_n\Psi^{*-1}\Phi'P_n{}'.$$

By the help of relations (4.36), (4.36') the expression for $A_nA_n{}^*$ can be transcribed into

$$A_nA_n{}^* = P_n{}'\overline{\Phi}\Psi^{-1}\Psi^{*-1}\Phi'P_n{}'.$$

The assertion on the spectrum of the matrix $\mathscr{A}_n\mathscr{A}_n{}^*$ will be proved if we verify that $(A_nA_n{}^*f, f) > (P_n{}'f, P_n{}'f)$.

Consider the operator $AA^* = \overline{\Phi}\Psi^{-1}\Psi^{*-1}\Phi'$. In the preceding subsection it has been shown that $\|\overline{\Phi}^{-1}\Psi\| < 1$. Similarly, it can be verified that $\|\Psi\overline{\Phi}^{-1}\| < 1$. As a consequence, $\|(AA^*)^{-1}\| < 1$ and $AA^* > E$; i.e., all the eigenvalues of $AA^*$ are greater than unity. Therefore,

$$(A_nA_n{}^*f, f) = (P_n{}'AA^*P_n{}'f, f) > (P_n{}'f, P_n{}'f),$$

and accordingly the eigenvalues of $A_nA_n{}^*$ are greater than unity.

We summarize the results obtained above in the following lemma.

**Lemma 4.3.** *Let $P_n$ be the projection operator onto an n-dimensional subspace $L_n = P_nL$ belonging to the spectral family of the operator $\Phi$. We introduce in $L_n$ an orthonormal basis $\{\xi_k\}$ and consider the matrix*

$$\mathscr{A}_n = \|\xi_i\overline{\Phi}\Psi^{-1}\xi_k\|.$$

*Then*

(1) *There exists a symmetric unitary matrix $U_n$ such that $U_n\mathscr{A}_nU_n$ is a real matrix,*

(2) *For vectors $t$, having real components $t_k$ with respect to the basis $\{\xi_k\}$, we have*

$$\sum_{i,k} t_i(U_n\mathscr{A}_nU_n)_{ik}t_k > \sum_k t_k{}^2. \tag{4.37}$$

We consider the space $L_n{}^* = (P_nL)^*$ and introduce in it a basis $\{\xi_k{}^*\}$.

The matrix $\overline{\mathscr{A}}_n = \|\xi_i{}^*\Phi\overline{\Psi}^{-1}\xi_k{}^*\|$ is complex conjugate to $\mathscr{A}_n$. Consequently, for vectors $\tau$ having real components $\tau_k$ with respect to the basis $\{\xi_k{}^*\}$, we have

$$\sum_{i,k} \tau_i(\overline{U}_n\overline{\mathscr{A}}_n\overline{U}_n)_{ik}\tau_k > \sum_k \tau_k{}^2. \tag{4.37'}$$

We now formulate a fundamental theorem of this subsection.

**Theorem 4.4.** *Let $\hat{A}$ be a bounded operator. Consider a canonical transformation $\hat{U}\hat{a}(\varphi)\hat{U}^{-1} = \hat{a}(\varphi\Phi) + \hat{a}^*(\varphi\Psi) + \varphi f$ which has the following properties:*

(1) *The operator $\Phi$ is Hermitian,*

(2) *The operator $\Psi$ has the inverse.*

*Let, further, $P_n$ be a monotonic sequence of operators of orthogonal projection onto a finite-dimensional space $L_n$, having the properties:*

(1) *The operators $P_n$ belong to the spectral family of projection operators of the operator $\Phi$,*

(2) *For $n \to \infty$ the sequence $P_n$ converges strongly to the identity operator.*

*Then the functional $B(a^*, a)$ corresponding to the normal form of the operator $\hat{B} = \hat{U}\hat{A}\hat{U}^{-1}$ is equal to*

$$B(a^*, a) = \lim_{n \to \infty} \int_{\alpha = U_n t, \, \alpha^* = \overline{U}_n \tau} \mathcal{K}_n(a^*, a \,|\, \alpha^*, \alpha) A(\alpha^*, \alpha) \, d^n t \, d^n \tau, \quad (4.38)$$

*where*

$$\mathcal{K}_n(a^*, a \,|\, \alpha^*, \alpha) = [\det P_n(\Psi\Psi^*)^{-1}P_n]^{1/2}$$

$$\times \exp\left[ -\tfrac{1}{2}(b_n - \alpha \quad b_n^* - \alpha^*)\mathcal{L}\begin{pmatrix} b_n - \alpha \\ b_n^* - \alpha^* \end{pmatrix} \right], \quad (4.39)$$

$$\mathcal{L} = \begin{pmatrix} \overline{\Phi}\Psi^{-1} & -E \\ -E & \Phi\overline{\Psi}^{-1} \end{pmatrix}, \quad (4.40)$$

$$b_n = \Phi P_n a + \Psi \overline{P}_n a^* + P_n f,$$

$$b_n^* = \overline{\Psi} P_n a + \overline{\Phi}\overline{P}_n a^* + \overline{P}_n f^*,$$

$P_n(\Psi\Psi^*)^{-1}P_n$ *is the matrix equal to $\|\xi_i(\Psi\Psi^*)^{-1}\xi_k\|$, where $\{\xi_k\}$ is an orthonormal basis in $L_n$, $U_n = \|\xi_i U\xi_k\|$ is a unitary symmetric matrix whose properties are described in Lemma 4.3, $\overline{U}_n = \|\xi_i^*\overline{U}\xi_k^*\|$ is its complex conjugate and $t \in L_n$, $\tau \in L_n^*$ are vectors having real components in the bases $\{\xi_k\}$ and $\{\xi_k^*\}$, respectively.*

Let the integration in (4.38) be chosen in such a way that the quadratic form in the exponent has a negative-definite real part (cf. Lemma 4.3).

We recall that the functional $A(a^*, a)$ corresponding to the normal form of the operator $\hat{A}$ is equal to $A(a^*, a) = (\hat{A}\hat{P}_{a^*}, \hat{P}_{a^*})$ (cf.

p. 35), where $\hat{P}_a$ is a Poisson vector with parameter $a$: $P_a(\sigma^*) = \exp(a\sigma^* - \tfrac{1}{2}a^*a)$. Evidently, $A(a^*, a)$ can also be written in the form

$$A(a^*, a) = \mathrm{Sp}\, \hat{A}\hat{\mathscr{P}}_{a^*,a},$$

where $\hat{\mathscr{P}}_{a',a}$ is the projection operator onto the Poisson vector[12]:

$$\mathscr{P}_{a^*,a}(\sigma^*, \sigma) = \exp(a\sigma^* + a^*\sigma - \sigma^*\sigma - a^*a).$$

Thus the functional $B_n(a^*, a) = \int \mathscr{K}_n A\, d^n t\, d^n\tau$ is equal to

$$B_n(a^*, a) = \int \mathscr{K}_n(a^*, a \,|\, \alpha^*, \alpha)\, \mathrm{Sp}\, \hat{\mathscr{A}}\hat{\mathscr{P}}_{\alpha^*\,\alpha}\, d^n t\, d^n\tau$$

$$= \mathrm{Sp}\, \hat{\mathscr{A}} \int \mathscr{K}_n(a^*, a \,|\, \alpha^*, \alpha)\hat{\mathscr{P}}_{\alpha^*,\alpha}\, d^n t\, d^n\tau. \qquad (4.41)$$

(The permutability of trace and integral will be confirmed at the end of the proof of the theorem.)

It turns out that $\hat{\mathscr{P}}^n_{a^*,a} = \int \mathscr{K}_n\hat{\mathscr{P}}_{\alpha^*,\alpha}\, d^n t\, d^n\tau$ is the projection operator onto the vector $\hat{\xi}_n(a^*)$. We shall show that for $n \to \infty$ the vector $\hat{\xi}_n(a^*)$ converges in the norm to $\hat{U}^{-1}\hat{P}_{a^*}$. Hence it will evidently follow that

$$B(a^*, a) = \lim B_n(a^*, a) = (\hat{A}\hat{U}^{-1}\hat{P}_a, \hat{U}^{-1}\hat{P}_a) = (\hat{U}\hat{A}\hat{U}^{-1}\hat{P}_a, \hat{P}_a),$$

i.e., that $B(a^*, a)$ is the functional corresponding to the operator $\hat{B} = \hat{U}\hat{A}\hat{U}^{-1}$.

We proceed to the calculation of the operator $\hat{\mathscr{P}}^n_{a^*,a}$. For this purpose we replace the operators $\hat{\mathscr{P}}_{a^*,a}$ and $\hat{\mathscr{P}}^n_{a^*,a}$ by their corresponding functionals $\mathscr{P}_{a^*,a}(\sigma^*, \sigma)$ and $\mathscr{P}^n_{a^*,a}(\sigma^*, \sigma)$:

$$\mathscr{P}_{a^*,a}(\sigma^*, \sigma) = e^{-(a^* - \sigma^*)(a - \sigma)},$$

$$\mathscr{P}^n_{a^*,a}(\sigma^*, \sigma) = (\det P_n(\Psi\Psi^*)^{-1}P_n)^{1/2}$$

$$\times \int\limits_{\alpha = U_{nt},\, \alpha^* = U_{n\tau}} \exp\Bigg[ -\tfrac{1}{2}(b_n - \alpha \quad b_n^* - \alpha^*)$$

$$\times \begin{pmatrix} \overline{\Phi}\Psi^{-1} & -E \\ -E & \Phi\overline{\Psi}^{-1} \end{pmatrix}\begin{pmatrix} b_n - \alpha \\ b_n^* - \alpha^* \end{pmatrix}$$

$$- (\alpha^* - \sigma^*)(\alpha - \sigma) \Bigg]\, d^n t\, d^n\tau. \qquad (4.42)$$

---

[12] Cf. expression (1.48) for the normal form of the projection operator.

In view of Lemma 4.3 the real part of the exponent is negative-definite. Forming the complete square and using relations (4.5), (4.8) and (4.36), (4.36'), we find for $\mathscr{P}_{a^*,a}^n(\sigma^*, \sigma)$,

$$\mathscr{P}_{a^*,a}^n(\sigma^*, \sigma) = (\det P_n(\Psi\Psi^*)^{-1}P_n)^{1/2}$$

$$\times (\det P_n'\overline{\Phi}\Psi^{-1}P_n \det P_n\Phi\overline{\Psi}^{-1}P_n')^{-1/2}$$

$$\times \exp\left[ \tfrac{1}{2}(b_n - \sigma_n \quad b_n^* - \sigma_n^*)\begin{pmatrix} \Psi\Phi^{-1} & -E \\ -E & \Psi\overline{\Phi}^{-1} \end{pmatrix} \right.$$

$$\times \left. \begin{pmatrix} b_n - \sigma_n \\ b_n^* - \sigma_n^* \end{pmatrix} - \tilde{\sigma}_n^*\tilde{\sigma}_n \right], \tag{4.43}$$

where $\sigma_n = P_n\sigma$, $\sigma_n^* = \overline{P}_n\sigma^*$, $\tilde{\sigma}_n = \sigma - \sigma_n$, $\tilde{\sigma}_n^* = \sigma^* - \sigma_n^*$.

From relations (4.36), (4.36') it follows that the factor before the exponential can be reduced by $(\det P_n(\Psi\Psi^*)^{-1}P_n)^{1/2}$. It is easy to show that the remaining factor is equal to $(\det P_n\Phi\Phi^*P_n)^{-1/2}$. With the help of relations (4.5), (4.8), $\mathscr{P}_{a^*,a}^n(\sigma^*, \sigma)$ can be transformed into

$$\mathscr{P}_{a^*,a}^n(\sigma^*, \sigma) = \zeta_{a^*,a}^n(\sigma^*)\overline{\zeta_{a^*,a}^n(\sigma^*)}\, e^{-\sigma^*\sigma}, \tag{4.44}$$

where

$$\zeta_{a^*,a}^n(\sigma^*) = (\det P_n\Phi\Phi^*P_n)^{-1/4}$$

$$\times \exp\left[ -\tfrac{1}{2}(\varphi_n - a_n \quad \varphi_n^* - a_n^*) \right.$$

$$\times \begin{pmatrix} \overline{\Phi}^{-1}\overline{\Psi} & E \\ E & \Phi^{-1}\Psi \end{pmatrix}\begin{pmatrix} \varphi_n - a_n \\ \varphi_n^* - a_n^* \end{pmatrix}$$

$$\left. + \tfrac{1}{2}\sigma^*P_n'\Phi^{*-1}\Psi'P_n'\sigma^* - \sigma^*\Phi^{*-1}(\varphi_n - a_n) \right],$$

$$\varphi_n = \Phi^*f_n - \Psi'f_n^*, \qquad \varphi_n^* = -\Psi^*f_n + \Phi'f_n^*.$$

For $n \to \infty$, we have $\det P_n\Phi\Phi^*P_n \to \det \Phi\Phi^*$, and $a_n$, $\varphi_n$ coverage in the norm of the Hilbert space $L$ to $a$, $\varphi = \Phi^*f - \Psi'f^*$, and finally the operator $P_n'\Phi^{*-1}\Psi'P_n'$ converges in the norm in the space of Hilbert-Schmidt operators to $\Phi^{*-1}\Psi'$. Hence it follows that the sequence of vectors $\hat{\xi}_{a^*,a}^n$, for which $\zeta_{a^*,a}^n(\sigma^*, \sigma)$ are generating functionals, converges in the norm to the vector $\overset{\circ}{\xi}_{a^*,a}$ whose generating functional is equal to

$$\xi_{a^*,a}(\sigma^*) = (\det \Phi\Phi^*)^{-1/4}$$

$$\times \exp\left[-\tfrac{1}{4}(\varphi - a \quad \varphi^* - a^*)\begin{pmatrix} \overline{\Phi}^{-1}\overline{\Psi} & E \\ E & \Phi^{-1}\Psi \end{pmatrix}\begin{pmatrix} \varphi - a \\ \varphi^* - a^* \end{pmatrix}\right.$$

$$\left. + \tfrac{1}{2}\sigma^*\Phi^{*-1}\Psi'\sigma^* - \sigma^*\Phi^{*-1}(\varphi - a)\right], \tag{4.45}$$

where

$$\varphi = \Phi^*f - \Psi'f^*, \quad \varphi^* = -\Psi^*f + \Phi'f^*.$$

Comparing (4.45) with (4.33), we find that $\overset{\circ}{\xi}_{a^*,a} = \hat{U}^{-1}\hat{P}_a$, where $\hat{P}_a$ is a Poisson vector.[13]

Finally, it follows from formula (4.44) that $\hat{\mathscr{P}}^n_{a^*,a}$ is the projection operator onto $\overset{\circ}{\xi}^n_{a^*,a}$ [cf. (1.48), the general form for the normal form of the projection operator onto a vector].

To terminate the proof of the theorem, one should ascertain the permutability of the trace and integral in (4.41).

Formula (4.41) has the form $\int F(\varphi_\alpha)d\mu_\alpha = F\left(\int \varphi_\alpha \, d\mu_\alpha\right)$, where $\varphi_\alpha = \mathscr{K}_n(a^*, a \,|\, \alpha^*, \alpha) \, \hat{\mathscr{P}}_{a^*,\alpha}$ is an element of a Banach space $\mathfrak{S}$ of trace-class operators and $F$ a continuous functional on this space. The permutability of the integral and trace will thus be proved if we establish that the integral sums converge to $\int \varphi_\alpha \, d\mu_\alpha$ in the norm of $\mathfrak{S}$.

We return to formula (4.42). It is easy to see that it is transformed into the form

$$\mathscr{P}^n_{a^*,a}(\sigma^*, \sigma) = c_n \int\limits_{\alpha = U_n t} \exp[-\tfrac{1}{2}\alpha\overline{\Phi}\Psi^{-1}\alpha + \alpha(\rho - \sigma^*)] \, dt$$

$$\times \int\limits_{\alpha^* = U_n \tau} \exp[-\tfrac{1}{2}\alpha^*\Phi\overline{\Psi}^{-1}\alpha^* + \alpha^*(\rho^* - \sigma)] \, d\tau, \tag{4.46}$$

where $c_n$ is a constant and $\rho$, $\rho^*$ signify expressions depending on $b_n$, $b_n^*$. By replacing the integral by the sum in (4.46), we obtain the operators $\hat{\mathscr{P}}^{n,\Sigma}_{a^*,a}$ which are evidently, up to the factor $c_n$, the projection operators

---

[13] In comparing (4.45) with (4.33) one should keep in mind that if a canonical transformation is given by operators $\Phi$, $\Psi$ and a vector $f$, then the inverse transformation is given by the operators $\Phi^*$, $-\Psi'$ and the vector $\varphi = \Phi^*f - \Psi'f^*$.

onto the vectors $\xi^{n,\Sigma}$. There corresponds to the last of these vectors the functionals

$$\zeta^{n,\Sigma}(\sigma^*) = \sum_{\alpha = U_n t} \Delta t \exp[-\tfrac{1}{2}\alpha\overline{\Phi}\Psi^{-1}\alpha + \alpha(\rho - \sigma^*)].$$

By decomposing $\zeta^{n,\Sigma}(\sigma^*)$ into a power series of $\sigma^*$ and estimating the individual terms, it is readily established that the sequence $\xi^{n,\Sigma}$ for the refinement of the subdivision converges in the norm to a vector $\xi^n$, to which there corresponds the functional

$$\zeta^n(\sigma^*) = \int_{\alpha = U_n t} \exp[-\tfrac{1}{2}\alpha\overline{\Phi}\Psi^{-1}\alpha + \alpha(\rho - \sigma^*)] \, d^n t. \qquad (4.47)$$

The corresponding estimates are not complicated and we shall omit them.

The convergence in norm of the vectors $\xi^{n,\Sigma}$ to the vector $\xi^n$ evidently implies that the sequence of the operators $\hat{\mathscr{P}}_{a^*,a}^{n,\Sigma}$ converges in the norm of $\mathfrak{S}$ to the operator given by the integral (4.46).

The proof proposed here is to a certain extent artificial and, moreover, does not carry over to the Fermi case, because there is no analogue of the Poisson vectors for fermions. If the number of degrees of freedom is finite, one may propose another proof of the theorem, which shows essentially the same legitimacy for both fermions and bosons. This proof (in the Fermi variant), for which formulas (4.38)–(4.40) are obtained at once, is left to Section 5.7.

We note in conclusion that formulas (4.38)–(4.40) are valid not only when the operator $\hat{A}$ is bounded. It is not difficult to establish their validity for the case when $\hat{A}$ is a polynomial operator. It appears that they hold for all operators $\hat{A}$ representable in the normal form, such that the operator $\hat{U}\hat{A}\hat{U}^{-1}$ also can be represented in the normal form.

7. EXAMPLES. Let a system have one degree of freedom. Consider the canonical transformation

$$\hat{b} = \hat{a}\,\mathrm{ch}\,\sigma + \varepsilon\hat{a}^*\,\mathrm{sh}\,\sigma, \qquad \hat{b}^* = \bar{\varepsilon}\hat{a}\,\mathrm{sh}\,\sigma + \hat{a}\,\mathrm{ch}\,\sigma$$

($|\varepsilon| = 1$ and $\sigma$ is any real number). It follows from Theorem 4.4 that in this case the canonical transformation of operators is given by the formula

$$B(a^*, a) = \frac{1}{|\text{sh }\sigma|} \int \exp\left\{-\frac{1}{2}\left[(b - \alpha)^2 \frac{\text{ch }\sigma}{\varepsilon \text{ sh }\sigma} + (b^* - \alpha^*)^2 \frac{\text{ch }\sigma}{\bar{\varepsilon} \text{ sh }\sigma}\right.\right.$$

$$\left.\left. - 2(b - \alpha)(b^* - \alpha^*)\right]\right\}A(\alpha^*, \alpha) \, d\alpha^*, \, d\alpha, \qquad (4.48)$$

where $b = a \text{ ch }\sigma + \varepsilon a^* \text{ sh }\sigma$, $b^* = \bar{\varepsilon}a \text{ sh }\sigma + a^* \text{ ch }\sigma$. The integral with respect to $d\alpha \, d\alpha^*$ should be taken along the contour on which $\alpha^2(\text{ch }\sigma/\varepsilon \text{ sh }\sigma) + \alpha^{*2} (\text{ch }\sigma/\bar{\varepsilon} \text{ sh }\sigma) - 2\alpha\alpha^* > 0$. According to the theorem, the contour is given by the condition $\alpha = ut$, $\alpha^* = \bar{u}\tau$, where $u = (\varepsilon \text{ sign }\sigma)^{1/2}$.

As the second example we consider the canonical transformation of the operator $\hat{A}$ to whose normal form there corresponds the generating functional $A$ of the form[14]

$$A(a^*, a) = \exp\left[-\frac{1}{2}(a \quad a^*)\begin{pmatrix} A_{11} & A_{12} \\ A_{21} & A_{22} \end{pmatrix}\begin{pmatrix} a \\ a^* \end{pmatrix}\right], \qquad A_{ik} = A'_{ki},$$

where the matrix $\mathscr{A} = \begin{pmatrix} A_{11} & A_{12} \\ A_{21} & A_{22} \end{pmatrix}$ satisfies the condition

$$\text{Re}(tU_n' \quad \tau U_n^*)(\mathscr{A} + \mathscr{L})\begin{pmatrix} U_n t \\ U_n \tau \end{pmatrix} > 0 \qquad (4.49)$$

for sufficiently large $n$. According to Theorem 4.4 the functional $B(a^*, a)$ corresponding to the normal form of the operator $\hat{B} = \hat{U}\hat{A}\hat{U}^{-1}$ is the limit of the functionals $B_n(a^*, a)$, where

$$B_n(a^*, a) = (\det P_n(\Psi\Psi^*)^{-1}P_n)^{1/2}$$

$$+ \int_{\alpha = U_n t, \, \alpha^* = U_n \tau} \exp\left[-\frac{1}{2}(b - \alpha \quad b^* - \alpha^*)\mathscr{L}\begin{pmatrix} b - \alpha \\ b^* - \alpha^* \end{pmatrix}\right.$$

$$\left. - \frac{1}{2}(\alpha \quad \alpha^*)\mathscr{A}\begin{pmatrix} \alpha \\ \alpha^* \end{pmatrix}\right] d^n\alpha \, d^n\alpha^*. \qquad (4.50)$$

[14] Cf. Berezin [1].

To calculate the integral (4.50) we single out in the exponent the complete square

$$(b - \alpha \quad b^* - \alpha^*)\mathscr{L}\begin{pmatrix} b - \alpha \\ b^* - \alpha^* \end{pmatrix} + (\alpha \quad \alpha^*)\mathscr{A}\begin{pmatrix} \alpha \\ \alpha^* \end{pmatrix}$$

$$= (x - \alpha \quad x^* - \alpha^*)(\mathscr{L} + \mathscr{A})\begin{pmatrix} x - \alpha \\ x^* - \alpha^* \end{pmatrix}$$

$$+ (b \quad b^*)(\mathscr{L} - \mathscr{L}(\mathscr{L} + \mathscr{A})^{-1}\mathscr{L})\begin{pmatrix} b \\ b^* \end{pmatrix}, \qquad (4.51)$$

where $\begin{pmatrix} x \\ x^* \end{pmatrix} = (\mathscr{L} + \mathscr{A})^{-1}\mathscr{L}\begin{pmatrix} b \\ b^* \end{pmatrix}$. We observe that, so long as $b$, $\alpha \in L_n$, $b^*$, $\alpha^* \in L_n^*$, and accordingly $\alpha = P_n\alpha$, $b = P_nb$, $\alpha^* = P_n'\alpha$, $b^* = P_n'b^*$, the matrices $\mathscr{A}$ and $\mathscr{L}$ in (4.50), (4.51) can be replaced by

$$\mathscr{A}_n = \begin{pmatrix} P_n' & 0 \\ 0 & P_n \end{pmatrix}\mathscr{A}\begin{pmatrix} P_n & 0 \\ 0 & P_n' \end{pmatrix}, \qquad \mathscr{L}_n = \begin{pmatrix} P_n' & 0 \\ 0 & P_n \end{pmatrix}\mathscr{L}\begin{pmatrix} P_n & 0 \\ 0 & P_n' \end{pmatrix}.$$

By our condition, beginning from some $n_0$,

$$\mathrm{Re}(tU_n' \quad \tau\bar{U}_n^*)(\mathscr{A}_n + \mathscr{L}_n)\begin{pmatrix} U_n t \\ \bar{U}_n\tau \end{pmatrix} > 0.$$

Consequently, the integral (4.50) can be calculated for $n > n_0$. As a result we obtain

$$B_n(a^*, a) = (\det P_n(\Psi\Psi^*)^{-1}P_n)^{1/2}[\det(\mathscr{A}_n + \mathscr{L}_n)]^{-1/2}$$

$$\times \exp\left[ -\tfrac{1}{2}(b \quad b^*)(\mathscr{L} - \mathscr{L}(\mathscr{L} + \mathscr{A})^{-1}\mathscr{L})\begin{pmatrix} b \\ b^* \end{pmatrix}\right]. \qquad (4.52)$$

By use of equality (4.36), it is not difficult to reduce the matrix $\mathscr{L}_n + \mathscr{A}_n$ to the form

$$\mathscr{A}_n + \mathscr{L}_n = \begin{pmatrix} P_n' & 0 \\ 0 & P_n \end{pmatrix}\begin{pmatrix} \bar{\Phi} + A_{11}\Psi & -\Psi + A_{12}\bar{\Psi} \\ -\Psi + A_{21}\Psi & \Phi + A_{22}\bar{\Psi} \end{pmatrix}$$

$$\times \begin{pmatrix} P_n' & 0 \\ 0 & P_n \end{pmatrix}\begin{pmatrix} \Psi^{-1} & 0 \\ 0 & \bar{\Psi}^{-1} \end{pmatrix}\begin{pmatrix} P_n & 0 \\ 0 & P_n' \end{pmatrix}.$$

Hence it turns out that

$$\det(\mathscr{A}_n + \mathscr{L}_n) = \det\begin{pmatrix} P_n' & 0 \\ 0 & P_n \end{pmatrix}\begin{pmatrix} \bar{\Phi} + A_{11}\Psi & (A_{12} - E)\bar{\Psi} \\ (A_{21} - E)\Psi & \Phi + A_{22}\bar{\Psi} \end{pmatrix}\begin{pmatrix} P_n & 0 \\ 0 & P_n' \end{pmatrix}$$

$$\times \det P_n'\Psi^{-1}P_n \det P_n\bar{\Psi}^{-1}P_n'. \qquad (4.53)$$

In view of (4.36), (4.36') we have

$$\det P_n{}'\Psi^{-1}P_n \det P_n\overline{\Psi}^{-1}P_n{}' = \det P_n(\Psi\Psi^*)^{-1}P_n.$$

Reducing by $\det P_n{}'\Psi^{-1}P_n \det P_n\overline{\Psi}^{-1}P_n{}'$ and passing to the limit as $n \to \infty$ we find the functional $B(a^*, a)$,

$$B(a^*, a) = \left[\det\begin{pmatrix} \overline{\Phi} + A_{11}\Psi & (A_{12} - E)\overline{\Psi} \\ (A_{21} - E)\Psi & \Phi + A_{22}\overline{\Psi} \end{pmatrix}\right]^{-1/2}$$

$$\times \exp\left[-\tfrac{1}{2}(b \quad b^*)(\mathscr{L} - \mathscr{L}(\mathscr{A} + \mathscr{L})^{-1}\mathscr{L})\begin{pmatrix} b \\ b^* \end{pmatrix}\right]. \quad (4.54)$$

We transform the exponent in (4.54) by representing the matrices $\mathscr{A} + \mathscr{L}$ and $\mathscr{L}$ in the form

$$\mathscr{A} + \mathscr{L} = \begin{pmatrix} \overline{\Phi} + A_{11}\Psi & -\overline{\Psi} + A_{12}\overline{\Psi} \\ -\Psi + A_{21}\Psi & \Phi + A_{22}\overline{\Psi} \end{pmatrix}\begin{pmatrix} \Psi^{-1} & 0 \\ 0 & \overline{\Psi}^{-1} \end{pmatrix},$$

$$\mathscr{L} = \begin{pmatrix} \overline{\Phi} & -\overline{\Psi} \\ -\Psi & \Phi \end{pmatrix}\begin{pmatrix} \Psi^{-1} & 0 \\ 0 & \overline{\Psi}^{-1} \end{pmatrix}.$$

Hence

$$\mathscr{L} - \mathscr{L}(\mathscr{A} + \mathscr{L})^{-1}\mathscr{L}$$

$$= \begin{pmatrix} \overline{\Phi} & -\overline{\Psi} \\ -\Psi & \Phi \end{pmatrix}\left[E - \begin{pmatrix} \overline{\Phi} + A_{11}\Psi & -\overline{\Psi} + A_{12}\overline{\Psi} \\ -\Psi + A_{21}\Psi & \Phi + A_{22}\overline{\Psi} \end{pmatrix}^{-1}\right.$$

$$\left.\times \begin{pmatrix} \overline{\Phi} & -\overline{\Psi} \\ -\Psi & \Phi \end{pmatrix}\right]\begin{pmatrix} \Psi^{-1} & 0 \\ 0 & \overline{\Psi}^{-1} \end{pmatrix}$$

$$= \begin{pmatrix} \overline{\Phi} & -\overline{\Psi} \\ -\Psi & \Phi \end{pmatrix}\begin{pmatrix} \overline{\Phi} + A_{11}\Psi & -\overline{\Psi} + A_{12}\overline{\Psi} \\ -\Psi + A_{21}\Psi & \Phi + A_{22}\overline{\Psi} \end{pmatrix}^{-1}$$

$$\times \left[\begin{pmatrix} \overline{\Phi} + A_{11}\Psi & -\overline{\Psi} + A_{12}\overline{\Psi} \\ -\Psi + A_{21}\Psi & \Phi + A_{22}\overline{\Psi} \end{pmatrix} - \begin{pmatrix} \overline{\Phi} & -\overline{\Psi} \\ -\Psi & \Phi \end{pmatrix}\right]\begin{pmatrix} \Psi^{-1} & 0 \\ 0 & \overline{\Psi}^{-1} \end{pmatrix}$$

$$= \begin{pmatrix} \overline{\Phi} & -\overline{\Psi} \\ -\Psi & \Phi \end{pmatrix}\begin{pmatrix} \overline{\Phi} + A_{11}\Psi & -\overline{\Psi} + A_{12}\overline{\Psi} \\ -\Psi + A_{21}\Psi & \Phi + A_{22}\overline{\Psi} \end{pmatrix}^{-1}\begin{pmatrix} A_{11} & A_{12} \\ A_{21} & A_{22} \end{pmatrix}.$$

As a result of these transformations we obtain for $B$ the final expression

$$B(a^*, a) = (\det C)^{-1/2} \exp\left[ -\tfrac{1}{2}(b \quad b^*)\begin{pmatrix} \overline{\Phi} & -\overline{\Psi} \\ -\Psi & \Phi \end{pmatrix}\right.$$

$$\times \left. C^{-1}\begin{pmatrix} A_{11} & A_{12} \\ A_{21} & A_{22} \end{pmatrix}\begin{pmatrix} b \\ b^* \end{pmatrix}\right], \qquad (4.55)$$

where

$$C = \begin{pmatrix} \overline{\Phi} + A_{11}\Psi & (A_{12} - E)\overline{\Psi} \\ (A_{21} - E)\Psi & \Phi + A_{22}\overline{\Psi} \end{pmatrix},$$

$$b = \Phi a + \Psi a^* + f, \qquad b^* = \overline{\Psi} a + \overline{\Phi} a^* + f^* \qquad (4.56)$$

Formula (4.55) has been derived under the assumption that $\Phi = \Phi^*$ and that the operator $\Psi^{-1}$ exists. We consider an arbitrary canonical transformation given by operators $\Phi$, $\Psi$ and a vector $f$. Let us represent $\Phi$ in the form $\Phi = V\Phi_1$, where $\Phi_1$ is an Hermitian positive-definite operator and $V$ is a unitary operator.

We represent the transformation being studied in the form of a superposition,

$$b_1 = \Phi_1 a + \Psi_1 a^* + f_1, \qquad b_1^* = \overline{\Psi}_1 a + \overline{\Phi}_1 a^* + f_1^*,$$

$$b = Vb_1, \quad b^* = \overline{V}b_1^*, \qquad \text{where } V\Psi_1 = \Psi, \quad Vf_1 = f.$$

By making use of formulas (4.35) and (4.55), we find that in this case,

$$B(a^*, a) = (\det C_1)^{-1/2} \exp\left[ -\tfrac{1}{2}(b \quad b^*)\begin{pmatrix} \overline{\Phi} & -\overline{\Psi} \\ -\Psi & \Phi \end{pmatrix}\right.$$

$$\times \left. C^{-1}\begin{pmatrix} A_{11} & A_{12} \\ A_{21} & A_{22} \end{pmatrix}\begin{pmatrix} b \\ b^* \end{pmatrix}\right], \qquad (4.57)$$

where $C$, $b$, $b^*$ are defined by formulas (4.56) and

$$C_1 = \begin{pmatrix} \overline{\Phi}_1 + A_{11}\Psi_1 & (A_{12} - E)\overline{\Psi}_1 \\ (A_{21} - E)\Psi_1 & \Phi_1 + A_{22}\overline{\Psi}_1 \end{pmatrix}.$$

We now remark that the operator $\Psi^{-1}$ does not enter explicitly into formulas (4.55), (4.57). Hence it follows evidently that these formulas are valid not only for the canonical transformations for which $\Psi^{-1}$ exists, but also for the transformations which can be approximated by such ones for which $\Psi^{-1}$ exists. In particular, it is not difficult to verify immediately that formulas (4.55) and (4.57) are valid for the case when $\Psi = 0$.

## 5. Fermi Case

1. DEFINITION. Let $L$ be a Hilbert space with involution, $\varphi \in L$, and $\hat{a}(\varphi)$, $\hat{a}^*(\varphi)$ be operators operating in the Hilbert space $\mathscr{H}$ and satisfying the Fermi commutation relations

$$\{\hat{a}(\varphi_1), \hat{a}^*(\varphi_2)\} = \varphi_1\varphi_2,$$

$$\{\hat{a}(\varphi_1), \hat{a}(\varphi_2)\} = \{\hat{a}^*(\varphi_1), \hat{a}^*(\varphi_2)\} = 0 \tag{5.1}$$

We consider in $L$ operators $\Phi$ and $\Psi$ having a common everywhere-dense domain of definition and possessing adjoint operators defined on a common everywhere-dense set $D$ which is invariant relative to the involution. We construct in $\mathscr{H}$ operators $\hat{b}(\varphi)$, $\hat{b}^*(\varphi)$, $\varphi \in D$:

$$\hat{b}(\varphi) = \hat{a}(\varphi\Phi) + \hat{a}^*(\varphi\Psi), \qquad \hat{b}^*(\varphi) = \hat{a}(\varphi\overline{\Psi}) + \hat{a}^*(\varphi\overline{\Phi}). \tag{5.2}$$

If the transformation (5.2) is reversible and the operators $\hat{b}(\varphi)$, $\hat{b}^*(\varphi)$ satisfy the Fermi commutation relations

$$\{\hat{b}(\varphi_1), \hat{b}^*(\varphi_2)\} = \varphi_1\varphi_2,$$

$$\{\hat{b}(\varphi_1), \hat{b}(\varphi_2)\} = \{\hat{b}^*(\varphi_1), \hat{b}^*(\varphi_2)\} = 0, \tag{5.1'}$$

then the transformation (5.2) is called a *linear canonical transformation*.

If the operators $\Phi$, $\Psi$ define a canonical transformation, then there are definite relations between them which will be found in the next subsection.

It will be said that a canonical transformation defined by operators $\Phi$, $\Psi$ *has the property* A if the operator $\Phi$ is represented in the form $\Phi = (\Phi\Phi^*)^{1/2}U$, where $U$ is a unitary operator. In the following we shall mainly consider such transformations.

It has been noted in Section 1 that if the space $L$ is finite-dimensional and if the operators $\hat{a}(\varphi)$, $\hat{a}^*(\varphi)$ and $\hat{b}(\varphi)$, $\hat{b}^*(\varphi)$ operate in the same space and satisfy the Fermi commutation relations, then

$$\hat{b}(\varphi) = \hat{U}\hat{a}(\varphi)\hat{U}^{-1}, \qquad \hat{b}^*(\varphi) = \hat{U}\hat{a}^*(\varphi)\hat{U}^{-1}, \tag{5.3}$$

where $\hat{U}$ is a unitary operator.

There are two possibilities in the infinite-dimensional case. If the canonical transformation is generated by a unitary operator $\hat{U}$, then it will be called *proper*; if the canonical transformation is such that there does not exist a unitary operator satisfying the condition (5.3), then it will be called *improper*.

2. RELATIONS BETWEEN THE OPERATORS $\Phi$ AND $\Psi$. We find, by substituting (5.2) into (5.1') and using (5.1), that in order that the transformation (5.2) be canonical it is necessary and sufficient that the operators $\Phi$ and $\Psi$ should satisfy the relations

$$\Phi\Psi' + \Psi\Phi' = 0, \qquad \overline{\Phi}\Psi^* + \overline{\Psi}\Phi^* = 0,$$
$$\Phi\Phi^* + \Psi\Psi^* = E, \qquad \overline{\Phi}\Phi' + \overline{\Psi}\Psi' = E. \tag{5.4}$$

The expressions in the left members of these equalities have the meaning of Hermitian forms on the dense set $D$ on which the operators $\Phi^*$, $\Psi^*$ are defined, for example,

$$(\Phi\Psi'f, g) = (\Psi'f, \Phi^*g), \qquad f, g \in D.$$

We turn our attention to the relation $\Phi\Phi^* + \Psi\Psi^* = E$. It follows evidently from this that the operators $\Phi$ and $\Psi$, giving a canonical transformation, are bounded. This fact does not have an analog in the Bose case.[15] We consider the matrix $\mathscr{A}$ consisting of operators $\Phi$ and $\Psi$,

$$\mathscr{A} = \begin{pmatrix} \Phi & \Psi \\ \Psi & \Phi \end{pmatrix}.$$

We shall refer later to the matrix $\mathscr{A}$ as the *matrix of a canonical transformation*.

It is easy to see that relations (5.4) are equivalent to saying that the matrix $\mathscr{A}$ has a right inverse which is given by the formula

$$\mathscr{A}^{-1} = \begin{pmatrix} \Phi^* & \Psi' \\ \Psi^* & \Phi' \end{pmatrix}. \tag{5.5}$$

By definition the canonical transformation is reversible. This means that the matrix $\mathscr{A}$ has a left inverse.

It is well known that if an operator has both left and right inverses, then these inverses coincide. Therefore the matrix (5.5) is not only the right inverse, but also the left inverse for $\mathscr{A}$.

---

[15] It follows from the result of Section 4.3 that if the Bose canonical transformation is proper, then operators $\Phi$ and $\Psi$ are bounded. It is not difficult in the Bose case to construct an example of the improper canonical transformation for which operators $\Phi$ and $\Psi$ are not bounded.

By making use of this fact, we obtain in addition to (5.4) the relations

$$\Phi^*\Psi + \Psi'\overline{\Phi} = 0, \qquad \Psi^*\Phi + \Phi'\overline{\Psi} = 0,$$
$$\Phi^*\Phi + \Psi'\overline{\Psi} = E, \qquad \Phi'\overline{\Phi} + \Psi^*\Psi = E. \tag{5.6}$$

It is easy to see that under the composition of canonical transformations the corresponding matrices are multiplied. From the circumstance that the matrix of a canonical transformation has a two-sided inverse, it thus follows that linear canonical transformations form a group.

Consider the matrix $U = (1/\sqrt{2})\begin{pmatrix} E & E \\ iE & -iE \end{pmatrix}$. We represent the matrix $U\mathscr{A}U^{-1}$ in the form

$$\mathscr{B} = U\mathscr{A}U^{-1} = \begin{pmatrix} A & B \\ C & D \end{pmatrix}. \tag{5.7}$$

The operators $A$, $B$, $C$, and $D$ are expressed in terms of $\Phi$, $\Psi$ as follows:

$$A = \operatorname{Re}(\Phi + \Psi), \qquad B = \operatorname{Im}(\Phi - \Psi),$$
$$C = -\operatorname{Im}(\Psi + \Phi), \qquad D = \operatorname{Re}(\Phi - \Psi). \tag{5.8}$$

Thus the matrix $\mathscr{B}$ is real.

Consider the matrix $I = \begin{pmatrix} 0 & E \\ E & 0 \end{pmatrix}$. It is easy to see that relations (5.4), (5.6) are equivalent to the relations

$$\mathscr{A}I\mathscr{A}' = I, \qquad \mathscr{A}'I\mathscr{A} = I. \tag{5.9}$$

We multiply the first of these relations from the left by $U$, from the right by $U'$, and the second from the left by $U'^{-1}$, from the right by $U^{-1}$. By observing that $UIU' = U'^{-1}IU^{-1} = E$, we obtain

$$\mathscr{B}\mathscr{B}' = E, \qquad \mathscr{B}'\mathscr{B} = E. \tag{5.10}$$

The converse is true: If the matrix $\mathscr{B}$ satisfies relations (5.10), then $\mathscr{A} = U^{-1}\mathscr{B}U$ satisfies relations (5.9), and hence it is the matrix of a canonical transformation.

Finite-dimensional matrices satisfying relations (5.10) are called *orthogonal*. They form a group, and moreover real orthogonal matrices form a compact group.

In the general case it is natural to call operators satisfying relations (5.10) *orthogonal* by analogy with the finite-dimensional case. They evidently form a group.

3. PROPER CANONICAL TRANSFORMATIONS. In this subsection we find criteria that a canonical transformation having the property A is proper (cf. Friedrichs' book [1]).

A fundamental theorem which establishes these criteria is based on the following lemma.

**Lemma 5.1.** *In order that a canonical transformation be proper, it is necessary and sufficient that there exist in the state space a vector F satisfying the equations*

$$\hat{b}(\varphi)\hat{F} = 0 \tag{5.11}$$

*for all $\varphi \in L$.*

This lemma, just like a similar lemma for bosons, is an immediate consequence of Theorem 1.4.

We formulate the fundamental theorem.

**Theorem 5.1.** *Let a canonical transformation having the property A be given by a matrix $\left(\begin{smallmatrix} \Phi & \Psi \\ \bar{\Psi} & \bar{\Phi} \end{smallmatrix}\right)$. In order that the transformation be proper, it is necessary and sufficient that the operator $\Psi$ be a Hilbert-Schmidt operator.*

The proof of this theorem is somewhat more complicated than that of the similar theorem in the Bose case. The complication is connected with the fact that in the Bose case the operator $\Phi$ has a bounded inverse for any canonical transformation, whereas this is not the case for fermions.

We first consider the case when the operators $\Phi$ and $\Phi^*$ have inverses (not bounded, maybe) defined on an everywhere-dense set. Then the general case is reduced to this case.

In the first case the proof of the theorem differs little from that of the corresponding theorem for bosons. Therefore we shall not carry out a similar argument, but limit ourselves only to a brief sketch.

Because of the circumstance that the operator $\Phi$ is bounded and has an inverse, just as in the Bose case, it is confirmed that $\Psi$ is a Hilbert-Schmidt operator. Further, after having established that $\Psi$ is a Hilbert-Schmidt operator, we observe that the relation $\Phi\Phi^* = E - \Psi\Psi^*$ implies that if the operator $\Phi\Phi^*$ has an inverse, then it has a *bounded* inverse. The same property is evidently possessed by $(\Phi\Phi^*)^{1/2}$.

By assumption the canonical transformation has the property A. That is, $\Phi = (\Phi\Phi^*)^{1/2}U$, where $U$ is a unitary operator.

Then it evidently follows that the operator $\Phi$ has a bounded inverse $\Phi^{-1} = U^{-1}(\Phi\Phi^*)^{-1/2}$. After having established that the operator $\Phi^{-1}$ is bounded, the sufficiency proof is not different from that in the Bose case.

The reduction of the general case to this case, when the operators $\Phi$ and $\Phi^*$ have inverses, is based on the following series of lemmas.

**Lemma 5.2.** *Let a proper canonical transformation be such that the operator $\Phi$ is equal to zero. Then the space $L$ is finite-dimensional.*

In fact, if $\Phi = 0$, then

$$\hat{b}(\varphi) = \hat{a}^*(\varphi\Psi).$$

Further, it follows from relations (5.4), (5.6) that in this case $\Psi$ is a unitary operator. Therefore, when $\varphi$ runs through $L$, $\varphi\Psi$ also runs through the whole space $L$. Consequently, equations (5.11) in this case are equivalent to the equations

$$\hat{a}^*(\varphi)\hat{F} = 0. \tag{5.12}$$

Concerning equations (5.12), if $L$ is infinite-dimensional it follows from them that $\hat{F} = 0$ (cf. Section 1.3).

The space $L$ is decomposed into the sum of two orthogonal subspaces, $L = L_1 + L_2$. We denote by $\mathscr{H}_i$ the subspace of $\mathscr{H}$ generated by operating with operators $\hat{a}^*(\varphi)$, $\varphi \in L_i$, on $\hat{\Phi}_0$. We consider a canonical transformation having the property that the subspaces $L_1$ and $L_2$ are invariant with respect to the right operation of the operators $\Phi$, $\Psi$, $\overline{\Phi}$, $\overline{\Psi}$ (cf. Introduction, Subsection 3). We denote by $\Phi_i$, $\Psi_i$, $\overline{\Phi}_i$, $\overline{\Psi}_i$ values of the operators $\Phi$, $\Psi$, $\overline{\Phi}$, $\overline{\Psi}$ on the subspace $L_i$. Evidently for $\varphi \in L_i$ the canonical transformation has the form

$$\hat{b}(\varphi) = \hat{a}(\varphi\Phi_i) + \hat{a}^*(\varphi\Psi_i),$$
$$\hat{b}^*(\varphi) = \hat{a}(\varphi\overline{\Psi}_i) + \hat{a}^*(\varphi\overline{\Phi}_i). \tag{5.13}$$

The space $\mathscr{H}_i$ is evidently invariant with respect to the operators $\hat{a}(\varphi)$, $\hat{a}^*(\varphi)$, $\hat{b}(\varphi)$, $\hat{b}^*(\varphi)$ for $\varphi \in L_i$. Therefore, formulas (5.13) may be regarded as a canonical transformation in $\mathscr{H}_i$. The transformation (5.13) will be called the *components* of the transformation with matrix $\left(\begin{smallmatrix} \Phi & \Psi \\ \overline{\Psi} & \overline{\Phi} \end{smallmatrix}\right)$. A transformation with matrix $\left(\begin{smallmatrix} \Phi & \Psi \\ \overline{\Psi} & \overline{\Phi} \end{smallmatrix}\right)$ having the property described above is called a *transformation decomposable into two components*.

The components (5.13) are said to be *proper* if the transformation (5.13) is proper, i.e., there exists in the space $\mathcal{H}_i$ a unitary operator $\hat{U}$ such that

$$\hat{b}(\varphi) = \hat{U}\hat{a}(\varphi)\hat{U}^{-1}, \qquad \hat{b}^*(\varphi) = \hat{U}\hat{a}^*(\varphi)\hat{U}^{-1}.$$

**Lemma 5.3.** *A canonical transformation decomposable into two components is proper if and only if both of its components are proper.*

We recall that there corresponds to every vector of the state space $\mathcal{H}$ an element of the Grassmann algebra $\mathcal{G}$ generated by the space $L$. Evidently if a vector $\hat{\Phi}$ belongs to $\mathcal{H}_i$, then the functional corresponding to it is an element of the subalgebra $\mathcal{G}_i \subset \mathcal{G}$ generated by the subspace $L_i$. Let the initial canonical transformation be proper, let $\hat{F}$ be a vector satisfying equations (5.11), and let $F(a^*)$ be a functional corresponding to it.

Consider the value of $F(a^*)$ on $L_1$. We first suppose that this value is equal to zero. Then it follows at once that $F(a^*) \in \mathcal{G}_2$. Let us apply to $F(a^*)$ the operator $\hat{b}(\varphi) = \int \varphi(x)\Phi(x, y)[\delta/\delta a^*(x)]\, dx\, dy + \int \varphi(x)\Psi(x, y)a^*(y)\, dx\, dy$ for $\varphi \in L_1$. From (5.11), on account of $F(a^*) \in \mathcal{G}_2$, it follows that $\int \varphi(x)\Psi(x, y)a^*(y)\, dy\, F(a^*) = 0$. Since the space $L_1$ is invariant with respect to $\Psi$, the last equation is equivalent to $\hat{a}^*(\varphi_1)\hat{F} = 0$, where $\varphi_1 = \varphi\Psi \in L_{\hat{1}}$. Again taking into consideration that $\hat{F} \in \mathcal{H}_2$, we arrive at the conclusion that the equation $\hat{a}^*(\varphi_1)\hat{F} = 0$, $\varphi_1 \in L_1$, has a solution only if $\varphi_1 = 0$ or, in other words, if the value of the operator $\Psi$ on $L_1$ is equal to zero. Thus in this case the first component of the canonical transformation has the form

$$\hat{b}(\varphi) = \hat{a}(\varphi\Phi_1), \quad \hat{b}^*(\varphi) = \hat{a}^*(\varphi\overline{\Phi}_1), \qquad \varphi \in L_1. \tag{5.14}$$

Evidently, the transformation (5.14) is proper and there corresponds to the vector $\hat{F}_1 \in \mathcal{H}_1$ satisfying the equation $\hat{b}(\varphi)\hat{F}_1 = 0$, $\varphi \in L_1$, the functional $F_1 \equiv 1$.

Let us consider the case when the value of $F(a^*)$ on $L_1$ is different from zero. We denote this value by $F_1(a^*)$. Evidently the vector $\hat{F}_1$ corresponding to $F_1(a^*)$ is the projection of $\hat{F}$ onto the space $\mathcal{H}_1$. Therefore $(\hat{F}_1, \hat{F}_1) < \infty$. We shall show that $\hat{b}(\varphi)\hat{F}_1 = 0$ for $\varphi \in L_1$.

Let $\hat{F} = \hat{F}_1 + \hat{T}$, where $\hat{T}$ is a vector orthogonal to $\mathcal{H}_1$. Since the space $\mathcal{H}_1$ is invariant with respect to the operators $\hat{b}^*(\varphi)$ for $\varphi \in L_1$, $\hat{b}(\varphi)\hat{T}$ for $\varphi \in L_1$ remains orthogonal to $\mathcal{H}_1$. On the other hand,

$\hat{b}(\varphi)\hat{F}_1 \in \mathscr{H}_1$. Therefore the equality $0 = \hat{b}(\varphi)\hat{F} = \hat{b}(\varphi)\hat{F}_1 + \hat{b}(\varphi)\hat{T}$ implies $\hat{b}(\varphi)\hat{F}_1 = 0$, which was to be proved.

Now let both components be proper, let $\hat{F}_i \in \mathscr{H}_i$ be vectors satisfying the equations $\hat{b}(\varphi)\hat{F}_i = 0$ for $\varphi \in L_i$, and let $F_i(a^*)$ be the functionals corresponding to these vectors. We consider the vector $\hat{F}$ to which the functional $F = F_1 F_2$ corresponds.

From formula (3.66) for the inner product it follows that $(\hat{F}, \hat{F}) = (\hat{F}_1, \hat{F}_1)(\hat{F}_2, \hat{F}_2)$; consequently, $(\hat{F}, \hat{F}) < \infty$, and thus $\hat{F}$ belongs to the state space.

We consider the operator on functionals which corresponds to $\hat{b}(\varphi)$ and denote it as before by $\hat{b}(\varphi)$:

$$\hat{b}(\varphi) = \int \varphi(x)\Phi(x, y) \frac{\delta}{\delta a^*(y)} \, dx \, dy + \int \varphi(x)\Psi(x, y)a^*(y) \, dy.$$

To complete the proof of the lemma, evidently it remains to verify that $\hat{b}(\varphi)F = 0$ for any $\varphi \in L$. If $\varphi \in L_1$, then $\hat{b}(\varphi)F = 0$ on account of $\hat{b}(\varphi)F_1 = 0$. If $\varphi \in L_2$, then we decompose $F_1$ into the sum of even and odd functionals, $F_1 = F_1'' + F_1'$. From formula (3.7) for the differentiation of the product[16] it follows immediately that in this case

$$\hat{b}(\varphi)F_1 F_2 = F_1''\hat{b}(\varphi)F_2 - F_1'\hat{b}(\varphi)F_2 = 0,$$

because $\hat{b}(\varphi)F_2 = 0$.

Thus $\hat{b}(\varphi)F = 0$ for any $\varphi$. The lemma is proved.

We consider a canonical transformation for which the operator $\Psi$ is equal to zero. It follows from relations (5.4), (5.6) that for such a transformation the operator $\Phi$ is an arbitrary unitary operator.

Let $\mathscr{A} = \begin{pmatrix} \Phi & \Psi \\ \bar{\Psi} & \bar{\Phi} \end{pmatrix}$ be the matrix of some proper transformation, and let $\mathscr{A}_1 = \begin{pmatrix} V_1 & 0 \\ 0 & \bar{V}_1 \end{pmatrix}$, $\mathscr{A}_2 = \begin{pmatrix} V_2 & 0 \\ 0 & \bar{V}_2 \end{pmatrix}$ be matrices of the canonical transformations just described. Consider the canonical transformation with the matrix $\mathscr{B} = \mathscr{A}_1 \mathscr{A} \mathscr{A}_2 = \begin{pmatrix} V_1\Phi V_2 & V_1\Psi \bar{V}_2 \\ \bar{V}_1\bar{\Psi} V_2 & \bar{V}_1\bar{\Phi}\bar{V}_2 \end{pmatrix}$. Evidently this canonical transformation will or will not be proper simultaneously with the primary transformation, and the condition of the theorem for this transformation is satisfied if and only if it is satisfied by the primary transformation.

Since the transformation has the property A, the operators $V_1$ and $V_2$ may be selected in such a way that $V_1\Phi V_2$ should be a real Hermi-

---

[16] Evidently this formula holds for the infinite-dimensional Grassmann algebra, just as in the finite-dimensional case.

tian operator.[17] As a consequence, it suffices to prove the theorem for the case when the operator $\Phi$ is real Hermitian.

Suppose $\Phi = \Phi^* = \overline{\Phi}$. We denote by $L_1$ the subspace on which $\Phi$ vanishes and by $L_2$ the orthogonal complement of $L_1$. Evidently, the operator $\Phi$ is inversible on $L_2$.

We shall show that the spaces $L_1$ and $L_2$ are invariant with respect to $\Psi$ and $\overline{\Psi}$. Let $f \in L_1$. From the condition (5.4), $\Phi\Psi' + \Psi\Phi' = 0$, by the aid of the relation $\Phi = \Phi'$, we obtain $0 = f\Phi\Psi' = -f\Psi\Phi$. Hence $f\Psi \in L_1$. Analogously, we obtain $f\overline{\Psi} = 0$ from the condition $\overline{\Phi}\Psi^* + \overline{\Psi}\Phi^* = 0$. Further, from the condition (5.6), $\Phi^*\Psi + \Psi'\overline{\Phi} = 0$ and $\Psi^*\Phi + \Phi'\overline{\Psi} = 0$, and the identities $\Phi^* = \overline{\Phi} = \Phi$, we find in the same way that $f\Psi' \in L_1$ and $f\Psi^* \in L_1$ and accordingly the space $L_1$ is invariant with respect to the operators $\Psi$, $\Psi^*$, $\Psi'$, $\overline{\Psi}$. Hence it follows that $L_2$ is invariant with respect to the same operators. Thus the canonical transformation splits into two components corresponding to the spaces $L_1$ and $L_2$. From Lemmas 5.2 and 5.3 it follows at once that the space $L_1$ is finite-dimensional and that the transformation is proper simultaneously with its component generated by the space $L_2$. Evidently, on the other hand, as long as the space $L_1$ is finite-dimensional, the operator $\Psi$ is a Hilbert-Schmidt operator if and only if its value in the space $L_2$ is a Hilbert-Schmidt operator. Thus the proof of the theorem is reduced to the case when the operators $\Phi$ and $\Phi^*$ have inverses. Beginning from this place, as stated above, the proof coincides with that of the similar theorem for bosons.

It should be noted that in the course of the proof we have established a fact which is valuable by itself. We shall formulate it as a separate lemma.

**Lemma 5.4.** *Let a proper canonical transformation with matrix* $\left( \begin{smallmatrix} \Phi & \Psi \\ \Psi & \Phi \end{smallmatrix} \right)$ *have the property* A. *Denote by* $L_1 \subset L$ *the eigensubspace for the operator* $\Phi$ *with eigenvalue* 0. *Then the space* $L_1$ *is finite-dimensional.*

We also note one more important proposition.

**Lemma 5.5.** *Consider a proper canonical transformation having the property that the eigensubspace* $L_1$ *of the operator* $\Phi$ *with eigenvalue* 0 *is finite-dimensional. Then there exists a family of canonical transformations*

---

[17] Cf. the Introduction, end of Subsection 3.

*depending on a parameter t such that the operator $\Phi_t^{-1}$ exists for $t \neq 0$ and $\Phi$ is the limit of $\Phi_t$ as $t \to 0$ in the strong sense, while $\Psi$ is the limit of $\Psi_t$ as $t \to 0$ in the strong sense.*

For the proof we represent the canonical transformation in the form of the product of two components, for one of which $\Phi^{-1}$ exists, and $\Phi = 0$ for the other, just as we have done in the proof of Theorem 5.1. The component with $\Phi = 0$ is a canonical transformation in a finite-dimensional space, having the matrix $\begin{pmatrix} 0 & \Psi_1 \\ \Psi_1 & 0 \end{pmatrix}$, where $\Psi_1$ is an arbitrary unitary matrix of even degree. It is not difficult to show, starting from elementary considerations of linear algebra, that there exists a family of matrices $\begin{pmatrix} \Phi_1(t) & \Psi_1(t) \\ \Psi_1(t) & \Phi_1(t) \end{pmatrix}$ satisfying the conditions (5.5), for which $\Phi_{1}{}^{-1}$ exists and $\begin{pmatrix} 0 & \Psi_1 \\ \Psi_1 & 0 \end{pmatrix}$ is its limit as $t \to 0$.

By using the canonical transformation with the matrix $\begin{pmatrix} \Phi_1(t) & \Psi(t) \\ \Psi_1(t) & \Phi(t) \end{pmatrix}$ as one of the components and the component of the initial transformation for which $\Phi^{-1}$ exists, we construct the required canonical transformation.

4. DETERMINANT OF THE MATRIX OF A PROPER CANONICAL TRANSFORMATION. Let $\mathscr{A} = \begin{pmatrix} \Phi & \Psi \\ \Psi & \Phi \end{pmatrix}$ be the matrix of a proper canonical transformation, for which the operator $\Phi$ is Hermitian and has the inverse $\Phi^{-1}$. Just as in the Bose case, we may convince ourselves that the matrix $\mathscr{A}$ has a determinant and that $\det \mathscr{A} = 1$.

5. CONSTRUCTION OF THE OPERATOR $\hat{U}$. We shall determine the generating functionals for the matrix and the normal forms of the operator $\hat{U}$ giving a proper linear canonical transformation.

**Theorem 5.2.** *Let an operator $\hat{U}$ give a proper canonical transformation $\hat{U}\hat{a}(\varphi)\hat{U}^{-1} = \hat{a}(\varphi\Phi) + \hat{a}^*(\varphi\Psi)$ such that the operator $\Phi$ has the two-sided inverse $\Phi^{-1}$. Then the generating functionals $U(a^*, a)$, $\tilde{U}(a^*, a)$ for the normal and matrix forms of $\hat{U}$ have the form*

$$\tilde{U}(a^*, a) = \theta \, (\det \Phi\Phi^*)^{1/4}$$

$$\times \exp[-\tfrac{1}{2}(a\overline{\Psi}\Phi^{-1}a - 2a^*\Phi^{-1}a + a^*\Phi^{-1}\Psi a^*)], \qquad (5.15)$$

$$U(a^*, a) = \tilde{U}(a^*, a) \, e^{-a^*a},$$

*where $\theta$ is an arbitrary number such that $|\theta| = 1$.*

Formulas (5.15) are proved verbatim just as the similar formulas were for bosons. Therefore we shall not dwell on their derivation.

We shall present also without derivation the expression for the functional $F$ corresponding to the transformed vacuum vector $\hat{F} = \hat{U}\hat{\Phi}_0$,

$$F(a^*) = \theta(\det \Phi\Phi^*)^{1/4} \exp(-\tfrac{1}{2}a^*\Phi^{-1}\Psi a^*). \qquad (5.16)$$

We remark that if the operator $\Phi$ has a two-sided inverse, then it may be represented in the form $\Phi = (\Phi\Phi^*)^{1/2}U$, where $U$ is a unitary operator. Consequently, the canonical transformation has the property A.

It can be shown that the expressions for the functionals $\tilde{U}(a^*, a)$, $U(a^*, a)$, $F(a^*)$ corresponding to an arbitrary proper canonical transformation having the property A may be obtained from (5.15) and (5.16) by a passage to the limit. However, we shall not discuss this further.

Formulas (5.15) assign to every proper canonical transformation a family of operators differing by a factor, $g \to \theta\hat{U}_g$, and moreover this correspondence is a projective representation: If

$$g_1 \to \theta\hat{U}_{g_1}, \quad g_2 \to \theta\hat{U}_{g_2}, \qquad \text{then } g_1 g_2 \to \theta\hat{U}_{g_1}\hat{U}_{g_2}.$$

Nonuniqueness in the correspondence $g \to \theta\hat{U}_g$ may be diminished if one considers, instead of the group of all proper canonical transformations, its subgroup $G$ defined as follows: The matrix $\left(\begin{smallmatrix} \Phi & \Psi \\ \Psi & \Phi \end{smallmatrix}\right)$ of a transformation from $g$ has the property that $\Phi = E + K$, where $K$ is a trace-class operator. For elements of the group $G$ we can choose $\theta$ in formula (5.15) in such a way that $\theta (\det \Phi\Phi^*)^{1/4} = (\det \Phi)^{1/2}$.

For such a choice of $\theta$ there remains only the nonuniqueness in choosing the sign of the root. By virtue of formula (3.69) or (3.70) for the product of operators, it is readily established that the two-valued representation thus obtained is a projective representation of the group $G$: If

$$g_1 \to \pm U_{g_1}, \quad g_2 \to \pm U_{g_2}, \qquad \text{then} \qquad g_1 g_2 \to \pm U_{g_1} U_{g_2}.$$

It is impossible to remove the remaining nonuniqueness in sign. This is proved word for word as in the case of the similar assertion for bosons (cf. p. 103).

The representation of the group we have obtained is called the *spinor representation*. The spinor representation of the finite-dimensional orthogonal group has been well investigated (cf., for example, Weyl's book [1]).

6. CANONICAL TRANSFORMATION OF OPERATORS. We consider a proper canonical transformation $\hat{U}\hat{a}(\varphi)\hat{U}^{-1} = \hat{a}(\varphi\Phi) + \hat{a}^*(\varphi\Psi)$. Let $\hat{A}$ and $\hat{B} = \hat{U}\hat{A}\hat{U}^{-1}$ be operators representable in the normal form. We express the functional $B(a^*, a)$ corresponding to the normal form of $\hat{B}$ in terms of the analogous functional $A(a^*, a)$. Let us first solve this problem for a special case when $\Psi = 0$.

Evidently, in this case

$$B(a^*, a) = A(\overline{\Phi}a^*, \Phi a); \tag{5.17}$$

i.e., the canonical transformation is reduced to a change of variables.

We observe that if $\Psi = 0$, then, as follows from relations (5.4), (5.6), $\Phi$ is an arbitrary unitary operator. We proceed to the general case.

Let the transformation have the property A. We represent the matrix of the transformation in the form

$$\begin{pmatrix} \Phi & \Psi \\ \overline{\Psi} & \overline{\Phi} \end{pmatrix} = \begin{pmatrix} \Phi_1 & \Psi_1 \\ \overline{\Psi}_1 & \overline{\Phi}_1 \end{pmatrix} \begin{pmatrix} V & 0 \\ 0 & \overline{V} \end{pmatrix}, \tag{5.18}$$

where $\Phi_1$ is an Hermitian operator and $V$ a unitary operator. Evidently, each factor in (5.18) is the matrix of a canonical transformation. For the case when the canonical transformation is given by the matrix $\begin{pmatrix} V & 0 \\ 0 & \overline{V} \end{pmatrix}$, the problem is solved by formula (5.17). Thus it remains to examine the canonical transformation for which the operator $\Phi_1$ is Hermitian. Evidently, this case presents the greatest interest.

**Theorem 5.3.** *Let* $\begin{pmatrix} \Phi & \Psi \\ \overline{\Psi} & \overline{\Phi} \end{pmatrix}$ *be the matrix of a proper canonical transformation, in which the operator* $\Psi$ *has an inverse and* $\Phi$ *is an Hermitian operator such that its eigensubspace with eigenvalue 0 is even-dimensional.*

*Assume that there exists a monotonic sequence of projection operators* $P_n$, *belonging to the spectral family of* $\Phi$, *such that the sequence converges strongly to the identity operator and that the subspaces* $P_n L$ *are finite-dimensional and have even dimension.*[18] *Then the functional* $B(a^*, a)$ *is equal to*

$$B(a^*, a) = \lim_{n \to \infty} \int \mathscr{K}_n(a^*, a \mid \alpha^*, \alpha) A(\alpha^*, \alpha) \, d^n\alpha^* \, d^n\alpha. \tag{5.19}$$

[18] It is evident that this condition is satisfied if the eigensubspaces are even-dimensional.

where

$\mathscr{H}_n(a^*, a \mid \alpha^*, \alpha)$

$$= (\det P_n \Psi \Psi^* P_n)^{1/2} \exp\left[ \tfrac{1}{2}(b - \alpha \quad b^* - \alpha^*) \mathscr{L} \begin{pmatrix} b - \alpha \\ b^* - \alpha^* \end{pmatrix} \right], \quad (5.20)$$

$$\mathscr{L} = \begin{pmatrix} \overline{\Phi}\Psi^{-1} & -E \\ E & -\Phi\overline{\Psi}^{-1} \end{pmatrix},$$

$b = \Phi a + \Psi a^*$, $b^* = \overline{\Psi} a + \overline{\Phi} a^*$, $\alpha \in P_n F$, $\alpha^* \in \overline{P}_n F^*$, and $F + F^*$ is the space of generators of the algebra to which $A(a^*, a)$ belongs.

For the proof of the theorem we note that according to formula (3.70) the functional $B(a^*, a)$ is equal to

$$B(a^*, a) = \int U(a^*, \alpha)V(\beta^*, a)A(\alpha^*, \beta)$$

$$\times \exp[-(\alpha^* - a^*)(\alpha - \beta) - (\beta^* - \alpha^*)(\beta - a)]\, \Pi d\alpha^*\, d\alpha\, d\beta^*\, d\beta, \quad (5.21)$$

where $U(a^*, a)$ is the functional corresponding to the normal form of the operator $\hat{U}$ which realizes the canonical transformation, and $V(a^*, a)$ is the functional corresponding to the normal form of the operator $\hat{V} = \hat{U}^{-1}$.

We consider the sequence of integrals

$$B_n(a^*, a) = \int U(a^*, \alpha)V(\beta^*, a)A(\alpha^*, \beta)$$

$$\times \exp[-(\alpha^* - a^*)(\alpha - \beta) - (\beta^* - \alpha^*)(\beta - a)]\, d^n\alpha\, d^n\alpha^*\, d^n\beta\, d^n\beta^*, \quad (5.22)$$

where $\alpha, \beta \in P_n F$, $\alpha^*, \beta^* \in \overline{P}_n F^*$. According to the definition of the continual integral we have

$$B(a^*, a) = \lim_{n \to \infty} B_n(a^*, a).$$

As $n$ is even, the integral (5.22) can be represented in the form

$$B_n(a^*, a) = \int \tilde{\mathscr{H}}_n(a^*, a \mid \alpha^*, \beta)A(\alpha^*, \beta)\, d^n\alpha^*\, d^n\beta, \quad (5.23)$$

where

$$\tilde{\mathscr{H}}_n(a^*, a \mid \alpha^*, \beta) = \int U(a^*, \alpha)V(\beta^*, a)$$

$$\times \exp[-(\alpha^* - a^*)(\alpha - \beta) - (\beta^* - \alpha^*)(\beta - a)]\, d^n\alpha\, d^n\beta^*.$$

We now assume the canonical transformation to be such that $\Phi^{-1}$ exists. In this case the functional $U(a^*, \alpha)$ is defined by formula (5.15). The functional $V(\beta^*, a)$ corresponds to the operator $\hat{U}^{-1}$, and therefore it is obtained by replacing the number $\theta$ in (5.15) by $\bar{\theta}$ and the operators $\Phi$, $\Psi$ by the corresponding elements $\Phi^*$, $\Psi'$ of the matrix $\left(\begin{smallmatrix} \Phi & \Psi \\ \overline{\Psi} & \overline{\Phi} \end{smallmatrix}\right)^{-1}$ $= \left(\begin{smallmatrix} \Phi^* & \Psi' \\ \overline{\Psi}* & \Phi' \end{smallmatrix}\right)$.

Thus the integrand in (5.23) is an exponential whose exponent is a polynomial of second degree with respect to the integration variables. Forming the complete square and calculating the Gauss integral, we obtain for $\tilde{\mathcal{K}}_n$ the expression

$$\tilde{\mathcal{K}}_n = (\det \Phi\Phi^*)^{1/2}(\det \bar{P}_n\overline{\Psi}\Phi^{-1}P_n)^{1/2}(\det P_n\Phi^{*-1}\Psi'\bar{P}_n)^{1/2}$$

$$\times \exp\{-\tfrac{1}{2}[(\alpha^* - a^*\Phi^{-1})\Phi\overline{\Psi}^{-1}(\alpha^* - \Phi'^{-1}a^*)$$

$$+ (\beta - a\overline{\Phi}^{-1})\Psi'^{-1}\Phi^*(\beta - \Phi^{*-1}a) + a^*\Phi^{-1}\Psi a^* + a\Psi^*\Phi^{-1}a$$

$$+ 2\alpha^*\beta + 2a^*a]\}. \tag{5.24}$$

The exponent of (5.24) after the replacement of $\beta$ by $\alpha$ coincides with that of (5.20). To confirm this one must represent the exponent of (5.20) by using the expressions for $b$, $b^*$ in terms of $a$, $a^*$, in the quadratic form of $a$, $a^*$, $\alpha$, $\alpha^*$ and establish the coincidence of the coefficients of this formula with the corresponding coefficients of the quadratic form in the exponent of (5.24). This leads to a simple but very laborious calculation by making repeated use of relations (5.4) and (5.6).

We shall omit these calculations and turn to the factor before the exponential.

We observe that the expression before the exponential, $\det \bar{P}_n\overline{\Psi}\Phi^{-1}P_n$, is the determinant of the matrix of the bilinear form $\alpha\overline{\Psi}\Phi^{-1}\beta$, $\alpha,\beta \in P_nF$. $\det P_n\Phi^{*-1}\Psi'\bar{P}_n$ has a similar meaning. By using the commutability of $P_n$ and $\Phi = \Phi^*$, we find that

$$\det \bar{P}_n\overline{\Psi}\Phi^{-1}P_n \det P_n\Phi^{*-1}\Psi'\bar{P}_n$$

$$= \det \bar{P}_n\overline{\Psi}P_n \det P_n\Psi'\bar{P}_n \det P_n\Phi^{-1}\Phi^{*-1}P_n.$$

Just as in the Bose case, it is not difficult to show that

$$\overline{\Psi}P_n = \bar{P}_n\overline{\Psi}. \tag{5.25}$$

Therefore, $\det \bar{P}_n \bar{\Psi} P_n \det P_n \Psi' \bar{P}_n = \det \bar{P}_n \bar{\Psi}\Psi' \bar{P}_n$. Evidently $\bar{P}_n \bar{\Psi}\Psi' \bar{P}_n$ is an Hermitian operator. Hence its determinant is a real number. Consequently, we have

$$\det \bar{P}_n \bar{\Psi}\Psi' \bar{P}_n = \det P_n \Psi\Psi^* P_n.$$

We finally remark that $\lim_{n \to \infty} \det P_n \Phi^{-1}\Phi^{*-1} P_n = (\det \Phi\Phi^*)^{-1}$. Therefore the functional $B(a^*, a)$ is equal not only to the limit of $B_n(a^*, a)$, but also to the limit of the functionals

$$\int \mathscr{K}_n(a^*, a \mid \alpha^*, \alpha) A(\alpha^*, \alpha) \, d^n\alpha^* \, d^n\alpha,$$

where

$$\mathscr{K}_n(a^*, a \mid \alpha^*, \alpha) = \left( \frac{\det \Phi\Phi^*}{\det P_n \Phi\Phi^* P_n} \right)^{1/2} \tilde{\mathscr{K}}_n(a^*, a \mid \alpha^*, \alpha).$$

From all that we have stated above, it is clear that the functional $\mathscr{K}_n$ defined by the last formula coincides with (5.20).

Thus the theorem is proved for the case when $\Phi^{-1}$ exists. The general case may be obtained by the aid of a passage to a limit, since the operator $\Phi^{-1}$ does not enter into formula (5.20). We shall not go into details, but only recall that, according to Lemma 5.5, if the eigen-subspace with eigenvalue 0 of the operator $\Phi$ is even-dimensional, then the matrix of the canonical transformation $\left( \begin{smallmatrix} \Phi & \Psi \\ \bar{\Psi} & \bar{\Phi} \end{smallmatrix} \right)$ can be approximated by the matrices $\left( \begin{smallmatrix} \Phi_t & \Psi_t \\ \bar{\Psi}_t & \bar{\Phi}_t \end{smallmatrix} \right)$ for which $\Phi_t^{-1}$ exists.

7. ANOTHER PROOF OF THEOREM 5.3. From the proof of the theorem which has been given above, it is not clear from where the final expression for the functional $\mathscr{K}_n$ originates. We shall present here another proof for which the kernel $\mathscr{K}_n$ is obtained at once in the final form, but which is effective only for the case when the number of degrees of freedom is finite. Evidently, if the number of degrees of freedom is finite, the functional $B(a^*, a)$ is expressed through $A(a^*, a)$ without the help of a limiting operation. We assume the number of degrees of freedom $n$ to be finite and seek an expression for $B$ in the form

$$B(a^*, a) = \int \mathscr{K}(a^*, a \mid \alpha^*, \alpha) A(\alpha^*, \alpha) \, d^n\alpha \, d^n\alpha^*, \qquad (5.26)$$

where $\mathscr{K}$ is an even element of the Grassmann algebra with $4n$ generators $a_k$, $a_k{}^*$, $\alpha_k$, $\alpha_k{}^*$.

We replace the operator $\hat{A}$ by $\hat{a}_k\hat{A}$. Then the operator $\hat{B} = \hat{U}\hat{A}\hat{U}^{-1}$ is replaced by $\hat{U}\hat{a}_k\hat{U}^{-1}\hat{B} = \sum_p (\Phi_{kp}\hat{a}_p + \Psi_{kp}\hat{a}_p{}^*)\hat{B}$, and the functionals $A$ and $B$ by $[(\partial/\partial a_k{}^*) + a_k]A$ and $\sum_p \{\Phi_{kp}[(\partial/\partial a_p{}^*) + a_p] + \Psi_{kp}a_p{}^*\}B$, respectively. Thus we obtain from (5.26) the identity

$$\int \sum_p \left(\Phi_{kp}a_p + \Psi_{kp}a_p{}^* + \Phi_{kp}\frac{\partial}{\partial a_p{}^*}\right)\mathscr{K}A\,d^n\alpha^*\,d^n\alpha$$

$$= \int \mathscr{K}\left(\frac{\partial}{\partial \alpha_k{}^*} + \alpha_k\right)A\,d^n\alpha^*\,d^n\alpha. \quad (5.27)$$

Integrating by parts in the right member of (5.27), we find that identity (5.27) is fulfilled if $\mathscr{K}$ satisfies the equation

$$\sum_p \left(\Phi_{kp}a_p + \Psi_{kp}a_p{}^* + \Phi_{kp}\frac{\partial}{\partial a_p{}^*}\right)\mathscr{K} = \mathscr{K}\left(\frac{\partial}{\partial \alpha_k{}^*} + \alpha_k\right). \quad (5.28)$$

Analogously, by replacing $\hat{A}$ by $\hat{a}_k{}^*\hat{A}$, $\hat{A}\hat{a}_k$ and $\hat{A}\hat{a}_k{}^*$, we obtain for $\mathscr{K}$ three more equations:

$$\sum_p \left(\overline{\Psi}_{kp}a_p + \overline{\Phi}_{kp}a_p{}^* + \overline{\Psi}_{kp}\frac{\partial}{\partial a_p{}^*}\right)\mathscr{K} = \mathscr{K}\alpha_k{}^*,$$

$$\mathscr{K}\sum_p \left(\Phi_{kp}a_p + \Psi_{kp}a_p{}^* + \Psi_{kp}\frac{\partial}{\partial a_p}\right) = \alpha_k\mathscr{K}, \quad (5.28')$$

$$\mathscr{K}\sum_p \left(\overline{\Psi}_{kp}a_p + \overline{\Phi}_{kp}a_p{}^* + \overline{\Phi}_{kp}\frac{\partial}{\partial a_p}\right) = \left(\alpha_k{}^* + \frac{\partial}{\partial \alpha_k}\right)\mathscr{K}$$

(in deriving the last two equations we have used the assumption of the evenness of $\mathscr{K}$).

In addition to equations (5.28), (5.28'), $\mathscr{K}$ satisfies the normalization condition

$$\int \mathscr{K}(a^*, a\,|\,\alpha^*, \alpha)\,d^n\alpha^*\,d^n\alpha = 1, \quad (5.29)$$

which signifies that under the canonical transformation the identity operator goes over into the identity operator.

It is not difficult to show that if equations (5.28), (5.28′) along with the condition (5.29) have a solution, then that solution is unique.[19]

We introduce the new variables $x_k = \sum_p(\Phi_{kp}a_p + \Psi_{kp}a_p{}^*) - \alpha_k$, $x_k{}^* = \sum_p(\Psi_{kp}a_p + \Phi_{kp}a_p{}^*) - \alpha_k{}^*$ and seek $\mathscr{H}$ in the form $\mathscr{H}(a^*, a \,|\, \alpha^*, \alpha) = F(x^*, x)$. It is not difficult to see that the first two equations of (5.28′) are transformed into the following equations for $F$:

$$x_k F + \sum_{p,s} \bar{\Phi}_{kp}\left(\Psi_{sp}\frac{\partial}{\partial x_s} + \Phi_{sp}\frac{\partial}{\partial x_s{}^*}\right)F - \frac{\partial}{\partial x_k{}^*}F = 0,$$

$$x_k{}^* F + \sum_{p,s} \Psi_{kp}\left(\Psi_{sp}\frac{\partial}{\partial x_s} + \Phi_{sp}\frac{\partial}{\partial x_s{}^*}\right)F = 0. \tag{5.30}$$

As for the remaining equations of (5.28′), they are shown to be consequences of these equations.[20]

The solution of equations (5.30) has the form

$$F = c\,\exp[\tfrac{1}{2}(xA_{11}x + 2xA_{12}x^* + x^*A_{22}x^*)].$$

Substituting $F$ into equations (5.30), we obtain for the definition of the matrices $A_{ik}$ four relations, from which we find that

$$A_{11} = \bar{\Phi}\Psi^{-1}, \qquad A_{22} = -\Phi\bar{\Psi}^{-1}, \qquad A_{12} = -E.$$

From the condition (5.29) it is found that the factor $c$ before the exponential is equal to $(\det \Psi\Psi^*)^{1/2}$.

We may carry out the proof of the corresponding theorem for bosons analogously, if the number of degrees of freedom is finite.

Unfortunately this deduction fails to apply to the general case.

---

[19] We denote by $K$ an operator on the operators which is induced by the solution of equations (5.28), (5.28′), (5.29), and by $\mathfrak{U}$ an operator on the operators which is induced by the unitary transformation $\hat{U}$: $\mathfrak{U}(\hat{A}) = \hat{U}\hat{A}\hat{U}^{-1}$. Evidently, the operator $\mathfrak{U}^{-1}K$ commutes with the operators of left and right multiplication by $\hat{a}_k$, $\hat{a}_k{}^*$. One can readily show that the operators of left and right multiplication by $\hat{a}_k$, $\hat{a}_k{}^*$ form an irreducible set in the space of operators. Therefore, $\mathfrak{U}^{-1}K = \lambda E$ or $K = \lambda\mathfrak{U}$. It follows from (5.29) that $\lambda = 1$.

[20] To verify this assertion, one should keep in mind that $(\partial/\partial x_p)F = -F(\partial/\partial x_p)$, because of the evenness of $F$.

8. EXAMPLE. As an example we consider a canonical transformation of an operator to whose normal form there corresponds a functional of the form

$$A = \exp[\tfrac{1}{2}(aA_{11}a + 2aA_{12}a^* + a^*A_{22}a^*)], \qquad A_{ij} = -A'_{ji}. \quad (5.31)$$

The application of formula (5.19) leads in this case to the calculation of the Gauss integral. As a result we obtain

$$B(a^*, a)$$

$$= (\det C)^{1/2} \exp\left[\tfrac{1}{2}(b \quad b^*)\begin{pmatrix} A_{11} & A_{12} \\ -A'_{12} & A_{22} \end{pmatrix} C^{-1} \begin{pmatrix} \Phi & \Psi \\ \Psi & \Phi \end{pmatrix}^{-1} \begin{pmatrix} b \\ b^* \end{pmatrix}\right]. \quad (5.32)$$

where

$$C = \begin{pmatrix} \Phi^* - \Psi'A_{11} & \Psi'(E - A_{12}) \\ \Psi^*(E - A'_{12}) & \Phi' + \Psi^*A_{22} \end{pmatrix},$$

$$b = \Phi a + \Psi a^*, \qquad b^* = \overline{\Psi}a + \overline{\Phi}a^*.$$

We shall not give the calculations, since they simply repeat similar calculations for bosons. We note only that it is necessary in transforming the factor before the exponential to use the fact that the subspace $P_nL$ is even-dimensional.

Formula (5.32) has been derived under the assumption that the operator $\Phi$ is Hermitian and nonnegative, while $\Psi$ has an inverse. Since this formula does not explicitly contain $\Psi^{-1}$, it remains valid for transformations for which $\Psi^{-1}$ does not exist, but which may be obtained from those having $\Psi^{-1}$ by a passage to a limit. It is not difficult to see also that formula (5.32) remains valid in the case when $\Phi$ is not Hermitian but is representable in the form $\Phi = SU$, where $S$ is an Hermitian nonnegative operator and $U$ is a unitary operator such that $U - E$ is a trace-class operator.

In the more general case when $\Phi = (\Phi\Phi^*)^{1/2}U$, $U$ being an arbitrary unitary operator, det $C$ cannot exist, because det $\Phi$ does not exist.

If, however, we replace det $C$ in (5.32) by det $C_1$, where

$$C_1 = \begin{pmatrix} S - \Psi_1'A_{11} & \Psi_1'(E - A_{12}) \\ \Psi_1^*(E - A'_{12}) & S' + \Psi_1^*A_{22} \end{pmatrix},$$

$$S = (\Phi\Phi^*)^{1/2}, \qquad \Psi_1 = \Psi U^{-1},$$

then formula (5.32) thus altered remains valid.

*Chapter III*

# Quadratic Operators

In this chapter operators are investigated which are expressed by creation and annihilation operators in the form of polynomials of at most second degree. Operators reduced to the normal form are studied in Section 6, and those not reduced to the normal form in Section 7. In Section 8 the canonical forms of quadratic operators are found, to which they are reducible by a proper linear canonical transformation.

Restrictions imposed on operator in Section 8 are highly stringent, although it would be very interesting to investigate more fully the reduction of quadratic operators to a canonical form.

It is to be noted that in the case of quadratic operators we meet with phenomena characteristic of operators of a more general type. As every quadratic expression of creation and annihilation operators cannot in general define an operator in the state space, it is possible to convert an operator, by a canonical transformation, into an expression not having an operator meaning, and vice versa. Very simple examples of this type will be considered at the end of Section 7.

The above-mentioned phenomena (in more complicated situations when the operator is not quadratic, but a polynomial of higher degree) are characteristic of field theory. These lead to infinities which are removed by the so-called *renormalizations* of mass and of wave functions. (The renormalization of wave functions is encountered in the Thirring model; cf. Section 9.)

## 6. Quadratic Operators Reduced to Normal Form

1. DEFINITION. As always we denote by $L$ a Hilbert space with involution. Let us realize $L$ in concordance with the involution in the

133

form of the space of square-integrable functions on a set $M$ provided with a measure. Further, let $\mathscr{H}$ be the state space (for bosons or fermions). An operator $\hat{H}$ in $\mathscr{H}$ is said to be quadratic if it has the form

$$\hat{H} = \tfrac{1}{2} \int [A(x, y)\hat{a}^*(x)\hat{a}^*(y) + B(x, y)\hat{a}(x)\hat{a}(y)$$

$$+ 2C(x, y)\hat{a}^*(x)\hat{a}(y)] \, dx \, dy$$

$$+ \int f(x)\hat{a}^*(x) \, dx + \int g(x)\hat{a}(x)dx + k. \tag{6.1}$$

The functions $A$, $B$, $C$ (generally speaking, the generalized functions) are kernels of operators in the space $L$, which we shall denote by the same letters; $f$ and $g$ are certain functions on $M$ and $k$ is a constant. If $k = f = g = 0$, the operator $\hat{H}$ will be called *homogeneous quadratic*. $\hat{a}^*$ and $\hat{a}$ in (6.1) and throughout all sections signify creation and annihilation operators for bosons or fermions.

We shall always assume that $A(x, y) = A(y, x)$, $B(x, y) = B(y, x)$ in the Bose case and that $A(x, y) = -A(y, x)$, $B(x, y) = -B(y, x)$ in the Fermi case. Passing from the kernels $A(x, y)$, $B(x, y)$ to the operators $A$, $B$, these equalities then mean that $A = A'$, $B = B'$ in the Bose case and $A = -A'$, $B = -B'$ in the Fermi case.

If (6.1) is a normal form, then the operator $\hat{H}$ will be called a *quadratic normal form*.

We recall that the vacuum vector $\hat{\Phi}_0$ is contained in the domain of definition of an operator in the normal form.

Let $\hat{H}$ be a quadratic normal form. Applying the operator $\hat{H}$ to $\hat{\Phi}_0$ we obtain

$$\hat{H}\hat{\Phi}_0 = \left[ \tfrac{1}{2} \int A(x, y)\hat{a}^*(x)\hat{a}^*(y) \, dx \, dy \right.$$

$$+ \left. \int f(x)\hat{a}^*(x) \, dx + k \right]\Phi_0. \tag{6.2}$$

Since $\hat{H}\hat{\Phi}_0 \in \mathscr{H}$, it follows from (6.2) that $\int |A(x, y)|^2 \, dx \, dy < \infty$ and $\int |f(x)|^2 \, dx < \infty$. In other words, $A$ is a Hilbert-Schmidt operator and $f \in L$.

2. SELF-ADJOINT QUADRATIC OPERATORS. We shall give one more definition. Let $\hat{H}$ be a formal series of operators $\hat{a}(x)$, $\hat{a}^*(x)$:

$$\hat{H} = \sum \int K(x_1^{(1)},\ldots, x_{n_1}^{(1)} \mid x_1^{(2)},\ldots, x_{n_2}^{(2)} \mid \ldots \mid x_1^{(p)},\ldots, x_{n_p}^{(p)})$$

$$\times \hat{a}^*(x_1^{(1)}) \cdots \hat{a}^*(x_{n_1}^{(1)}) \hat{a}(x_1^{(2)}) \cdots \hat{a}^*(x_{n_p}^{(p)})$$

$$\times d^{n_1 + \cdots + n_p} x_1^{(1)} \cdots x_{n_p}^{(p)},$$

where $K(x_1^{(1)},\ldots, x_{n_p}^{(p)})$ are generalized functions. Regarding $\hat{H}$ as an operator, we apply it to a vector $\hat{\Phi} \in \mathcal{H}$.

As a result we obtain a formal expression of the form

$$\hat{\Phi}' = \sum_n \frac{1}{(n!)^{1/2}} \int K_n(x_1,\ldots, x_n)\hat{a}^*(x_1) \cdots \hat{a}^*(x_n)\, d^n x\, \hat{\Phi}_0.$$

The set $D_{\hat{H}}$ consisting of vectors $\hat{\Phi} \in \mathcal{H}$, for which $K_n(x_1,\ldots, x_n)$ are square-integrable functions satisfying the condition $\sum_n \int |K_n|^2\, d^n x < \infty$, is called the *natural domain of definition of $\hat{H}$*.

Generally speaking, we may suppose that $D_{\hat{H}}$ consists only of the zero vector. In this case $\hat{H}$ does not have the meaning of an operator.

We return now to the quadratic operator. Evidently, if $\hat{H}$ is a self-adjoint operator of the form (6.1), then $B = A^*$, $C$ is an Hermitian operator, and $g = f^*$.

It turns out that these conditions are sufficient for the self-adjointness of the quadratic normal form.

**Theorem 6.1.** *Let $A$ be a Hilbert-Schmidt operator in $L$, $C = C^*$ an Hermitian operator in $L$, and $f \in L$. Then*
(1) *The operator*

$$\hat{H} = \tfrac{1}{2} \int [A(x, y)\hat{a}^*(x)\hat{a}^*(y) + \bar{A}(y, x)\hat{a}(x)\hat{a}(y)$$

$$+ 2C(x, y)\hat{a}^*(x)\hat{a}(y)]\, dx\, dy$$

$$+ \int f(x)\hat{a}^*(x)\, dx + \int f^*(x)\hat{a}(x)\, dx, \qquad (6.3)$$

*considered on the natural domain of definition, is self-adjoint.*

(2) *The operator $\hat{H}$, considered on the set of finite vectors entering into the domain of definition of the operator $\hat{C} = \int C(x, y)\hat{a}^*(x)\hat{a}(y)\, dx\, dy$, is symmetric and has the deficiency indices (0, 0).*

We shall limit ourselves to the proof of the second assertion, since the first assertion follows from this in an obvious way. We note first of all that the operator

$$\hat{C} = \int C(x, y)\hat{a}^*(x)\hat{a}(y)\, dx\, dy$$

has the diagonal matrix form

$$\hat{C} = \begin{pmatrix} 0 & & & \\ & C_1 & 0 & \\ & & C_2 & \\ & 0 & & \\ & & & \end{pmatrix}$$

The operators $C_n$ are defined in a natural way on the set $D \cap \mathcal{H}^n$, where $D$ is the domain of definition of $\hat{H}$ described in the condition of the theorem. We shall show that the operators $C_n$ are self-adjoint.

According to a theorem on spectral types, the space $L$ may be realized by means of square-integrable functions in such a way that the operator $C$ should be an operator involving multiplication by a function. We denote this function by $c(x)$ and will assume that the space $L$ is realized in the indicated way. In this realization $C_n$ is the operation of multiplying by $c(x_1) + \cdots + c(x_n)$. Hence the self-adjointness of the operator $C_n$ follows.

We consider the matrix of the operator $\hat{H}$. It can be readily seen that it has the form

$$K = \begin{pmatrix} 0 & f_1^* & A_1^* & 0 & 0 & 0 & \cdots \\ f_1 & C_1 & f_2^* & A_2^* & 0 & 0 & \cdots \\ A_1 & f_2 & C_2 & f_3^* & A_3^* & 0 & \cdots \\ 0 & A_2 & f_3 & C_3 & f_4^* & A_4^* & \cdots \\ & & & & & & \end{pmatrix}. \tag{6.4}$$

As remarked above, the $C_n$ are self-adjoint operators.

The matrix $K$ is close in form to the Jacobi matrix. Therefore, without making more precise the form of the operators $f_n$, $A_n$, being elements of $K$, we can prove, following Carleman,[1] the following lemma.

**Lemma 6.1.** *In order that the operator given by the matrix $K$ on finite vectors entering into the domain of definition of the operator $C$ have null deficiency indices, it is sufficient that*

$$\sum_n [\max(\|A_n\|, \|A_{n+1}\|, \|f_{n+1}\|)]^{-1} = \infty. \tag{6.5}$$

The adjoint of the operator of which we have spoken in the condition of the lemma is also given by the matrix (6.4), but this time its domain of definition consists of all vectors that the matrix $K$ does not transform out of the Hilbert space. Therefore the lemma will be proved if we verify that from (6.5) and the condition

$$K\hat{\Phi} = z\hat{\Phi}, \qquad \text{Im } z \neq 0, \qquad (\hat{\Phi}, \hat{\Phi}) < \infty \tag{6.6}$$

it follows that $\hat{\Phi} = 0$.

Let

$$\hat{\Phi} = \begin{pmatrix} \Phi_0 \\ \Phi_1 \\ \Phi_2 \\ \vdots \end{pmatrix}$$

The equation $K\hat{\Phi} = z\hat{\Phi}$ gives

$$z\Phi_k = A_{k-1}\Phi_{k-2} + f_k\Phi_{k-1} + C_k\Phi_k + f_{k+1}^*\Phi_{k+1} + A_{k+1}^*\Phi_{k+2}.$$

Taking the inner products of this equality by $\Phi_k$ from the right and left, and subtracting them, we obtain

$$(z - \bar{z})(\Phi_k, \Phi_k) = (A_{k-1}\Phi_{k-2}, \Phi_k) + (f_k\Phi_{k-1}, \Phi_k)$$
$$+ (f_{k+1}^*\Phi_{k+1}, \Phi_k) + (A_{k+1}^*\Phi_{k+2}, \Phi_k)$$
$$- (\Phi_k, A_{k-1}\Phi_{k-2}) - (\Phi_k, f_k\Phi_{k-1})$$
$$- (\Phi_k, f_{k+1}^*\Phi_{k+1}) - (\Phi_k, A_{k+1}^*\Phi_{k+2}). \tag{6.7}$$

---

[1] Cf. Carleman [1] or Ahiezer [1].

[The term $(C_k \Phi_k, \Phi_k)$ cancels due to the self-adjointness of $C_k$.] Further we have, from (6.7),

$$
(z - \bar{z}) \sum_{k=0}^{n} (\Phi_k, \Phi_k) = (A_n^* \Phi_{n+1}, \Phi_{n-1}) + (A_{n+1}^* \Phi_{n+2}, \Phi_n)
$$
$$
- (A_n \Phi_{n-1}, \Phi_{n+1}) - (A_{n+1} \Phi_n, \Phi_{n+2})
$$
$$
+ (f_{n+1}^* \Phi_{n+1}, \Phi_n) - (f_{n+1} \Phi_n, \Phi_{n+1}).
$$

Hence

$$
2|\operatorname{Im} z| \sum_{k=0}^{n} (\Phi_k, \Phi_k) \leq \max(\|A_n\|, \|A_{n+1}\|, \|f_{n+1}\|)
$$
$$
\times (\|\Phi_{n-1}\|^2 + \|\Phi_{n+2}\|^2 + 2\|\Phi_n\|^2 + 2\|\Phi_{n+1}\|^2).
$$

If $\hat{\Phi} \neq 0$, then there exists an $n_0$ such that $\sum_{k=0}^{n_0} (\Phi_k, \Phi_k) = c > 0$. As a consequence, for $n \geq n_0$,

$$
\|\Phi_{n-1}\|^2 + \|\Phi_{n+2}\|^2 + 2\|\Phi_n\|^2 + 2\|\Phi_{n+1}\|^2
$$
$$
> \frac{2|\operatorname{Im} z|c}{\max(\|A_n\|, \|A_{n+1}\|, \|f_{n+1}\|)}. \quad (6.8)
$$

Summing in the limits from $n_0$ to $N$ and supplementing the left member by the missing terms, we obtain

$$
6 \sum_{n=n_0}^{N} \|\Phi_n\|^2 > 2c |\operatorname{Im} z| \sum_{n=n_0}^{N} [\max(\|A_n\|, \|A_{n+1}\|, \|f_{n+1}\|)]^{-1}.
$$

Thus, if (6.5) is fulfilled, $\sum_n \|\Phi_n\|^2 = \infty$. The lemma is proved.

To apply this lemma to the proof of the theorem we have to estimate $\|A_n\|$ and $\|f_n\|$. Passing to the functionals, we obtain that the integrals $\int A(x, y) \hat{a}^*(x) \hat{a}^*(y) \, dx \, dy$ and $\int f(x) \hat{a}^*(x) \, dx$ are the operators of multiplication by $\int A(x, y) a^*(x) a^*(y) \, dx \, dy$ and $\int f(x) a^*(x) \, dx$, respectively. Hence it is easily found that

$$
\|A_n\| \leq [n(n + 1)]^{1/2} \|A\|_2, \qquad \|f_n\| \leq n^{1/2} \|f\|,
$$

where

$$
\|A\|_2 = \left( \int |A(x, y)|^2 \, dx \, dy \right)^{1/2}, \qquad \|f\| = \left( \int |f(x)|^2 \, dx \right)^{1/2}.
$$

Thus the condition (6.5) is satisfied. The theorem is proved.

3. NORMAL FORM OF THE OPERATOR $e^{it\hat{H}}$. BOSE CASE. Let $\hat{H}$ be a self-adjoint quadratic operator. The operator $e^{it\hat{H}}$ is unitary, and accordingly it is bounded and reducible to the normal form. Before formulating a fundamental theorem on the normal form of the operator $e^{it\hat{H}}$, we shall prove some auxiliary propositions.

**Lemma 6.2.** *Let an operator $A$ in a Hilbert space $H$ have the form $A = S + T$, where $S$ is a self-adjoint operator and $T$ a bounded operator. Then*

*(1) There exists a bounded operator $U(t) = e^{itA}$ which is a solution of the equation*

$$\frac{1}{i}\frac{dU}{dt} = UA \qquad (6.9)$$

*with the initial condition $U(0) = E$, and moreover this solution is unique within the class of bounded operators.*

*(2) If*

$$W(t) = \int_0^t e^{i\tau S} T e^{-i\tau S}\, d\tau$$

*is a Hilbert-Schmidt operator and the function*

$$\rho(t) = [\mathrm{Sp}\ W(t)W^*(t)]^{1/2}$$

*is locally integrable, then*

$$e^{it(S+T)} = e^{itS} + K,$$

*where $K$ is a Hilbert-Schmidt operator.*

Consider the operator $V(t) = U(t)e^{-itS}$. It is easy to see that the first assertion of the lemma will be proved if we verify that $V(t)$ is the unique solution, within the class of bounded operators, of the equation

$$\frac{1}{i}\frac{dV}{dt} = V(t)T(t), \qquad (6.10)$$

with the initial condition $V(0) = E$. Here $T(t)$ denotes the operator $T(t) = e^{itS}Te^{-itS}$. Because of the initial condition $V(0) = E$, we obtain from (6.10) the integral equation

$$V(t) = E + i\int_0^t V(\tau)T(\tau)\, d\tau. \qquad (6.11)$$

The uniqueness of the solution of this equation within the class of bounded operators is proved by standard arguments.

We represent the solution of equation (6.11) in the form of a series of successive approximations:

$$V(t) = \sum V_n(t),$$

$$V_n(t) = i \int_0^i V_{n-1}(\tau)T(\tau)\,d\tau, \qquad V_0 = E. \tag{6.12}$$

We note that

$$\|T(\tau)\| = \|T\|. \tag{6.13}$$

By making use of (6.13) we obtain for $\|V_n\|$ the inequality

$$\|V_n(t)\| \leq \|T\| \int_0^t \|V_{n-1}(\tau)\|\,d\tau. \tag{6.14}$$

From (6.14), on account of $V_0 = E$ and hence $\|V_0\| = 1$, we obtain

$$\|V_n(t)\| \leq \frac{t^n \|T\|^n}{n!}.$$

Thus the series $\sum_n V_n(t)$ converges in norm and we obtain for the norm of its sum the estimate

$$\|V(t)\| \leq e^{t\|T\|}. \tag{6.15}$$

Evidently, the constructed operator $V(t)$ satisfies equation (6.11) and accordingly the differential equation (6.10) with the initial condition $V(0) = E$.

We remark that it follows from the uniqueness of the solution of equation (6.9) under the initial condition $U(0) = E$ that $U(t) = e^{itA}$ has all the usual properties of an exponential.

We proceed to the second assertion of the lemma. Let $K$ be a Hilbert-Schmidt operator, and $\|K\|_2 = (\operatorname{Sp} KK^*)^{1/2}$. Returning to (6.12) we find that

$$\|V_1(t)\|_2 = [\operatorname{Sp} W(t)W^*(t)]^{1/2} = \rho(t),$$

and for $n \geq 2$

$$\|V_n(t)\|_2 \leq \|T\| \int_0^t \|V_{n-1}(\tau)\|_2\,d\tau. \tag{6.16}$$

Hence

$$\|V_n(t)\|_2 \le \|T\|^{n-1} \int_0^t \frac{(t-\tau)^{n-2}}{(n-2)!}\, \rho(\tau)\, d\tau, \qquad n \ge 2. \qquad (6.17)$$

Thus $V(t) = E + K_1$, where $K_1 = \sum_{n=1}^\infty V_n(t)$ and

$$V(t) = E + K_1, \qquad \text{where} \quad K_1 = \sum_{n=1}^\infty V_n(t).$$

Passing to the operator $e^{it(S+T)}$, it is found that $e^{it(S+T)} = (E + K_1)e^{itS} = e^{itS} + K$, $K$ being a Hilbert-Schmidt operator. The lemma is completely proved.

**Lemma 6.3.** *Let $C = C^*$ be a self-adjoint operator in a Hilbert space $L$ with involution and let $A = A'$ be a bounded operator having the property that*

$$F(t) = \int_0^t \exp[-iC\tau]\, A \exp[-i\bar{C}\tau]\, d\tau \qquad (6.18)$$

*is a Hilbert-Schmidt operator and the function $\rho(t) = [\mathrm{Sp}\, F(t)F^*(t)]^{1/2}$ is locally integrable. Consider in the Hilbert space $\mathscr{E} = L \oplus L^*$ an operator given by the matrix*

$$\mathscr{A} = \begin{pmatrix} -C & -A \\ \bar{A} & \bar{C} \end{pmatrix}.$$

*Then the operator $e^{it\mathscr{A}}$ exists and has the matrix $\begin{pmatrix} \Phi & \Psi \\ \bar{\Psi} & \bar{\Phi} \end{pmatrix}$, which is the matrix of a proper Bose canonical transformation.*

The existence of $e^{it\mathscr{A}}$ follows obviously from Lemma 6.2.

We shall show that $e^{it\mathscr{A}}$ is the matrix of a canonical transformation. Consider the matrix $I = \begin{pmatrix} 0 & E \\ -E & 0 \end{pmatrix}$. It is easy to see that $I\mathscr{A}' + \mathscr{A}I = 0$. By the use of this identity, we find

$$\frac{d}{dt}\, e^{it\mathscr{A}} I\, e^{it\mathscr{A}'} = 0.$$

Consequently,

$$I(t) = e^{it\mathscr{A}} I\, e^{it\mathscr{A}'} = I(0) = I.$$

Since $e^{it\mathscr{A}'} = (e^{it\mathscr{A}})'$ and the matrix $e^{it\mathscr{A}}$ has a two-sided inverse, $e^{it\mathscr{A}}$ is the matrix of a canonical transformation according to Section 4.2.

Using the second assertion of Lemma 6.2 we find that $e^{it\mathscr{A}}$ $= \exp\left[it\left(\begin{smallmatrix} -C & 0 \\ 0 & C \end{smallmatrix}\right)\right] + K$, where $K$ is a Hilbert-Schmidt operator. Evidently $K = \left(\begin{smallmatrix} \Phi_1 & \Psi \\ \bar{\Psi} & \bar{\Phi}_1 \end{smallmatrix}\right)$ with $\Phi_1 = \Phi - e^{-itC}$. As a consequence, $\Psi$ is a Hilbert-Schmidt operator and hence $e^{it\mathscr{A}}$ is the matrix of a proper canonical transformation.

**Lemma 6.4.** *Let $A$ and $C$ be the same as in Lemma 6.3, and in addition to the condition of Lemma 6.3, let $F(t)\bar{A}$ be a trace-class operator, for which $\rho_1(t) = \mathrm{Sp}\,\{F(t)\bar{A}[F(t)\bar{A}]^*\}^{1/2}$ is locally integrable. Then the operator $\Phi e^{itC} - E$ is of trace class.*

Let

$$V(t) = \begin{pmatrix} E + \tilde{\Phi}(t) & \tilde{\Psi}(t) \\ \bar{\tilde{\Psi}}(t) & E + \bar{\tilde{\Phi}}(t) \end{pmatrix} = e^{it(S+T)}\, e^{-itS},$$

where

$$S = \begin{pmatrix} -C & 0 \\ 0 & C \end{pmatrix}, \qquad T = \begin{pmatrix} 0 & -A \\ \bar{A} & 0 \end{pmatrix}.$$

We turn back to the method of successive approximations (6.12) determining $V(t)$. For elements

$$V_n(t) = \begin{pmatrix} E + \tilde{\Phi}_n & \tilde{\Psi}_n \\ \bar{\tilde{\Psi}}_n & E + \bar{\tilde{\Phi}}_n \end{pmatrix}$$

we obtain the recursion formulas

$$\tilde{\Phi}_n(t) = i \int_0^t \tilde{\Psi}_{n-1}(\tau)\bar{A}(\tau)\, d\tau,$$

$$\tilde{\Psi}_n(t) = i \int_0^t \tilde{\Phi}_{n-1}(\tau)A(\tau)\, d\tau, \qquad (6.19)$$

$$\tilde{\Phi}_1(t) \equiv 0, \qquad \tilde{\Psi}_1(t) = i \int_0^t A(\tau)\, d\tau,$$

where $A(\tau) = e^{-i\tau C}Ae^{-i\tau C}$ and $\bar{A}(\tau) = e^{i\tau C}\bar{A}e^{i\tau C}$. Let $\|K\|_1 = \mathrm{Sp}(KK^*)^{1/2}$. From (6.19) and (6.18) it is immediately obvious that $\tilde{\Psi}_1(t) = iF(t)$, $\tilde{\Psi}_2(t) \equiv 0$, $\Phi_2(t) = -\int_0^t F(\tau)\bar{A}(\tau)\, d\tau$, and consequently,

$$\|\tilde{\Phi}_2(t)\|_1 \le \int_0^t \rho_1(\tau)\, d\tau = \rho_2(t).$$

For $n > 2$, using the well-known inequality $\|KQ\|_1 \leq \|K\|_1 \|Q\|$, we obtain the estimate

$$\|\tilde{\Phi}_n(t)\|_1 \leq \|A\| \int_0^t \|\Psi_{n-1}(\tau)\|_1 \, d\tau, \qquad \|\Psi_n(t)\|_1 \leq \|A\| \int_0^t \|\Phi_{n-1}(\tau)\|_1 \, d\tau.$$

Hence

$$\|\tilde{\Phi}_n(t)\|_1 \leq \|A\|^{n-2} \int_0^t \frac{(t-\tau)^{n-3}}{(n-3)!} \, \rho_2(\tau) \, d\tau.$$

Consequently, $\tilde{\Phi}$ is a trace-class operator.

We now formulate a fundamental theorem.

**Theorem 6.2.** *Let*

$$\hat{H} = \tfrac{1}{2} \int (\hat{a}^* A \hat{a}^* + \hat{a} \bar{A} \hat{a} + 2\hat{a}^* C \hat{a}) \, dx \, dy$$

$$+ \int (\hat{a}^* f + f^* \hat{a}) \, dx \tag{6.20}$$

*be a self-adjoint quadratic normal form. Further, let*

$$\mathscr{A} = \begin{pmatrix} -C & -A \\ \bar{A} & C \end{pmatrix} \quad and \quad e^{it\mathscr{A}} = \begin{pmatrix} \Phi & \Psi \\ \bar{\Psi} & \bar{\Phi} \end{pmatrix}.$$

*Then the operator $e^{it\hat{H}}$ has its normal and matrix forms, to which there correspond the functionals*[2]

$$U(a^*, a) = \tilde{U}(a^*, a)e^{-a^*a}, \tag{6.21}$$

$$\tilde{U}(a^*, a) = c \exp\left[ \tfrac{1}{2}(a \quad a^*) \begin{pmatrix} \bar{\Psi}\bar{\Phi}^{-1} & \Phi'^{-1} \\ \Phi^{-1} & -\Phi^{-1}\Psi \end{pmatrix} \begin{pmatrix} a \\ a^* \end{pmatrix} \right.$$

$$\left. + a(g^* - \bar{\Psi}\bar{\Phi}^{-1}g) - a^*\Phi^{-1}g \right], \tag{6.22}$$

*where*

$$c = (\det \Phi e^{iCt})^{-1/2} \exp\left[ i \int_0^t (g\Phi'^{-1}\bar{A}\Phi^{-1}g - f^*\Phi^{-1}g) \, d\tau \right], \tag{6.23}$$

$$\begin{pmatrix} g \\ g^* \end{pmatrix} = i \int_0^t \exp\left[ i\tau \begin{pmatrix} -C & -A \\ \bar{A} & C \end{pmatrix} \right] d\tau \begin{pmatrix} -f \\ f^* \end{pmatrix}. \tag{6.24}$$

[2] The determinant in (6.23) exists, since in view of Lemma 6.4 the operator $\Phi e^{itC} - E$ is of trace class.

*Proof.* Comparing formulas (6.22) and (4.26), we find that there corresponds to the functional (6.22) an operator $\hat{U}$ which is unitary up to a factor. It is sufficient to verify that $\hat{U}$ satisfies the equation

$$\frac{1}{i}\frac{d\hat{U}}{dt} = \hat{H}\hat{U} \tag{6.25}$$

and the initial condition $\hat{U}(0) = E$. The initial condition follows from (6.22)–(6.24) in an obvious way. To verify equation (6.25) one should take into account that in view of (1.22) it is equivalent to the following equation for the functional $\tilde{U}$ corresponding to the matrix form of the operator $\hat{U}$:

$$\frac{1}{i}\frac{d\tilde{U}}{dt} = \left[\frac{1}{2}\left(a^*Aa^* + \frac{\delta}{\delta a^*}\,\bar{A}\,\frac{\delta}{\delta a^*} + 2a^*C\frac{\delta}{\delta a^*}\right)\right.$$

$$\left. + fa^* + f^*\frac{\delta}{\delta a^*}\right]\tilde{U}. \tag{6.26}$$

The corresponding calculations are very unwieldy, although the idea is simple. We shall omit them, but in the next subsection we shall give an alternative proof which bypasses these calculations.

4. ANOTHER PROOF OF THEOREM 6.2. We consider a proof of Theorem 6.2 which is not completely rigorous, but leads at once to formulas (6.22)–(6.24).

We shall show that the operator $\hat{U}(t) = e^{it\hat{H}}$ generates a linear canonical transformation. Consider the operators

$$\hat{a}(\varphi, t) = e^{it\hat{H}}\hat{a}(\varphi)e^{-it\hat{H}},$$

$$\hat{a}^*(\varphi, t) = e^{it\hat{H}}\hat{a}^*(\varphi)e^{-it\hat{H}}. \tag{6.27}$$

Differentiating with respect to $t$, it is found that $\hat{a}(\varphi, t)$, $\hat{a}^*(\varphi, t)$ satisfy the equations

$$\frac{1}{i}\frac{d\hat{a}(\varphi, t)}{dt} = [\hat{H}, \hat{a}(\varphi, t)],$$

$$\frac{1}{i}\frac{d\hat{a}^*(\varphi, t)}{dt} = [\hat{H}, \hat{a}^*(\varphi, t)]. \tag{6.28}$$

Let

$$\hat{A} = \sum_{m,n} \int K_{mn}(x_1,\ldots, x_m \,|\, y_1,\ldots, y_n)$$

$$\times \, \hat{a}^*(x_1) \cdots \hat{a}^*(x_m)\hat{a}(y_1) \cdots \hat{a}(y_n) \, d^m x \, d^n y$$

be an arbitrary operator in the normal form. We denote by $\hat{A}(t)$ the operator

$$\hat{A}(t) = \sum_{m,n} \int K_{mn}(x_1,\ldots, x_m \,|\, y_1,\ldots, y_n)$$

$$\times \, \hat{a}^*(x_1, t) \cdots \hat{a}^*(x_m, t)\hat{a}(y_1, t) \cdots \hat{a}(y_n, t) \, d^m x \, d^n y,$$

where $\hat{a}(x, t)$, $\hat{a}^*(x, t)$ are defined by formula (6.27). Evidently $\hat{A}(t) = e^{it\hat{H}}\hat{A}e^{-it\hat{H}}$. We consider, in particular, the operator $\hat{A} = \hat{H}$. It is evident that $\hat{H}(t) = e^{it\hat{H}}\hat{H}e^{-it\hat{H}} = \hat{H}$.

By making use of this fact, we substitute in (6.28) the operator $\hat{H}(t)$ instead of $\hat{H}$. Evidently the operators $\hat{a}(\varphi, t)$, $\hat{a}^*(\varphi, t)$ satisfy one and the same commutation relations for all $t$. Therefore, we can accomplish the commutation in the right members of (6.28). As a result we obtain finally the system of equations

$$\frac{1}{i}\frac{d}{dt}\hat{a}(\varphi) = -\hat{a}(\varphi C) - \hat{a}^*(\varphi A) - \varphi f,$$

$$\frac{1}{i}\frac{d}{dt}\hat{a}^*(\varphi) = \hat{a}(\varphi \bar{A}) + \hat{a}^*(\varphi \bar{C}) + \varphi f^*. \tag{6.29}$$

Integrating this system, we find

$$\hat{a}(\varphi, t) = \hat{a}(\varphi \Phi) + \hat{a}^*(\varphi \Psi) + \varphi g,$$

$$\hat{a}^*(\varphi, t) = \hat{a}(\varphi \bar{\Psi}) + \hat{a}^*(\varphi \bar{\Phi}) + \varphi g^*, \tag{6.30}$$

where

$$\begin{pmatrix} \Phi & \Psi \\ \bar{\Psi} & \bar{\Phi} \end{pmatrix} = \exp\left[it\begin{pmatrix} -C & -A \\ \bar{A} & \bar{C} \end{pmatrix}\right],$$

$$\begin{pmatrix} g \\ g^* \end{pmatrix} = i\int_0^t \exp\left[i\tau\begin{pmatrix} -C & -A \\ \bar{A} & \bar{C} \end{pmatrix}\right] d\tau \begin{pmatrix} -f \\ f^* \end{pmatrix}.$$

Thus (6.27) is a linear canonical transformation. Therefore the functional $\tilde{U}(a^*, a)$, corresponding to the matrix form of the operator $\hat{U} = e^{it\hat{H}}$ up to a factor independent of $a$, $a^*$, is defined by formula

(4.26). Thus we have obtained for $\tilde{U}(a^*, a)$ the formula (6.22) with a coefficient $c$ which is not yet determined. In order to find $c$, we substitute (6.22) into equation (6.26) and put $a = a^* = 0$.

As a result we obtain

$$\frac{1}{i}\frac{dc}{dt} = (-\tfrac{1}{2}\,\text{Sp}\,\Phi^{-1}\Psi\bar{A} + g\Phi'^{-1}\bar{A}\Phi^{-1}g - f^*\Phi^{-1}g)c.$$

We set

$$c = c_1 \exp\left[i\int_0^t (g\Phi'^{-1}\bar{A}\Phi^{-1}g - f^*\Phi^{-1}g)\,d\tau\right].$$

Then the equation for $c_1$,

$$\frac{1}{i}\frac{dc_1}{dt} = -\tfrac{1}{2}\,\text{Sp}(\Phi^{-1}\Psi\bar{A})c_1, \tag{6.31}$$

is obtained. We shall seek $c_1$ in the form $c_1 = (\det M)^{-1/2}$. From the formula $\det M = e^{\text{Sp}\,\ln M}$ it is found that

$$\frac{d}{dt}\det M = \text{Sp}\left(\frac{d}{dt}\ln M\right)\det M = \text{Sp}\left(M^{-1}\frac{dM}{dt}\right)\det M.$$

Thus we obtain for the operator $M$ the equation

$$\frac{1}{i}\,\text{Sp}\,M^{-1}\frac{dM}{dt} = \text{Sp}\,\Phi^{-1}\Psi\bar{A}. \tag{6.32}$$

Recalling that the operators $\Phi$, $\Psi$ are the solution of the equation

$$\frac{1}{i}\frac{d}{dt}\begin{pmatrix}\Phi & \Psi \\ \Psi & \Phi\end{pmatrix} = \begin{pmatrix}\Phi & \Psi \\ \Psi & \Phi\end{pmatrix}\begin{pmatrix}-C & -A \\ \bar{A} & \bar{C}\end{pmatrix}, \tag{6.33}$$

we have

$$\frac{1}{i}\Phi^{-1}\frac{d\Phi}{dt} = -C + \Phi^{-1}\Psi\bar{A}. \tag{6.34}$$

We now set $M = \Phi e^{itC}$. In view of (6.34) it turns out that the $M$ satisfies Eq. (6.32). Thus

$$c_1 = (\det \Phi e^{itC})^{-1/2}, \tag{6.35}$$

$$c = (\det \Phi e^{itC})^{-1/2} \exp i\int_0^t (g\Phi'^{-1}\bar{A}\Phi^{-1}g - f^*\Phi^{-1}g)\,d\tau. \tag{6.36}$$

5. NORMAL FORM OF THE OPERATOR $\hat{U}(t) = e^{it\hat{H}}$. FERMI CASE. Before formulating a fundamental theorem of this subsection, we note the following lemma.

**Lemma 6.5.** *Let $C$ be a self-adjoint operator in a Hilbert space $L$ with involution and let $A = -A'$ be a skew-symmetric operator having the property that the operator*

$$F(t) = \int_0^t e^{-iC\tau} A e^{-i\bar{C}\tau} \, d\tau$$

*is a Hilbert-Schmidt operator, let $F(t)\bar{A}$ be a trace-class operator, and let $\rho(t) = [\mathrm{Sp}\, A(t)A^*(t)]^{1/2}$ and $\rho_1(t) = \mathrm{Sp}\,\{F(t)\bar{A}[F(t)\bar{A}]^*\}^{1/2}$ be locally integrable. Consider in the Hilbert space $\mathscr{E} = L \oplus L^*$ the operator*

$$\mathscr{A} = \begin{pmatrix} -C & -A \\ \bar{A} & \bar{C} \end{pmatrix}.$$

*Then*

(1) *There exists the operator $e^{it\mathscr{A}} = \begin{pmatrix} \Phi & \Psi \\ \bar{\Psi} & \bar{\Phi} \end{pmatrix}$ and, moreover, $e^{it\mathscr{A}}$ is the matrix of a proper Fermi canonical transformation.*

(2) *The operator $\Phi e^{itC} - E$ is of trace class.*

The proof of this lemma is not different in its essentials from that of Lemmas 6.3 and 6.4. We now formulate a theorem.

**Theorem 6.3.** *Let*

$$\hat{H} = \tfrac{1}{2} \int (\hat{a}^* A \hat{a}^* - \hat{a} \bar{A} \hat{a} + 2\hat{a}^* C \hat{a}) \, dx \, dy \tag{6.37}$$

*be a self-adjoint quadratic normal form. Then the normal and matrix forms of the operator $\hat{U} = e^{it\hat{H}}$ are given by the formulas*

$$U(a^*, a) = \tilde{U}(a^*, a)e^{-a^*a},$$

$$\tilde{U}(a^*, a) = (\det \Phi e^{iCt})^{1/2}$$

$$\times \exp\left[ -\tfrac{1}{2}(a \quad a^*) \begin{pmatrix} \bar{\Psi}\Phi^{-1} & \Phi'^{-1} \\ -\Phi^{-1} & \Phi^{-1}\Psi \end{pmatrix} \begin{pmatrix} a \\ a^* \end{pmatrix} \right], \tag{6.38}$$

*where the operators $\Phi$, $\Psi$ are defined by the equation*

$$\begin{pmatrix} \Phi & \Psi \\ \bar{\Psi} & \bar{\Phi} \end{pmatrix} = \exp\left[ it \begin{pmatrix} -C & -A \\ \bar{A} & \bar{C} \end{pmatrix} \right]. \tag{6.39}$$

Formula (6.38) is valid under the condition that the operator $\Phi^{-1}$ exists. In the case when $\Phi^{-1}$ does not exist, but the transformation $\begin{pmatrix} \Phi & \Psi \\ \bar{\Psi} & \bar{\Phi} \end{pmatrix}$ possesses the property A, the corresponding formula may be obtained from (6.38) by a passage to a limit. The proof of Theorem 6.3 differs from that of Theorem 6.2 only by the simplification connected with the homogeneity of the operator $\hat{H}$.

6. RESOLVENT OF A QUADRATIC OPERATOR. Let $\hat{H}$ be the simplest quadratic operator $\hat{H} = \hat{a}^{*}C\hat{a}$. There corresponds to the matrix form of the resolvent of the operator $\hat{H}$ the functional

$$\tilde{R}(z) = \int_{0}^{1} \exp(a^{*}\xi^{C}a)\xi^{-z-1}\, d\xi \qquad \text{Im } z \neq 0. \qquad (6.40)$$

Formula (6.40) holds equally for fermions and for bosons.

For the proof we realize the space $L$ in such a way that the operator $C$ is an operator of multiplication by a function, and then expand the functional (6.40) into a series, when we can immediately confirm the validity of formula (6.40).

## 7. Quadratic Operators Not Reduced to Normal Form

We consider the formal expression

$$\hat{H} = \tfrac{1}{2} \int [A(x, y)\hat{a}^{*}(x)\hat{a}^{*}(y) + \bar{A}(y, x)\hat{a}(x)\hat{a}(y)$$
$$+ 2C(x, y)\hat{a}^{*}(x)\hat{a}(y)]\, dx\, dy$$
$$+ \int (f(x)\hat{a}^{*}(x) + f^{*}(x)\hat{a}(x))\, dx + k. \qquad (7.1)$$

Here $A(x, y)$ and $C(x, y)$ are generalized functions serving as kernels of operators $A$ and $C$ in the space $L$, $C$ being a self-adjoint operator, $f(x)$ a generalized function, and $k$ a constant. $f(x) \equiv 0$ in the Fermi case.

We shall always assume that there exists in $L$ a dense domain $\Delta$ invariant with respect to the involution, on which the operators $C$, $A$, $\bar{A}$ are defined and the generalized function $f$ gives a linear functional $(f, g^{*}), g \in \Delta$.

In this section we discover conditions for the existence of a dense domain in the state space, on which the operator given by formula (7.1) is defined as a self-adjoint operator.

1. NECESSARY CONDITIONS. We consider the differential equations for the functions $a(x, t)$, $a^*(x, t)$ which are square-integrable with respect to $x$,[3]

$$\frac{1}{i} \frac{da(t)}{dt} = -Ca(t) - Aa^*(t) - f,$$

$$\frac{1}{i} \frac{da^*(t)}{dt} = \bar{A}a(t) + \bar{C}a^*(t) + f^*. \tag{7.2}$$

($f = f^* = 0$ in the Fermi case.) The terms in the right member of (7.2) are in general generalized functions on the set $\Delta$. For instance, $(Ca(t), p) = (a(t), Cp)$ for $p \in \Delta$. The latter inner product exists, since $a(t) \in L$, $\Delta$ is contained in the domain of definition of $C$, and hence $Cp \in L$. If one desires, one can exclude generalized functions from our consideration. Then (7.2) should be written as follows:

$$\frac{1}{i} \frac{d}{dt} (a(t), p) = -(a(t), Cp) - (a^*(t), A^*p) - (f, p),$$

$$\frac{1}{i} \frac{d}{dt} (a^*(t), p) = (a(t), A'p) + (a^*(t), C'p) + (f^*, p).$$

The solution of the system (7.2) under the initial condition $a(x, 0) = a(x)$, $a^*(x, 0) = a^*(x)$ has the form $a(t) = \Phi(t)a + \Psi(t)a^* + g(t)$, $a^*(t) = \bar{\Psi}(t)a + \bar{\Phi}(t)a^* + g^*(t)$. By replacing the functionals $a$, $a^*$ by the operator $\hat{a}$, $\hat{a}^*$, respectively, we obtain the relations

$$\hat{a}(t) = \Phi(t)\hat{a} + \Psi(t)\hat{a}^* + g(t),$$

$$\hat{a}^*(t) = \bar{\Psi}(t)\hat{a} + \bar{\Phi}(t)\hat{a}^* + g^*(t). \tag{7.3}$$

[$g(t) = 0$ in the Fermi case.]

In Sections 6.4 and 6.5 it was shown that (7.3) is a canonical transformation.

---

[3] In (7.2) and later the argument $x$ in $a(x, t)$, $a^*(x, t)$, $\hat{a}(x, t)$, $\hat{a}^*(x, t)$ is omitted: $Ca(t) = \int C(x, y)a(y, t)\, dy$, etc.

**Theorem 7.1.** *Let the operators A, C and the function f be such that equations (7.2) have a unique solution. Then, in order that there exist a dense set D in the state space, on which the operator given by formula (7.1) is defined and self-adjoint, it is necessary that the canonical transformation (7.3) be proper.*

Suppose that formula (7.1) gives a self-adjoint operator. In such a case there exists the unitary operator $e^{it\hat{H}} = \hat{U}(t)$.

To prove the theorem it is sufficient to verify that the operators $\hat{a}(t) = \hat{U}(t)\hat{a}\hat{U}^{-1}(t)$, $\hat{a}^*(t) = \hat{U}(t)\hat{a}^*\hat{U}^{-1}(t)$ are expressed in terms of $\hat{a}$, $\hat{a}^*$ by formulas (7.3). We shall give an heuristic argument.

From the differentiation it turns out, as on p. 145, that $\hat{a}(t)$, $\hat{a}^*(t)$ satisfy equations (7.2). Integrating them we obtain (7.3).

The strict proof follows this idea. We shall begin with the Fermi case. First we remark that if vectors $\hat{\varphi}$, $\hat{\psi}$ belong to the domain of definition of the operator $\hat{H}$ and $p \in L$, then the function

$$\alpha(t) = (e^{it\hat{H}}\hat{a}(p)e^{-it\hat{H}}\hat{\varphi}, \hat{\psi})$$

is differentiable. Consider the function

$$\alpha(t, \tau) = \frac{\alpha(t + \tau) - \alpha(t)}{\tau}.$$

It is convenient to represent this function in the form of a sum of three terms:

$$\alpha(t, \tau) = \alpha_1(t, \tau) + \alpha_2(t, \tau) + \alpha_3(t, \tau),$$

where

$$\alpha_1(t, \tau) = \frac{1}{\tau}((e^{i(t+\tau)\hat{H}} - e^{it\hat{H}})\hat{a}(p)e^{-it\hat{H}}\hat{\varphi}, \hat{\psi}),$$

$$\alpha_2(t, \tau) = \frac{1}{\tau}(e^{it\hat{H}}\hat{a}(p)(e^{-i(t+\tau)\hat{H}} - e^{-it\hat{H}})\hat{\varphi}, \hat{\psi}),$$

$$\alpha_3(t, \tau) = \frac{1}{\tau}((e^{i(t+\tau)\hat{H}} - e^{it\hat{H}})\hat{a}(p)(e^{-i(t+\tau)\hat{H}} - e^{-it\hat{H}})\hat{\varphi}, \hat{\psi}).$$

Since the operator $\hat{H}$ is self-adjoint, the state space $\mathscr{H}$ can be realized as a space of square-integrable functions $\varphi(\lambda)$ in such a way that the operator $\hat{H}$ is an operator of multiplication by a measurable function

$h(\lambda)$. With this realization of the space $\mathscr{H}$ we obtain for the function $\alpha_1(t, \tau)$ the following expression:

$$\alpha_1(t, \tau) = \int (\{\exp[i(t + \tau)h(\lambda)] - \exp[ith(\lambda)]\}/\tau)\varphi_t(\lambda)\overline{\psi}(\lambda)\, d\lambda, \quad (7.4)$$

where $\varphi_t(\lambda)$, $\psi(\lambda)$ are the functions corresponding to the vectors $\hat{a}(p)e^{-it\hat{H}}\hat{\varphi}$, $\hat{\psi}$. The integrand of (7.4) allows an obvious estimate.

$$|(\{\exp[i(t + \tau)h(\lambda)] - \exp[ith(\lambda)]\}/\tau)\varphi_t(\lambda)\overline{\psi}(\lambda)|$$

$$= 2\frac{|\sin(\tau/2)h(\lambda)|}{\tau}|\varphi_t(\lambda)|\,|\psi(\lambda)|$$

$$\le |\varphi_t(\lambda)|\,|h(\lambda)\psi(\lambda)|.$$

The function in the right member of this inequality is integrable:

$$\int |\varphi_t(\lambda)|\,|h(\lambda)\psi(\lambda)|\, d\lambda \le \left[\int |\varphi_t(\lambda)|^2\, d\lambda \int |h(\lambda)\psi(\lambda)|^2\, d\lambda\right]^{1/2}$$

$$= \|\hat{a}(p)e^{it\hat{H}}\hat{\varphi}\|\,\|\hat{H}\psi\| < \|\hat{a}(p)\|\,\|\hat{\varphi}\|\,\|\hat{H}\hat{\psi}\|.$$

Therefore, we can apply to the integral (7.4) Lebesgue's theorem on the passage to the limit under the integral sign. Passing to the limit we then obtain

$$\lim_{\tau \to 0} \alpha_1(t, \tau) = i\int e^{ith(\lambda)}h(\lambda)\varphi_t(\lambda)\overline{\psi}(\lambda)\, d\lambda$$

$$= i(\hat{H}e^{it\hat{H}}\hat{a}(p)e^{-it\hat{H}}\hat{\varphi}, \hat{\psi}).$$

Similarly, it is found that

$$\lim_{\tau \to 0} \alpha_2(t, \tau) = -i(e^{it\hat{H}}\hat{a}(p)e^{-it\hat{H}}\hat{H}\hat{\varphi}, \hat{\psi}).$$

The function $\alpha_3(t, \tau)$ allows the estimate

$$|\alpha_3(t, \tau)| \le \frac{1}{\tau}\|(e^{-i(t+\tau)\hat{H}} - e^{-it\hat{H}})\hat{\psi}\|\,\|(e^{-i(t+\tau)\hat{H}} - e^{-it\hat{H}})\hat{\varphi}\|\,\|\hat{a}(p)\|.$$

To estimate the first factor in the right member of this inequality, it is convenient to consider the same realization as in the study of $\alpha_1(t, \tau)$.

We have (in the same notation)

$$\frac{1}{\tau^2} \|(e^{-i(t+\tau)\hat{H}} - e^{-it\hat{H}})\hat{\psi}\|^2 = 2 \int \left| \sin \frac{\tau h(\lambda)}{2} \right|^2 |\psi(\lambda)|^2 \, d\lambda$$

$$\leq \int h^2(\lambda) |\psi(\lambda)|^2 \, d\lambda = \|\hat{H}\hat{\psi}\|^2.$$

With this realization it is also found that

$$\|(e^{-i(t+\tau)\hat{H}} - e^{-it\hat{H}})\hat{\varphi}\|^2 = 2 \int \sin^2 \frac{\tau h(\lambda)}{2} |\varphi(\lambda)|^2 \, d\lambda,$$

where $\varphi(\lambda)$ is the function corresponding to the vector $\hat{\varphi}$. The final estimate for $\alpha_3(t, \tau)$ is

$$|\alpha_3(t, \tau)| \leq 2\|\hat{a}(p)\| \, \|\hat{H}\hat{\psi}\| \left[ \int \sin^2 \frac{\tau h(\lambda)}{2} |\varphi(\lambda)|^2 \, d\lambda \right]^{1/2}. \qquad (7.5)$$

In the right member of (7.5) we can easily pass to the limit as $\tau \to 0$. As a result we obtain

$$\lim_{\tau \to 0} \alpha_3(t, \tau) = 0.$$

Turning back to $\alpha(t, \tau)$, it has been established first that there exists a limit of this function as $\tau \to 0$, and second that this limit is equal to

$$\lim_{\tau \to 0} \alpha(t, \tau) = ([\hat{H}, e^{it\hat{H}}\hat{a}(p)e^{-it\hat{H}}]\hat{\varphi}, \hat{\psi}). \qquad (7.6)$$

Recalling the connection between the functions $\alpha(t)$ and $\alpha(t, \tau)$, we find that the function $\alpha(t)$ is differentiable, and its derivative is equal to the right member of (7.6).

It is to be noted that we have made use only of the boundedness of $\hat{a}(p)$ to derive this result.

We denote for brevity the operator $e^{it\hat{H}}\hat{a}(p)e^{-it\hat{H}}$ by $\hat{a}(p, t)$. From now on we shall assume that $p \in \Delta$. Repeating the argument given on p. 145 it is found that

$$[\hat{H}, \hat{a}(p, t)] = -\hat{a}(pC, t) - \hat{a}^*(pA, t).$$

We observe that the linear functional $(\hat{a}(p, t)\hat{\varphi}, \hat{\psi})$ with the argument $p$ is bounded:

$$|(\hat{a}(p, t)\hat{\varphi}, \hat{\psi})| \leq \|\hat{a}(p, t)\| \, \|\hat{\varphi}\| \, \|\hat{\psi}\| = \|\hat{a}(p, 0)\| \, \|\hat{\varphi}\| \, \|\hat{\psi}\| \leq \|p\| \, \|\hat{\varphi}\| \, \|\hat{\psi}\|.$$

(We have used the fact that $\|\hat{a}(p, 0)\| \leq \|p\|$ [cf. p. 14].)

From the boundedness of this functional it follows that there exists a function $a(x, t)$, square-integrable with respect to $x$, such that

$$(\hat{a}(p, t)\hat{\varphi}, \hat{\psi}) = \int p(x)a(x, t) \, dx.$$

Using this function we find that

$$\frac{d}{dt} \int p(x)a(x, t) \, dx = - \int p(x)(C(x, y)a(y, t) + A(x, y)a^*(y, t)) \, dx \, dy.$$

$$(7.7)$$

As we have already noted, equation (7.7) is equivalent to the first equation of the system (7.2). The second equation of (7.2) may be derived similarly. Integrating these equations and making use of the definition of the function $a(x, t)$, we obtain

$$(\hat{a}(p, t)\hat{\varphi}, \hat{\psi}) = (\hat{a}(p\Phi, 0)\hat{\varphi}, \hat{\psi}) + (\hat{a}^*(p\Psi, 0)\hat{\varphi}, \hat{\psi},$$

$$(\hat{a}^*(p, t)\hat{\varphi}, \hat{\psi}) = (\hat{a}(p\overline{\Psi}, 0)\hat{\varphi}, \hat{\psi}) + (\hat{a}^*(p\overline{\Phi}, 0)\hat{\varphi}, \hat{\psi}).$$

Since these identities hold for every $\hat{\varphi}, \hat{\psi}$ in a dense set, relations (7.3) follow from them.

We proceed to consider the Bose case.

The preceding arguments become invalid, since the operator $\hat{a}(p)$ is unbounded. Consider in this connection the operator

$$\hat{A} = e^{i(\hat{a}(p) + \hat{a}^*(p))}, \qquad p = p^* \in L.$$

It should be noted that according to (6.22)–(6.24) there corresponds to the matrix form of this operator the functional

$$\tilde{A} = \exp[a^*a + i(ap + a^*p) - p^2/2]$$

The operator $\hat{A}$ is unitary and hence bounded. Repeating the previous argument we find that the operator $\hat{A}(t) = e^{it\hat{H}}\hat{A}e^{it\hat{H}}$ satisfies the differential equation

$$\frac{1}{i}\frac{d}{dt}(\hat{A}(t)\hat{\varphi}, \hat{\psi}) = ([\hat{H}, \hat{A}]\hat{\varphi}, \hat{\psi}), \tag{7.8}$$

where $\hat{\varphi}$, $\hat{\psi}$ are elements in the domain of definition of $\hat{H}$. We shall first of all show that any solution of equation (7.8) in the class of bounded operators has the form $\hat{A}(t) = e^{it\hat{H}}\hat{A}(0)e^{-it\hat{H}}$.

We observe as a preliminary that this assertion is correct if one considers Hilbert-Schmidt operators instead of bounded operators. In fact, in the space of Hilbert-Schmidt operators, equation (7.8) can be written in the form

$$\frac{1}{i}\frac{d}{dt}(\hat{A}(t), \hat{B}) = (\mathfrak{H}\,\hat{A}, \hat{B}),$$

where $\mathfrak{H}$ is the operator in the space of Hilbert-Schmidt operators which is defined by the formula $\mathfrak{H}\hat{A} = [\hat{H}, \hat{A}]$, $\hat{B}$ is an element in the domain of definition of the operator $\mathfrak{H}$, and the inner product is given by the formula $(\hat{A}, \hat{B}) = \mathrm{Sp}\,\hat{A}\hat{B}^*$. The operator $\mathfrak{H}$ is self-adjoint, and hence from the spectral theorem it follows that equation (7.8) in this case has the unique solution $\hat{A}(t) = e^{it\mathfrak{H}}\,\hat{A}(0) = e^{it\hat{H}}\hat{A}(0)e^{-it\hat{H}}$.

We pass to the general case. Let $\hat{A}(t)$ be a solution of equation (7.8) in the class of bounded operators and $\hat{B}(t)$ be a solution of the same equation in the class of Hilbert-Schmidt operators. It is not difficult to verify that the operator $\hat{C}(t) = \hat{A}(t)\hat{B}(t)$ also satisfies equation (7.8).

We now recall that the product of a bounded operator and a Hilbert-Schmidt operator is also a Hilbert-Schmidt operator. Therefore, $\hat{C}(t)$ is a Hilbert-Schmidt operator and accordingly $\hat{C}(t) = e^{it\hat{H}}\hat{C}(0)e^{-it\hat{H}}$, namely,

$$\hat{A}(t)\hat{B}(t) = \hat{A}(t)e^{it\hat{H}}\hat{B}(0)e^{-it\hat{H}} = e^{it\hat{H}}\hat{A}(0)\hat{B}(0)e^{-it\hat{H}}.$$

Taking into account that $\hat{B}(0)$ may be an arbitrary Hilbert-Schmidt operator, it is concluded from this that $\hat{A}(t) = e^{it\hat{H}}\hat{A}(0)e^{-it\hat{H}}$. Let us now construct the explicit solution of equation (7.8) with the initial condition $\hat{A}(0) = e^{i(\hat{a}(p) + \hat{a}^*(p))}$.

It is supposed that there corresponds to the matrix form of the operator $\hat{A}(t)$ the functional

$$\tilde{A}(t) = \exp[a^*a + i(\sigma(t)a^* + \sigma^*(t)a) - \kappa(t)].$$

In such a case there corresponds to the matrix form of the operator $\hat{B} = [\hat{H}, \hat{A}]$ the functional

$$\hat{B}(t) = \tfrac{1}{2}(2ia^*C\sigma - 2ia^*A\sigma^* - 2ia\bar{C}\sigma^* + 2ia\bar{A}\sigma$$
$$- \sigma\bar{A}\sigma + \sigma^*A\sigma^*) + if^*\sigma - if\sigma^*.$$

The functions $\sigma$, $\sigma^*$, $\kappa$ are subject to the system of equations

$$\frac{1}{i}\frac{d\sigma}{dt} = C\sigma - A\sigma^*,$$

$$\frac{1}{i}\frac{d\sigma^*}{dt} = \bar{A}\sigma - \bar{C}\sigma^*, \tag{7.9}$$

$$\frac{1}{i}\frac{d\kappa}{dt} = \tfrac{1}{2}(\sigma\bar{A}\sigma - \sigma^*A\sigma^*) - if^*\sigma + if\sigma^*.$$

For this system we give the initial conditions:

$$\sigma(0) = \sigma^*(0) = p, \qquad \kappa(0) = \frac{p^2}{2}. \tag{7.10}$$

The system (7.9), similar to (7.2), has a unique solution. This follows from the fact that the matrix of the right member of (7.9) is connected with the matrix of the right member of (7.2) by the relation

$$\begin{pmatrix} -C & -A \\ \bar{A} & \bar{C} \end{pmatrix} = -\begin{pmatrix} E & 0 \\ 0 & -E \end{pmatrix}\begin{pmatrix} C & -A \\ \bar{A} & -\bar{C} \end{pmatrix}\begin{pmatrix} E & 0 \\ 0 & -E \end{pmatrix}.$$

Using this relation, and on account of the initial conditions (7.10), we obtain

$$\sigma(t) = \Phi(-t)p - \Psi(-t)p,$$

$$\sigma^*(t) = -\bar{\Psi}(-t)p + \bar{\Phi}(-t)p,$$

$$\kappa(t) = -ip(g(t) + g^*(t)) + \tfrac{1}{2}p(\Phi(t) + \bar{\Psi}(t))(\Psi'(t) + \Phi^*(t))p,$$

where $\Phi(t)$, $\Psi(t)$, $g(t)$ are the same as in (7.3).
  We now observe that

$$\begin{pmatrix} \Phi(-t) & \Psi(-t) \\ \bar{\Psi}(-t) & \bar{\Phi}(-t) \end{pmatrix} = \begin{pmatrix} \Phi(t) & \Psi(t) \\ \bar{\Psi}(t) & \bar{\Phi}(t) \end{pmatrix}^{-1}.$$

Because of formula (4.7), we obtain after simple transformations the final expression for the functional $\tilde{A}(t)$:

$$\tilde{A}(t) = \exp[ip(\Phi a + \Psi a^* + g) + ip(\bar{\Psi}a + \bar{\Phi}a^* + g^*)$$
$$- \tfrac{1}{2}p(\Phi + \bar{\Psi})(\Psi' + \Phi^*)p].$$

Therefore, again recalling formulas (6.22)–(6.24), we find that the functional $\tilde{A}(t)$ corresponds to the matrix form of the operator

$$\hat{A}(t) = \exp[ip(\Phi\hat{a} + \Psi\hat{a}^* + g) + ip(\overline{\Psi}\hat{a} + \overline{\Phi}\hat{a}^* + g^*)]. \qquad (7.11)$$

Evidently the operator $\hat{A}(t)$ is bounded and satisfies equation (7.8) and the initial condition $\hat{A}(0) = e^{it\hat{H}}\hat{A}(0)e^{-it\hat{H}}$, and accordingly

$$e^{it\hat{H}}(\hat{a}(p) + \hat{a}^*(p))e^{-it\hat{H}}$$
$$= p(\Phi(t)\hat{a} + \Psi(t)\hat{a}^* + g(t)) + p(\overline{\Psi}(t)\hat{a} + \overline{\Phi}(t)\hat{a}^* + g^*(t)).$$

Analogously, by considering the operator $\hat{B} = e^{\hat{a}(p) - \hat{a}^*(p)}$, it can be established that

$$e^{it\hat{H}}(\hat{a}(p) - \hat{a}^*(p))e^{-it\hat{H}}$$
$$= p(\Phi(t)\hat{a} + \Psi(t)\hat{a}^* + g(t)) - p(\overline{\Psi}(t)\hat{a} + \overline{\Phi}(t)\hat{a}^* + g^*(t)).$$

From these last two equalities it follows that the operators

$$\hat{a}(t) = e^{it\hat{H}}\hat{a}e^{-it\hat{H}}, \qquad \hat{a}^*(t) = e^{it\hat{H}}\hat{a}^*e^{-it\hat{H}}$$

are expressed in terms of $\hat{a}$, $\hat{a}^*$ by formulas (7.3).

2. SUFFICIENT CONDITIONS.

**Theorem 7.2.** *In order that there exist a dense domain D on which the operator $\hat{H}$ given by (7.1) is self-adjoint, it is sufficient that, besides the condition of Theorem 7.1, the following condition be satisfied.*

(1) *$\Phi e^{itC}$ is a trace-class operator.*

(2) *The inner products $g\Phi'^{-1}\overline{A}\Phi^{-1}g$ and $f^*\Phi^{-1}g$ encountered in (6.23) have a meaning and are locally integrable functions of t.*

If these conditions are fulfilled, the matrix and normal forms of the operators $e^{it\hat{H}}$ are given by formulas (6.21)–(6.24) for bosons, and by formula (6.38) for fermions.

If the conditions of the theorem are fulfilled, then there exist functionals defined by formulas (6.21)–(6.24) or (6.38). It can be readily verified, with the aid of the formulas for the product of operators, that the operators defined by these functionals are unitary and form a one-parameter group $\hat{U}(t)$. Since $\hat{U}(t)$ is a one-parameter group, there exists a self-adjoint operator $\hat{K}$ such that $e^{it\hat{K}} = \hat{U}(t)$. It is possible to verify in addition that the functional $\tilde{U}(t)$ satisfies equation (6.26). Hence, it turns out that $\hat{K} = \hat{H}$.

The corresponding calculations are very unwieldy and we shall omit them, especially by virtue of the fact that in the next subsection we shall give a more convenient sufficient condition, which appears also to be sufficiently close to a necessary condition.

It can be shown that if the conditions of Theorem 7.1 are fulfilled, but those of Theorem 7.2 are not, then the operator $\hat{H}$ differs from a self-adjoint operator by infinite terms. See the following subsections for the details of this phenomenon.[4]

3. REDUCTION OF THE OPERATOR (7.1) TO NORMAL FORM. We recall that (7.1) is a normal form if

$$\int |A(x, y)|^2 \, dx \, dy < \infty, \qquad \int |f(x)|^2 \, dx < \infty.$$

Let us denote by $D_1$ a set of functions on which the generalized function $f(x)$ gives a functional, and by $D_2$ a set of operators $X$ in $L$ such that the operator $AX$ is of trace class. Further, denote by $\tilde{C}$ an operator in the space of operators $\tilde{C}X = CX + XC'$.

**Theorem 7.3.** *Let the operator $A$ and the generalized function $f$ satisfy the conditions*

(1) $(C - z)^{-1}f \in D_1, \quad (\tilde{C} - z)^{-1}A \in D_2 \qquad (\text{Im } z \neq 0),$ (7.12)

(2) $\|A\| < \infty.$

*Then, there exists a proper linear canonical transformation which transforms the operator* (7.1) *into the quadratic normal form.*[5]

Since the quadratic normal form provides a self-adjoint operator on the natural domain of definition, we obtain the following corollary from Theorem 7.3:

---

[4] Although $\hat{H}$ in this case does not have a direct operator meaning (i.e., without addition of an infinite constant), the $\hat{H}$, nevertheless, has the meaning of a bilinear form (cf. p. 22). In general the quadratic expression, not being an operator, often provides a bilinear form (cf. examples on p. 165 *et seq*).

[5] It is not difficult to verify that from the conditions (7.12) there immediately follows the second condition of Theorem 7.2 and also the conditions of Lemmas 6.3, 6.4, 6.5, and thus the first condition of Theorem 7.2. Therefore, if an operator satisfies the condition (7.12). then Theorems 6.2 and 6.3 remain valid for this operator.

**Corollary 7.1.** *If the conditions of Theorem 7.3 are satisfied, then the natural domain of definition $D_A$ of the operator (7.1) is dense and the operator (7.1) with the domain of definition $D_A$ is self-adjoint.*

For the proof of the theorem we shall limit ourselves to the Bose case. The proof of the theorem in the Fermi case differs only by a simplification connected with the fact that $f = 0$ in this case.

It is remarked that if the space $L$ is realized in such a way that $C$ is an operator of multiplication by a function $c(x)$, then the conditions (7.12) signify that

$$\int \frac{|f(x)|^2}{|c(x) - z|} \, dx < \infty, \qquad \int \frac{|A(x, y)|^2 \, dx \, dy}{|c(x) + c(y) - z|} < \infty. \qquad (7.12')$$

Evidently, if the conditions (7.12') [and thus (7.12)] are fulfilled for at least one complex number $z$, then these are fulfilled for all $z$ for which $\text{Im } z \neq 0$.

It follows from (7.12') that if $C$ is an operator of multiplication by a function, then $f(x)$ and $A(x, y)$ are locally square-integrable functions.

It is noted that the conditions of the theorem imply that $(C - z)^{-1}f \in L$ and $(\tilde{C} - z)^{-1}A$ is a Hilbert-Schmidt operator. To prove these assertions it suffices to turn to the conditions (7.12) written in the form (7.12').

To prove the theorem we consider first of all the functions $\sigma$, $\sigma^*$ defined by the equations

$$(C - z)\sigma + A\sigma^* + f = 0, \qquad \bar{A}\sigma + (\bar{C} - \bar{z})\sigma^* + f^* = 0. \qquad (7.13)$$

By eliminating $\sigma^*$ from the second equation, we obtain the equation for $\sigma$,

$$[C - A(\bar{C} - \bar{z})^{-1}\bar{A} - z]\sigma = A(\bar{C} - \bar{z})^{-1}f^* - f. \qquad (7.13')$$

We denote the right member of (7.13') by $g$; i.e., $g = A(\bar{C} - \bar{z})^{-1}f^* - f$. Since $\|A\| < \infty$ and $(C - z)^{-1}f \in L$, we have $\bar{A}(C - z)^{-1}f \in L$ and $A(\bar{C} - \bar{z})^{-1}f^* \in L$. Consequently, $(C - z)^{-1}g \in L$. The solution of equation (7.13') can be written in the form

$$\sigma = \sum [(C - z)^{-1}A(\bar{C} - \bar{z})^{-1}\bar{A}]^n(C - z)^{-1}g. \qquad (7.14)$$

For sufficiently large $|\text{Im } z|$ we have

$$\|(C - z)^{-1}A(\bar{C} - \bar{z})^{-1}\bar{A}\| < 1.$$

Therefore, for sufficiently large $|\text{Im } z|$ the series (7.14) defines a function $\sigma \in L$. Evidently the function defined by this series is the solution of equation (7.13′).

In what follows $z$ will be supposed to be fixed in such a way that the functions $\sigma, \sigma^*$ should belong to $L$.

We consider the canonical transformation

$$\hat{a}(x) \to \hat{a}(x) + \sigma(x), \qquad \hat{a}^*(x) \to \hat{a}^*(x) + \sigma^*(x). \qquad (7.15)$$

According to Theorem 4.1, the transformation (7.15) is proper. Let us apply this transformation to the operator $\hat{H}$.

As a result we obtain the operator

$$\hat{H}_1 = \int C(x, y)(\hat{a}^*(x) + \sigma^*(x))(\hat{a}(y) + \sigma(y)) \, dx \, dy + \cdots.$$

By formally removing the parentheses in this expression, $\hat{H}$ reduces to[6]

$$\hat{H}_1 = \hat{a}^*C\hat{a} + \tfrac{1}{2}\hat{a}^*A\hat{a}^* + \tfrac{1}{2}\hat{a}\bar{A}\hat{a} + \bar{z}\sigma^*\hat{a} + z\sigma\hat{a}^* + k + k_1,$$
$$k_1 = \sigma^*C\sigma + \tfrac{1}{2}\sigma^*A\sigma^* + \tfrac{1}{2}\sigma\bar{A}\sigma + f^*\sigma + f\sigma^*. \qquad (7.16)$$

To justify this operation, one should verify that the constant $k_1$ is finite.

It follows from (7.14), (7.13) that the function $\sigma$ is of the form $\sigma = -(C - z)^{-1}f + (C - z)^{-1}f_1$, where $f_1 \in L$. Since $(C - z)^{-1}f \in D_1$ by the condition of the theorem, we have $|f^*\sigma| \le |f^*(C - z)^{-1}f| + |f^*(C - z)^{-1}f_1| < \infty$. Further, $|\sigma\bar{A}\sigma| < \infty$ since $\|A\| < \infty$ and $\sigma \in L$, and we have

$$\sigma^*C\sigma = \sigma^*(C - z)\sigma + z\sigma^*\sigma = \sigma^*(-f + f_1) + z\sigma^*\sigma$$

$$= (-f^*(C - \bar{z})^{-1} + f_1^*(C - \bar{z})^{-1})(-f + f_1^*) + z\sigma^*\sigma$$

$$= f^*(C - \bar{z})^{-1}f - f^*(C - \bar{z})^{-1}f_1^* - f_1^*(C - \bar{z})^{-1}f$$

$$+ f_1^*(C - \bar{z})^{-1}f_1^* + z\sigma^*\sigma.$$

All of these terms have a meaning by virtue of the condition of the theorem.

---

[6] In (7.16) and later we shall use the abbreviation $\hat{a}^*C\hat{a} = \int C(x, y)a^*(x)a(y) \, dx \, dy$, etc.

Thus the operator $\hat{H}_1$ obtained as a result of the canonical transformation has the same form as $\hat{H}$, with the difference that the linear terms of $\hat{H}_1$ are of the form $\bar{z}\sigma^*\hat{a} + z\sigma\hat{a}^*$, $\sigma \in L$.

We now consider the homogeneous canonical transformation

$$\hat{a} \rightarrow \Phi\hat{a} + \Psi\hat{a}^*, \qquad \hat{a}^* \rightarrow \bar{\Psi}\hat{a} + \bar{\Phi}\hat{a}^*, \qquad (7.17)$$

where

$$\begin{pmatrix} \Phi & \Psi' \\ \bar{\Psi} & \bar{\Phi} \end{pmatrix} = \exp\begin{pmatrix} 0 & -B \\ -\bar{B} & 0 \end{pmatrix} = \begin{pmatrix} \mathrm{ch}(B\bar{B})^{1/2} & -B\,\dfrac{\mathrm{sh}(\bar{B}B)^{1/2}}{(\bar{B}B)^{1/2}} \\ -\bar{B}\,\dfrac{\mathrm{sh}(B\bar{B})^{1/2}}{(B\bar{B})^{1/2}} & \mathrm{ch}(\bar{B}B)^{1/2} \end{pmatrix}, \quad (7.18)$$

$$B = (\tilde{C} - z)^{-1}A.^{7} \qquad (7.19)$$

The condition of the theorem implies that the operators $BA$, $\bar{B}A$, $AB$, $A\bar{B}$ are of trace class and that $B$ is a Hilbert-Schmidt operator. From this latter circumstance it follows that the operators $\mathrm{sh}(\bar{B}B)^{1/2}/(\bar{B}B)^{1/2}$ and $B[\mathrm{sh}(\bar{B}B)^{1/2}/(\bar{B}B)^{1/2}]$ also are Hilbert-Schmidt operators. Thus, according to Theorem 4.1, the transformation (7.17) is proper.

By applying the transformation (7.17) to the operator $\hat{H}_1$, we obtain the operator

$$\hat{H}_2 = (\hat{a}\Psi^* + \hat{a}^*\Phi^*)C(\Phi\hat{a} + \Psi\hat{a}^*) + \cdots$$

We remove the parentheses in this expression and put $\hat{a}$ and $\hat{a}^*$ in the ordinary order. In order that this procedure lead to the identity transformation, it is necessary that the constant appearing there,

$$k_2 = \mathrm{Sp}(\Psi^*C\Psi + \tfrac{1}{2}\Psi^*A\bar{\Phi} + \tfrac{1}{2}\Phi'\bar{A}\Psi), \qquad (7.20)$$

should have the meaning. It will be convenient to postpone the analysis of the constant $k_2$ to the end of the proof of the theorem.

It turns out that the canonical transformation (7.17) converts $\hat{H}_1$ into a quadratic normal form.

---

[7] We recall that $\tilde{C}$ is an operator on operators: $\tilde{C}X = CX + XC'$. Thus it follows from (7.19) that $CB + BC' = zB + A$. It is noted that from the condition $A = A'$ there follows the result $B = B'$.

We introduce one important formula. From equality (7.19), because of $\bar{C} = C'$, which follows from the self-adjointness of $C$, we find[7] that $CB + BC' = zB + A$ and $\bar{B}C + C'\bar{B} = \bar{z}\bar{B} + \bar{A}$. Hence we obtain

$$CB\bar{B} = B\bar{B}C + R_1, \qquad R_1 = A\bar{B} - B\bar{A} + (z - \bar{z})B\bar{B}. \qquad (7.21)$$

Evidently $R_1$ is a Hilbert-Schmidt operator. We denote by $\| \ \|_2$ the norm in the space of Hilbert-Schmidt operators: $\|X\|_2 = (\text{Sp } XX^*)^{1/2}$. It is found from (7.21) that

$$C(B\bar{B})^n = (B\bar{B})^n C + R_n, \qquad \|R_n\|_2 \leq n\|B\bar{B}\|^{n-1}\|R_1\|_2. \qquad (7.22)$$

Let $f(z) = \sum_n a_n z^n$ be an analytic function whose radius of convergence is greater than $\|B\bar{B}\|$. By making use of (7.22) we obtain

$$Cf(B\bar{B}) = f(B\bar{B})C + R_f, \qquad (7.23)$$

where $R_f$ is a Hilbert-Schmidt operator, for which

$$\|R_f\|_2 \leq \|R_1\|_2 \tilde{f}'(\|B\bar{B}\|).$$

Here we have denoted by $\tilde{f}(z)$ the function

$$\tilde{f}(z) = \sum_n |a_n| z^n.$$

We now consider the terms in $\hat{H}_2$ which contain two creation operators. These terms are of the form $\hat{a}^* A_2 \hat{a}^*$, where

$$A_2 = \tfrac{1}{2}(\Phi^* C\Psi + \Psi' C'\bar{\Phi}) + \tfrac{1}{2}\Phi^* A\bar{\Phi} + \tfrac{1}{2}\Psi'\bar{A}\Psi. \qquad (7.24)$$

The last term in (7.24) is a Hilbert-Schmidt operator, since $\bar{A}$ is a bounded operator and $\Psi$ a Hilbert-Schmidt operator.

For the analysis of the remaining terms we make use of equality (7.18):

$$\Phi^* C\Psi + \Psi' C'\bar{\Phi} + \Phi^* A\bar{\Phi}$$

$$= -\left[ \text{ch}(\bar{B}B)^{1/2} \, CB \, \frac{\text{sh}(\bar{B}B)^{1/2}}{(B\bar{B})^{1/2}} + \frac{\text{sh}(B\bar{B})^{1/2}}{(B\bar{B})^{1/2}} \, BC' \, \text{ch}(\bar{B}B)^{1/2} \right]$$

$$+ \text{ch}(B\bar{B})^{1/2} \, A \, \text{ch}(\bar{B}B)^{1/2}. \qquad (7.25)$$

We denote the expression in the parentheses of (7.25) by $K$. $K$ is transformed by means of equalities (7.19) and (7.23) as follows:

$$K = C \operatorname{ch}(B\bar{B})^{1/2} \frac{\operatorname{sh}(\bar{B}B)^{1/2}}{(\bar{B}B)^{1/2}} - R_{\operatorname{ch}} B \frac{\operatorname{sh}(\bar{B}B)^{1/2}}{(\bar{B}B)^{1/2}}$$

$$- C \frac{\operatorname{sh}(B\bar{B})^{1/2}}{(B\bar{B})^{1/2}} B \operatorname{ch}(\bar{B}B)^{1/2} + R_{\operatorname{sh}} B \operatorname{ch}(\bar{B}B)^{1/2}$$

$$+ z \frac{\operatorname{sh}(B\bar{B})^{1/2}}{(B\bar{B})^{1/2}} B \operatorname{ch}(\bar{B}B)^{1/2} + \frac{\operatorname{sh}(B\bar{B})^{1/2}}{(B\bar{B})^{1/2}} A \operatorname{ch}(\bar{B}B)^{1/2}.$$

All terms in this expression, except the terms containing $C$ and the last term, are Hilbert-Schmidt operators. Denote their sum by $R$. The terms containing $C$ mutually cancel, as is seen from a chain of equalities[8]

$$\operatorname{ch}(B\bar{B})^{1/2} B \frac{\operatorname{sh}(\bar{B}B)^{1/2}}{(\bar{B}B)^{1/2}} = B \operatorname{ch}(\bar{B}B) \frac{\operatorname{sh}(\bar{B}B)^{1/2}}{(\bar{B}B)^{1/2}}$$

$$= B \frac{\operatorname{sh}(\bar{B}B)^{1/2}}{(\bar{B}B)^{1/2}} \operatorname{ch}(\bar{B}B)^{1/2}$$

$$= \frac{\operatorname{sh}(B\bar{B})^{1/2}}{(B\bar{B})^{1/2}} B \operatorname{ch}(\bar{B}B)^{1/2}.$$

We now note that $[\operatorname{sh}(B\bar{B})^{1/2}/(B\bar{B})^{1/2}] A \operatorname{ch}(\bar{B}B)^{1/2} = A + R_1$, where $R_1$ is a Hilbert-Schmidt operator. This is easily confirmed by decomposing, for example, $\operatorname{sh}(B\bar{B})^{1/2}/(B\bar{B})^{1/2}$ and $\operatorname{ch}(\bar{B}B)^{1/2}$ into series. In a similar way, it may be shown that the last term of formula (7.25) has the form $A + R_2$, where $R_2$ is a Hilbert-Schmidt operator. Thus, after canceling the terms with opposite signs, (7.25) becomes the alternative form

$$\Phi^* C \Psi + \Psi' C' \bar{\Phi} + \Phi^* A \bar{\Phi} = R + R_1 + R_2.$$

Consequently, $A_2$ is a Hilbert-Schmidt operator.

The terms in $\hat{H}_2$ depending linearly on the creation and annihilation operators have the form $f_2 \hat{a}^* + f_2^* \hat{a}$, where

$$f_2 = z\sigma\bar{\Phi} + \bar{z}\sigma^*\Psi. \tag{7.26}$$

Since $\bar{\Phi}$, $\Psi$ are bounded operators, it turns out that $f_2 \in L$.

---

[8] These equalities are based on the identity $f(B\bar{B})B = Bf(\bar{B}B)$. In the case when $f$ is an analytic function in a disk of radius $> \|B\bar{B}\|$, the identity $f(B\bar{B})B = Bf(\bar{B}B)$ can be established by expanding the left and right members into series.

The terms in $\hat{H}_2$ which contain the product $\hat{a}^*\hat{a}$ have the form $\hat{a}^*C_2\hat{a}$, where

$$C_2 = \Phi^*C\Phi + \Psi'C'\overline{\Psi} + \Phi^*A\overline{\Psi} + \Psi'\overline{A}\Phi. \tag{7.27}$$

Starting from (7.18), (7.19), and (7.23), we find that $\Phi^*C\Phi = C[\text{ch}(B\overline{B})^{1/2}]^2 + R_1$ and $\Psi'C'\overline{\Psi} = -C[\text{sh}(B\overline{B})^{1/2}]^2 + R_2$, where $R_1$, $R_2$ are bounded operators. Thus $C_2 = C + R$, where $\|R\| < \infty$ and $R = R^*$. Consequently, $C_2$ is a self-adjoint operator. We pass to the analysis of the constant (7.20).

First we shall show that the operator $\Psi^*A\overline{\Phi}$ has a trace. By making use of (7.18) we obtain for $\Psi^*A\overline{\Phi}$ the expression

$$\Psi^*A\overline{\Phi} = -\frac{\text{sh}(\overline{B}B)^{1/2}}{(\overline{B}B)^{1/2}}\,\overline{B}A\,\text{ch}(\overline{B}B)^{1/2}.$$

The operators $\text{sh}(\overline{B}B)^{1/2}/(\overline{B}B)^{1/2}$ and $\text{ch}(\overline{B}B)^{1/2}$ are bounded. The operator $\overline{B}A$ is of trace class by virtue of the condition of the theorem. Thus the operator $\Psi^*A\overline{\Psi}$ has a trace. Analogously, it can be established that the operator $\Phi'\overline{A}\Psi$ has a trace.

Let us proceed to the operator $\Psi^*C\Psi$. We remark that if it has a trace, the operator $(\Psi^*C\Psi)' = \Psi'C'\overline{\Psi}$ also has a trace and $\text{Sp}\,\Psi^*C\Psi = \text{Sp}\,\Psi'C'\overline{\Psi}$. We now carry out the formal calculation

$\text{Sp}\,\Psi^*C\Psi$

$$= \tfrac{1}{2}\,\text{Sp}(\Psi^*C\Psi + \Psi'C'\overline{\Psi})$$

$$= \tfrac{1}{2}\,\text{Sp}\left[\frac{\text{sh}(\overline{B}B)^{1/2}}{(\overline{B}B)^{1/2}}\,\overline{B}CB\,\frac{\text{sh}(\overline{B}B)^{1/2}}{(\overline{B}B)^{1/2}} + \frac{\text{sh}(B\overline{B})^{1/2}}{(B\overline{B})^{1/2}}\,BC'\overline{B}\,\frac{\text{sh}(B\overline{B})^{1/2}}{(B\overline{B})^{1/2}}\right]$$

$$= \tfrac{1}{2}\,\text{Sp}\left\{CB\left[\frac{\text{sh}(\overline{B}B)^{1/2}}{(\overline{B}B)^{1/2}}\right]^2\overline{B} + (-CB + zB + A)\overline{B}\left[\frac{\text{sh}(B\overline{B})^{1/2}}{(B\overline{B})^{1/2}}\right]^2\right\}.$$

It is easy to see that[9] $[\text{sh}(\overline{B}B)^{1/2}/(\overline{B}B)^{1/2}]^2\overline{B} = \overline{B}[\text{sh}(B\overline{B})^{1/2}/(B\overline{B})^{1/2}]^2$. Therefore, as a result of the calculation we obtain

$$\text{Sp}\,\Psi^*C\Psi = \tfrac{1}{2}\,\text{Sp}\left\{(A + zB)\overline{B}\left[\frac{\text{sh}(B\overline{B})^{1/2}}{(B\overline{B})^{1/2}}\right]^2\right\}. \tag{7.28}$$

[9] Cf. the footnote on p. 162.

In view of the assumption of the theorem the operator under the sign of the trace is of trace class.

The calculation we have carried out is correct if the operator $\bar{B}CB$ is of trace class. Thus, in this case we obtain for $\hat{H}_2$ the expression

$$\hat{H}_2 = \hat{a}^*C_2\hat{a} + \tfrac{1}{2}(\hat{a}^*A_2\hat{a}^* + \hat{a}\bar{A}_2\hat{a}) + f_2\hat{a}^* + f_2^*\hat{a} + k_2, \quad (7.29)$$

where

$$k_2 = k + k_1 + \tfrac{1}{2}\,\mathrm{Sp}\left\{(A + zB)\bar{B}\left[\frac{\mathrm{sh}(B\bar{B})^{1/2}}{(B\bar{B})^{1/2}}\right]^2\right\}$$

$$+ \tfrac{1}{2}\mathrm{Sp}\,\Psi^*A\bar{\Phi} + \tfrac{1}{2}\,\mathrm{Sp}\,\Phi'\bar{A}\Psi, \quad (7.30)$$

$A_2$ is a Hilbert-Schmidt operator and $f_2 \in L$. Now we shall remove the assumption that the operator $\bar{B}CB$ is a trace-class operator.

We consider the realization of the space $L$ by means of square-integrable functions on a set $M$, in which $C$ is an operator of multiplication by a function. In this realization the operator $A$ is given by a locally square-integrable kernel $A(x, y)$. Consider a family of sets $D_n$ of finite measure such that $D_n \subset D_{n+1} \subset M$ and $\cup\, D_n = M$. We denote by $A(n)$ the operator with kernel $A(n\,|\,x, y) = \chi_n(x)\chi_n(y)A(x, y)$, where $\chi_n(x)$ is the characteristic function of the set $D_n$. We denote also by $\hat{H}(n)$, $\Phi(n)$, $B(n)$, etc., the operators obtained from $\hat{H}$, $\Phi$, $B$, etc., by replacing $A$ by $A(n)$. Evidently the operator $\bar{B}(n)CB(n)$ has an absolutely convergent trace. Therefore the following transformations are all well founded: $\hat{H}(n) = \hat{U}(n)\hat{H}_2(n)\hat{U}^{-1}(n)$, where $\hat{U}(n)$ is a unitary operator defined by the product of canonical transformations (7.15) and (7.17) with the understanding that $\Phi$ and $\Psi$ in (7.17) are to be replaced by $\Phi(n)$ and $\Psi(n)$, respectively.

From formulas (7.18), (7.24), (7.26), (7.27) it follows that for $n \to \infty$ the operators $C_2(n)$, $A_2(n)$ and the functions $f_2(n)$ converge strongly to $C_2, A_2, f_2$, respectively. Then it follows from (7.30) that $k_2(n) \to k_2$. Consequently, the operators $\hat{H}_2(n)$ converge strongly to $\hat{H}_2$ on the set of finite vectors and $\hat{U}(n)$ converges strongly to $\hat{U}$. Therefore, the sequence of operators $\hat{H}(n) = \hat{U}(n)\hat{H}_2(n)\hat{U}^{-1}(n)$ converges strongly on a certain dense set. Evidently its limit is the operator $\hat{H}$. Thus, $\hat{H} = \hat{U}\hat{H}_2\hat{U}^{-1}$, where $\hat{U}$ is the unitary operator defined by the product of the canonical transformations (7.15) and (7.17).

The theorem is proved.

*Remark.* We replace the condition of the theorem by the weaker condition

$$(C - z)^{-1}f \in L,$$

$$(\tilde{C} - z)^{-1}A \text{ is a Hilbert-Schmidt operator.}[10]$$

(7.31)

We consider the unitary operator $\hat{U}$ defined by the product of the canonical transformations (7.15), (7.17) and the operator $\hat{H}_2 = \hat{U}^{-1}\hat{H}\hat{U}$. The proof of the theorem tells us that $\hat{H}_2$ is given as before by formula (7.29), in which $A_2$ is a Hilbert-Schmidt operator and $f \in L$. The difference consists only of the fact that the constant $k_2$ here is shown to be infinite. Evidently, if $k_2 = \infty$, then (7.29) and the starting expression (7.1) of the operators are not defined. It is natural, however, to connect with them the regularized operator $\hat{H}_{2 \text{ reg}}$ obtained from $\hat{H}_2$ by replacing the "infinite constant" $k_2$ by some real number and $\hat{H}_{\text{reg}} = \hat{U}\hat{H}_{2 \text{ reg}} \hat{U}^{-1}$.

4. EXAMPLES. In this subsection $k$ runs through a real Euclidean space and $dk$ is the Lebesgue measure.

(1) Consider the expression

$$\hat{H} = \int \omega(k)\hat{a}^*(k)\hat{a}(k) \, dk$$

$$+ \int (f(k)\hat{a}^*(k)\hat{a}^*(-k) + f^*(k)\hat{a}(-k)\hat{a}(k)) \, dk.$$

(7.32)

In this case the operators $C$ and $A$ are given by the kernels

$$C(k, k') = \omega(k)\delta(k - k'), \qquad A(k, k') = f(k)\delta(k + k').$$

Operators $\Phi(t)$, $\Psi(t)$ obtained by solving the system (7.2) are given by similar kernels

$$\Phi(t, k, k') = \varphi(t, k)\delta(k - k'), \qquad \Psi(t, k, k') = \psi(t)\delta(k + k'). \quad (7.33)$$

It follows from (7.33) that the canonical transformation defined by the operators $\Phi$ and $\Psi$ is improper. Thus the expression (7.32) does

---

[10] It is not difficult to verify that the conditions of Lemmas 6.3 and 6.4, and the conditions of Theorem 7.1 follow from (7.31). The fact that the conditions (7.31) follows from (7.12) becomes clear immediately if one writes the condition (7.12) in the form (7.12').

not define a self-adjoint operator in both the Fermi and Bose cases.[11]

(2) Consider the simplest Bose expression

$$\hat{H} = \int \omega(k)\hat{a}^*(k)\hat{a}(k) \, dk$$

$$+ g \int \left( f(k)\hat{a}^*(k) + f^*(k)\hat{a}(k) \right) dk, \qquad \omega(k) > \omega_0 > 0. \quad (7.34)$$

(a) First let

$$\int |f(k)|^2 \, dk < \infty. \tag{7.35}$$

In this case, according to Theorem 6.1, $\hat{H}$ is a self-adjoint operator, in the domain of definition in which finite vectors are included. If one considers $\hat{H}$ only on finite vectors, then a symmetric operator with null deficiency indices is obtained.

(b) Let the condition (7.35) not be fulfilled, but instead the condition

$$\int \frac{|f(k)|^2}{\omega(k)} \, dk < \infty \tag{7.36}$$

be valid. In this case, as is easily verified, the conditions of Theorem 7.3 are satisfied. We observe that, in the first as well as the second cases, by means of the canonical transformations

$$\hat{a}(k) = \hat{b}(k) - g\frac{f(k)}{\omega(k)}, \qquad \hat{a}^*(k) = \hat{b}^*(k) - g\frac{f^*(k)}{\omega(k)} \tag{7.37}$$

the operator $\hat{H}$ may be brought into the form

$$\hat{H}_1 = \int \omega(k)\hat{b}^*(k)b(k) \, dk + g^2 \int \frac{|f(k)|^2}{\omega(k)} \, dk. \tag{7.38}$$

By making use of the canonical transformation (7.37) and formula (4.26), it is not difficult to find the domain of definition $D_g$ of the

---

[11] It appears that the natural domain of definition (cf. Section 6.2) of the quadratic form (7.32) consists only of the zero vector. One can readily verify, however, that the expression (7.32) has the meaning of a bilinear form with an everywhere-dense domain of definition (cf. p. 22).

operator (7.34). In case (b) $D_g$ consists of vectors to which there correspond functionals of the form

$$e^{g(f/\omega)a^*}\Phi\left(a^* - g\frac{f}{\omega}\right), \tag{7.39}$$

where $\Phi$ is the functional corresponding to the vector

$$\hat{\Phi} = \sum_n \frac{1}{(n!)^{1/2}} \int \Phi_n(k_1,..., k_n)\hat{a}^*(k_1) \cdots \hat{a}^*(k_n)\, d^n k\, \hat{\Phi}_0$$

taken from the domain of definition of $\hat{H}_1$:

$$\sum_n \int (\omega(k_1) + \cdots + \omega(k_n))^2 |\Phi_n(k_1,..., k_n)|^2\, d^n k < \infty. \tag{7.40}$$

From formulas (7.39) and (7.40) it follows easily that the domain $D_g$ depends essentially on $g$: If $g \neq g'$, then $D_g \cap D_{g'} = 0$ [under the condition $\int |f(k)|^2\, dk = \infty$].

(c) Now let neither the condition (7.35) nor (7.36) be satisfied, but

$$\int \frac{|f(k)|^2}{\omega^2(k)}\, dk < \infty. \tag{7.41}$$

In this case the conditions of Theorem 7.1 and the conditions (7.31) are satisfied, but the conditions of Theorems 7.2 and 7.3 are not. The canonical transformation (7.37) remains proper. Carrying out this transformation, we obtain (7.38), but the constant in this case is infinite, since

$$\int \frac{|f(k)|^2}{\omega(k)}\, dk = \infty.$$

Hence, it evidently follows that the expression (7.34) does not have a direct operator meaning. However, the regularized operator

$$\hat{H}_{reg} = \int \omega(k)\left(\hat{a}^* + g\frac{f^*}{\omega}\right)\left(\hat{a} + g\frac{f}{\omega}\right)\, dk \tag{7.42}$$

has a meaning (it is impossible to remove the parentheses!).

The domain of definition of the operator (7.42) is given as before by formulas (7.39), (7.40).

A rather extensive literature has been devoted to the operator (7.42).[12] This operator and some of its generalizations interest us as the simplest models in quantum field theory. It is characteristic of these models, however, that the condition (7.41) is not fulfilled. Therefore the canonical transformation (7.37) is no longer proper.

However, it remains proper if one extends the state space by introducing an indefinite metric, as was done by Berezin [3, 4]. But the analysis of the problems arising here falls outside the scope of this book.

## 8. Canonical Form of a Quadratic Operator

In this section we shall find out the simplest form to which the quadratic operator can be reduced by a proper linear canonical transformation.

This problem is not solved in its full extent in the present section: We restrict ourselves to the case when the initial operator is real, homogeneous, self-adjoint, and reduced to normal form. However, the last restriction is relaxed to some extent by Theorem 7.3.

The canonical forms in the Bose and Fermi cases are identical, but it is convenient to give their expositions separately.

### 1. Bose Case

**Theorem 8.1.** *Let a self-adjoint operator $\hat{H}$ reduced to the normal form be*

$$\hat{H} = \tfrac{1}{2}(\hat{a}^*T\hat{a}^* + \hat{a}\bar{T}\hat{a} + 2\hat{a}^*S\hat{a}), \quad T = \bar{T}, \quad S = \bar{S}, \quad \|S\| < \infty. \quad (8.1)$$

*If*

$$S \pm T > \mu E > 0,$$

*where $\mu$ is a real number, then by a proper linear canonical transformation the operator $\hat{H}$ is reduced to the form*

$$\hat{H} = \hat{a}^*\Omega\hat{a} + k, \qquad (8.2)$$

*where $\Omega$ is a self-adjoint operator and $k$ a constant.*

---

[12] Cf. Tomonaga [1], Edwards and Peierls [1], van Hove [1], and Greenberg and Schweber [1]. Detailed discussions of the problems in field theory connected with this operator are given in the books by Schweber [1] and Henley and Thirring [1].

We provisionally omit that $S = \bar{S}$, $T = \bar{T}$, $\|S\| < \infty$. Before proving the theorem we remark that under the linear canonical transformation the operator (8.1) goes over into an operator of the same form plus a constant, and moreover the matrix of the quadratic part of the operator (8.1) is transformed according to the rule

$$\begin{pmatrix} \bar{T} & \bar{S} \\ S & T \end{pmatrix} \rightarrow \begin{pmatrix} \Phi & \Psi \\ \bar{\Psi} & \bar{\Phi} \end{pmatrix}' \begin{pmatrix} \bar{T} & \bar{S} \\ S & T \end{pmatrix} \begin{pmatrix} \Phi & \Psi \\ \bar{\Psi} & \bar{\Phi} \end{pmatrix}. \tag{8.3}$$

It follows from (8.3) that the matrix

$$\begin{pmatrix} 0 & -E \\ E & 0 \end{pmatrix} \begin{pmatrix} \bar{T} & \bar{S} \\ S & T \end{pmatrix} = \begin{pmatrix} -S & -T \\ \bar{T} & \bar{S} \end{pmatrix}$$

is transformed according to the rule

$$\begin{pmatrix} -S & -T \\ \bar{T} & \bar{S} \end{pmatrix} \rightarrow \begin{pmatrix} \Phi & \Psi \\ \bar{\Psi} & \bar{\Phi} \end{pmatrix}^{-1} \begin{pmatrix} -S & -T \\ \bar{T} & \bar{S} \end{pmatrix} \begin{pmatrix} \Phi & \Psi \\ \bar{\Psi} & \bar{\Phi} \end{pmatrix}. \tag{8.4}$$

Let

$$\bar{V}(t) = \exp\left[ it \begin{pmatrix} -S & -T \\ \bar{T} & \bar{S} \end{pmatrix} \right]. \tag{8.5}$$

By virtue of Lemma 6.3, $\bar{V}(t)$ is the matrix of a proper canonical transformation.

We denote by $G_0$ the group of canonical transformations given by matrices of the form $\begin{pmatrix} \Phi & 0 \\ 0 & \bar{\Phi} \end{pmatrix}$. We shall prove that if the conditions of the theorem are satisfied, then there exists a proper canonical transformation with a matrix $\sigma$ such that $\sigma \bar{V}(t)\sigma^{-1} \in G_0$. Evidently the assertion of the theorem will follow from this fact.

The proof for the existence of such a matrix will be carried out as follows. We shall find a set $Z$ on which the group of proper canonical transformations acts, and such that the subgroup $G_0$ consists of all transformations leaving fixed a certain point $Z_0 \in Z$. Further, we shall show that if the conditions of Theorem 8.1 are fulfilled, then there also exists for the transformations $\bar{V}(t)$ a fixed point $Z_1 \in Z$ which does not depend on $t$.

Next we shall find a transformation $\sigma$ carrying $Z_1$ into $Z_0$. Evidently this transformation has the required property $\sigma \bar{V}(t)\sigma^{-1}$ leaves fixed the point $Z_0$ and accordingly belongs to $G_0$. It will be convenient for us in this subsection to give the canonical transformations by the real matrices [cf. (4.11)]

$$\begin{pmatrix} A & B \\ C & D \end{pmatrix} = U \begin{pmatrix} \Phi & \Psi \\ \overline{\Psi} & \overline{\Phi} \end{pmatrix} U^{-1}, \qquad U = \frac{1}{\sqrt{2}} \begin{pmatrix} E & E \\ -iE & iE \end{pmatrix}. \qquad (8.6)$$

In such a representation the group $G_0$ consists of matrices

$$\begin{pmatrix} A & B \\ -B & A \end{pmatrix}. \qquad (8.7)$$

We note that it follows from (8.6) that

$$\Psi = \tfrac{1}{2}(A - D) + \frac{i}{2}(B + C).$$

Therefore, if the canonical transformation is proper, then $A - D$ and $B + C$ are Hilbert-Schmidt operators.

W denote by $\tilde{Z}$ the set of symmetric operators $Z$ in $L$ of the form $Z = X + iY$, where $X$, $Y$ are real operators and $Y > 0$.

We denote by $Z \subset \tilde{Z}$ the subset of $\tilde{Z}$ which consists of operators having the supplementary property that $Z - iE$ is a Hilbert-Schmidt operator. Let $\sigma = \begin{pmatrix} A & B \\ C & D \end{pmatrix}$ be a matrix corresponding to a canonical transformation and $Z \in \tilde{Z}$. We define the operation of the element $\sigma$ on the set $\tilde{Z}$ by means of the formula

$$\sigma Z = (AZ + B)(CZ + D)^{-1}. \qquad (8.8)$$

By making use of the relations between $A$, $B$, $C$, $D$ following from (4.13), it is not difficult to show that $(\sigma Z)' = \sigma Z$. We shall find the imaginary part of $\sigma Z$:

$(1/2i)(\sigma Z - \overline{\sigma Z})$

$\quad = (1/2i)((\sigma Z)' - \overline{\sigma Z})$

$\quad = (1/2i)[(ZC' + D')^{-1}(ZA' + B') - (A\overline{Z} + B)(C\overline{Z} + D)^{-1}]$

$\quad = (1/2i)(ZC' + D')^{-1}$

$\qquad \times [(ZA' + B')(C\overline{Z} + D) - (ZC' + D')(A\overline{Z} + B)](C\overline{Z} + D)^{-1}$

$\quad = (ZC' + D')^{-1} Y (C\overline{Z} + D)^{-1}, \qquad (8.9)$

where $Y = (1/2i)(Z - \bar{Z})$. The last equality in (8.9) is obtained with the help of (4.13). It follows from (8.9) that $(1/2i)(\sigma Z - \overline{\sigma Z}) > 0$, i.e., that $\sigma Z \in \check{Z}$. Thus $\sigma$ is a transformation of the set $\check{Z}$. It can be readily verified that the point $Z_0 = iE \in \check{Z}$ remains fixed only under a transformation $\sigma$ that is of the form (8.7). We shall find the condition that $Z \in \check{Z}$ is a fixed point relative to transformations given by the matrices (8.5).

Let

$$V(t) = \begin{pmatrix} \Phi & \Psi \\ \bar{\Psi} & \bar{\Phi} \end{pmatrix} = \exp\left[ it \begin{pmatrix} -S & -T \\ \bar{T} & \bar{S} \end{pmatrix} \right], \qquad W(t) = UV(t)U^{-1},$$

where $U$ is defined by formula (8.6). Evidently

$$W(t) = \exp\left[ t \begin{pmatrix} \alpha & \beta \\ -\gamma & \delta \end{pmatrix} \right], \qquad \begin{pmatrix} \alpha & \beta \\ -\gamma & \delta \end{pmatrix} = iU \begin{pmatrix} -S & -T \\ \bar{T} & \bar{S} \end{pmatrix} U^{-1},$$

and $\alpha$, $\beta$, $\gamma$, $\delta$ are expressed in terms of $S$ and $T$ by the formulas

$$\alpha = \mathrm{Im}(S + T), \qquad \beta = \mathrm{Re}(S - T), \qquad \gamma = \mathrm{Re}(S + T), \qquad \delta = -\alpha'. \tag{8.10}$$

(The last equality is due to the fact that $\bar{S} = S'$, $T = T'$.) Now let $Z \in \check{Z}$ and $Z(t) = W(t)Z$:

$$Z(t) = (AZ + B)(CZ + D)^{-1}. \tag{8.11}$$

We find the derivative $dZ(t)/dt$:

$$\frac{dZ(t)}{dt} = (\dot{A}Z + \dot{B})(CZ + D)^{-1}$$

$$- (AZ + B)(CZ + D)^{-1}(\dot{C}Z + \dot{D})(CZ + D)^{-1}$$

$$= (\dot{A}Z + \dot{B})(CZ + D)^{-1}$$

$$- (ZC' + D')^{-1}(ZA' + B')(\dot{C}Z + \dot{D})(CZ + D)^{-1}$$

$$= (ZC' + D')^{-1}$$

$$\times [(ZC' + D')(\dot{A}Z + \dot{B}) - (ZA' + B')(\dot{C}Z + \dot{D})](CZ + D)^{-1}. \tag{8.12}$$

For brevity we have denoted derivatives with respect to $t$ by dots. In carrying out the above calculation we have made use of the fact that

$$(AZ + B)(CZ + D)^{-1} = [(AZ + B)(CZ + D)^{-1}]'.$$

It follows from (8.10) that

$$\frac{d}{dt}\begin{pmatrix} A & B \\ C & D \end{pmatrix} = \begin{pmatrix} A & B \\ C & D \end{pmatrix}\begin{pmatrix} \alpha & \beta \\ -\gamma & -\alpha' \end{pmatrix}.$$

By using these equalities and the relations between $A$, $B$, $C$, $D$ arising from (4.13), we can simplify the expression in the square brackets of (8.12). As a result we obtain for $dZ(t)/dt$ the final expression

$$\frac{dZ(t)}{dt} = (ZC' + D')^{-1}(Z\gamma Z + \alpha Z + Z\alpha' + \beta)(CZ + D)^{-1}. \quad (8.13)$$

Evidently the condition $dZ(t)/dt = 0$ is necessary and sufficient that $Z(t) \equiv Z(0)$; i.e., the point $Z = Z(0)$ should be fixed relative to the transformations $W(t)$. Thus it is found from (8.13) that in order that the point $Z$ should be fixed relative to $W(t)$, it is necessary and sufficient that the operator $Z$ should satisfy the equation

$$Z\gamma Z + \alpha Z + Z\alpha' + \beta = 0. \quad (8.14)$$

We now recall that $S$ and $T$ are symmetric operators and $S \pm T > \mu E > 0$. It then follows from (8.10) that these conditions are equivalent to the following:

$$\alpha = 0, \qquad \beta > \mu E > 0, \qquad \gamma > \mu E > 0. \quad (8.15)$$

By solving equation (8.14), because of (8.15), we find[13]

$$Z = i\gamma^{-1/2}(\gamma^{1/2}\beta\gamma^{1/2})^{1/2}\gamma^{-1/2}. \quad (8.16)$$

We shall now show that $Z$ belongs not only to $\tilde{Z}$ but also to $Z$. It is noted that (8.10) under the conditions $S = \bar{S}$, $T = \bar{T}$ implies $T = \frac{1}{2}(\gamma - \beta)$. Recall that $\hat{H}$ is the normal form, and accordingly $T$ is a Hilbert-Schmidt operator. Substituting $\beta = \gamma - 2T$ into the right member of (8.16) we have

$$\gamma^{1/2}\beta\gamma^{1/2} = \gamma^2 - 2\gamma^{1/2}T\gamma^{1/2} = \gamma^2 + K_1.$$

---

[13] The other solutions of equation (8.14) do not belong to $\tilde{Z}$.

Since $\|\gamma\| < \infty$, $K_1$ is a Hilbert-Schmidt operator.

By making use of inequalities (8.15) for $\beta$ and $\gamma$, it is easily found that $\gamma^2 + K_1 > \mu_1 E > 0$.

In Subsection 3 it will be proved that the conditions $\gamma > \mu E > 0$, $\gamma^2 + K_1 > \mu_1 E > 0$, $K_1$ being a Hilbert-Schmidt operator, imply that $(\gamma^2 + K_1)^{1/2} = \gamma + K_2$, where $K_2$ is a Hilbert-Schmidt operator.

As is easily seen, these conditions are fulfilled. Furthermore, it follows from (8.15) that $\gamma^{-1/2}$ is a bounded operator. Therefore, $Z = i\gamma^{-1/2}(\gamma^{1/2}\beta\gamma^{1/2})^{1/2}\gamma^{-1/2} = iE + K$, where $K$ is a Hilbert-Schmidt operator.

Thus we have established that $Z \in \mathbf{Z}$. Now let $Z_1 = X_1 + iY_1$ be a fixed element of $\mathbf{Z}$, in which $X_1$, $Y_1 - E$ are real symmetric Hilbert-Schmidt operators and $Y_1 > 0$. We put

$$A = Y_1^{-1/2}, \qquad D = Y_1^{1/2}, \qquad B = -Y_1^{-1/2}X_1, \qquad C = 0.$$

Evidently $(AZ_1 + B)D^{-1} = iE$. In addition, $B$ is a Hilbert-Schmidt operator and $A - D$ also is a Hilbert-Schmidt operator, and the matrix $\left(\begin{smallmatrix} A & B \\ 0 & D \end{smallmatrix}\right)$ satisfies the conditions (4.13).

Thus there exists a proper canonical transformation such that the corresponding transformation of the set $\mathbf{Z}$ carries $Z_1$ into $Z_0 = iE$. The theorem is proved.

## 2. FERMI CASE.

**Theorem 8.2.** *Let a self-adjoint operator $\hat{H}$ reduced to the normal form be*

$$\hat{H} = \tfrac{1}{2}(\hat{a}^*T\hat{a}^* - \hat{a}\bar{T}\hat{a} + 2\hat{a}^*S\hat{a}), \qquad T = \bar{T}, \quad S = \bar{S}, \qquad (8.17)$$

*where $[S, T]$ is a Hilbert-Schmidt operator, $S > \mu E > 0$, $S^2 - [S, T] - T^2 > \mu E > 0$. Then the operator $\hat{H}$ is reduced by a proper linear canonical transformation to the form*

$$\hat{H} = \hat{a}^*\Omega\hat{a} + k, \qquad (8.18)$$

*where $k$ is a constant.*

The proof is based on the same idea used in the proof of Theorem 8.1. We consider the matrix

$$V(t) = \begin{pmatrix} \Phi & \Psi \\ \bar{\Psi} & \bar{\Phi} \end{pmatrix} = \exp\left[ it\begin{pmatrix} -S & -T \\ \bar{T} & \bar{S} \end{pmatrix} \right]. \qquad (8.19)$$

According to Lemma 6.5, $V(t)$ is the matrix of a proper canonical transformation.

We denote by $G_0$ the group of canonical transformations given by the matrices of the form $\begin{pmatrix} \Phi & 0 \\ 0 & \bar{\Phi} \end{pmatrix}$. Just as in the Bose case, it is established that the theorem to be proved is equivalent to the following statement: Under the conditions of Theorem 8.2, there exists a proper linear canonical transformation with a matrix $\sigma$ such that $\sigma U(t)\sigma^{-1} \in G_0$.

The proof of this latter statement is performed with the aid of a fixed-point theorem according to the same plan as for the proof of the similar statement in the Bose case.

We pass from the matrices $\begin{pmatrix} \Phi & \Psi \\ \bar{\Psi} & \bar{\Phi} \end{pmatrix}$ to the real matrices

$$\begin{pmatrix} A & B \\ C & D \end{pmatrix} = \frac{1}{2}\begin{pmatrix} E & E \\ iE & -iE \end{pmatrix}\begin{pmatrix} \Phi & \Psi \\ \bar{\Psi} & \bar{\Phi} \end{pmatrix}\begin{pmatrix} E & -iE \\ E & iE \end{pmatrix}. \tag{8.20}$$

In view of (5.10),

$$\begin{pmatrix} A & B \\ C & D \end{pmatrix}\begin{pmatrix} A' & C' \\ B' & D' \end{pmatrix} = \begin{pmatrix} A' & C' \\ B' & D' \end{pmatrix}\begin{pmatrix} A & B \\ C & D \end{pmatrix} = \begin{pmatrix} E & 0 \\ 0 & E \end{pmatrix}. \tag{8.21}$$

We note that there correspond to matrices of the form $\begin{pmatrix} \Phi & 0 \\ 0 & \bar{\Phi} \end{pmatrix}$ real matrices of the form

$$\begin{pmatrix} A & B \\ -B & A \end{pmatrix}. \tag{8.22}$$

In exactly the same way as in the Bose case, since $V(t)$ has the form (8.19), $W(t) = \frac{1}{2}\begin{pmatrix} E & E \\ iE & -iE \end{pmatrix}V(t)\begin{pmatrix} E & -iE \\ E & iE \end{pmatrix}$ has the form

$$W(t) = \begin{pmatrix} A & B \\ C & D \end{pmatrix} = \exp\left[t\begin{pmatrix} \alpha & -\beta \\ \gamma & \delta \end{pmatrix}\right], \tag{8.23}$$

where

$$\alpha = \operatorname{Im}(T + S), \qquad \beta = \operatorname{Re}(S - T), \qquad \delta = \operatorname{Im}(S - T), \qquad \gamma = \beta'. \tag{8.24}$$

(The last equality is due to the fact that $\bar{S} = S'$, $T' = -T$.) We consider the set $\tilde{\mathbf{Z}}$ of operators $Z$ in $L$ satisfying the conditions

$$Z'Z = ZZ' = -E. \tag{8.25}$$

We denote by $\mathbf{Z} \subset \tilde{\mathbf{Z}}$ the subset of $\tilde{\mathbf{Z}}$ consisting of elements of the form $Z = iE + K$, where $K$ is a Hilbert-Schmidt operator.

From the relations between $A$, $B$, $C$, $D$ which arise from (8.21), it follows that if $Z \in \tilde{Z}$, then also $Z_1 \in \tilde{Z}$, where

$$Z_1 = (AZ + B)(CZ + D)^{-1}. \tag{8.26}$$

Thus there corresponds to every canonical transformation a transformation in $\tilde{Z}$. We denote by $G_0$ the group of transformations (8.26) leaving fixed the point $Z_0 = iE$.

It is readily verified that $G_0$ consists of transformations generated by matrices of the form (8.22).

We can now find the condition that a point $Z \in \tilde{Z}$ is fixed relative to transformations generated by the operators (8.23). Let

$$Z(t) = (AZ + B)(CZ + D)^{-1}.$$

By differentiating $Z(t)$ with respect to $t$ we have

$$\frac{dZ(t)}{dt} = (\dot{A}Z + \dot{B})(CZ + D)^{-1}$$

$$- (AZ + B)(CZ + D)^{-1}(\dot{C}Z + \dot{D})(CZ + D)^{-1}$$

$$= (\dot{A}Z + \dot{B})(CZ + D)^{-1}$$

$$+ (Z'A' + B')^{-1}(Z'C' + D')(\dot{C}Z + \dot{D})(CZ + D)^{-1}$$

$$= (Z'A' + B')^{-1}$$

$$\times [(Z'C' + D')(\dot{C}Z + \dot{D}) + (Z'A' + B')(\dot{A}Z + \dot{B})](CZ + D)^{-1}. \tag{8.27}$$

In carrying out the calculation we have used the fact that the operator $Z_1$ of the form (8.26) has the property $-Z_1 = (Z_1')^{-1}$. For brevity we have denoted derivatives with respect to $t$ by dots. It follows from (8.23) that

$$\frac{d}{dt}\begin{pmatrix} A & B \\ C & D \end{pmatrix} = \begin{pmatrix} A & B \\ C & D \end{pmatrix}\begin{pmatrix} \alpha & -\beta \\ \gamma & \delta \end{pmatrix}. \tag{8.28}$$

By making use of (8.28), as well as relations (8.25) and (8.21), we can transform the expression in the square brackets of (8.27) into the form

$$Z'\alpha Z + \gamma Z - Z'\beta + \delta.$$

In order that the point $Z = Z(0)$ be fixed under the transformations given by the matrices (8.23), it is necessary and sufficient that $dZ(t)/dt \equiv 0$. Thus, in order that the point $Z$ be fixed, it is necessary and sufficient that the operator $Z$ should satisfy the equation

$$Z'\alpha Z + \gamma Z - Z'\beta + \delta = 0. \tag{8.29}$$

We now recall that $S = \bar{S}$, $T = \bar{T}$ by the condition of the theorem. Hence, by (8.24), it follows that $\alpha = \delta = 0$. Taking into account, in addition, that $\beta = \gamma'$, we find the final equation for $Z$:

$$\gamma Z = Z'\gamma', \tag{8.30}$$

from which we have

$$Z = i\gamma^{-1}(\gamma\gamma')^{1/2}.$$

It is easy to see that $Z$ satisfies the condition (8.25) and accordingly belongs to $\tilde{\mathbf{Z}}$. We shall show that $Z \in \mathbf{Z}$. Expressing $\gamma$ in terms of $S$ and $T$, we obtain

$$\gamma\gamma' = S^2 - T^2 - [S, T].$$

By the condition of the theorem $K_1 = T^2 + [S, T]$ is a Hilbert-Schmidt operator, $S > \mu E > 0$ and $S^2 - K_1 > \mu E > 0$. Therefore $(\gamma\gamma')^{1/2} = (S^2 - K_1{}^2)^{1/2} = S + K_2$, where $K_2$ is a Hilbert-Schmidt operator.[14] Further, $\gamma^{-1}S = (S + T)^{-1}S = E + Y$. The condition of the theorem implies that $\gamma^{-1} = (S + T)^{-1}$ is a bounded operator. Therefore $Y = (S + T)^{-1}S - E = -(S + T)^{-1}T$ is a Hilbert-Schmidt operator. Furthermore, it follows from the boundedness of the operator $(S + T)^{-1}$ that $(S + T)^{-1}K_2$ is a Hilbert-Schmidt operator. Thus we arrive at the conclusion that

$$Z = i(E + K), \qquad K = \bar{K}, \tag{8.31}$$

where $K$ is a Hilbert-Schmidt operator, i.e., that $Z \in \mathbf{Z}$.

We shall now show that any element in $\mathbf{Z}$ of the form (8.31) can be carried into the point $Z_0 = iE$ by a translation to which there corresponds a proper canonical transformation. We require that the transformation given by the matrix $\left(\begin{smallmatrix} A & 0 \\ 0 & D \end{smallmatrix}\right)$ should carry the element (8.31) into $Z_0 = iE$. We obtain for the operators $A$ and $D$ the equation

$$A(E + K)D^{-1} = E. \tag{8.32}$$

---

[14] Cf. Section 8.3.

It is noted that, as is seen from (8.25), the operators $E + K$ and $E + K'$ commute. Since, in addition, $K = \overline{K}$, $K$ is a normal operator. Therefore the operator $E + K$ has the square root $(E + K)^{1/2}$, which is defined as usual by means of spectral decomposition. We put

$$A = (E + K)^{-1/2}, \qquad D = (E + K)^{1/2}. \qquad (8.33)$$

From what we have stated above, it is clear that $AA' = A'A = DD'$ $= D'D = E$. Therefore the matrix $\begin{pmatrix} A & 0 \\ 0 & D \end{pmatrix}$ gives a canonical transformation. We shall show that the operator $(E + K)^{-1}$ is bounded. In fact, $Z^{-1} = -Z'$. Therefore, $(E + K)^{-1} = E + K'$. Since $K$ is a Hilbert-Schmidt operator, $K'$ has the same property, and accordingly it is bounded. The boundedness of the operator $(E + K)^{-1/2}$ obviously follows from that of the operator $(E + K)^{-1}$.

From (8.20) it is easily found that, under the condition $B = C = 0$, in order that the canonical transformation be proper, it is necessary and sufficient that $A - D$ should be a Hilbert-Schmidt operator. This fact easily follows from (8.33) and the boundedness of the operator $(E + K)^{-1/2}$. The theorem is proved.

In conclusion we remark that the sets considered in the proof of Theorems 8.1 and 8.2, on which the group of canonical transformations acts, are infinite-dimensional analogues of the classical complex symmetric spaces. (Cf. Siegel's lecture note [1] for a description of these spaces which is closest to that used in Subsections 1 and 2.)

### 3. COMPLETION OF THE PROOF OF THEOREMS 8.1 AND 8.2.

**Lemma 8.1.** *Let $C$ and $K$ be self-adjoint operators, for which $C > \mu E$ and $C^2 + K > \mu_1^2 E$ with $\mu, \mu_1 > 0$. Consider the operator*

$$X = (C^2 + K)^{1/2} - C. \qquad (8.34)$$

(1) *If $K$ is a trace-class operator, then $X$ is also a trace-class operator.*
(2) *If $K$ is a Hilbert-Schmidt operator, then $X$ is also a Hilbert-Schmidt operator.*

The second assertion of this lemma serves to complete the proof of Theorems 8.1 and 8.2. First we shall prove the first assertion.

We consider a special case. Suppose that $K \geq 0$ and $C$ has a pure point spectrum. It is remarked that if $K \geq 0$, then $X \geq 0$ also. In fact, since the obvious inequality $C^2 + K \geq C^2$ holds, it follows, according to a well-known theorem of Heinz [1], that $(C^2 + K)^{1/2} \geq C$.

We now rewrite equality (8.34) in the form

$$X^2 + CX + XC = K. \tag{8.35}$$

Let $\{\xi_k\}$ be an orthonormal basis consisting of eigenvectors of the operator $C$, and let $P_n$ be the projection operator onto the subspace spanned by vectors $\xi_1, \ldots, \xi_n$. Let $A$ be an arbitrary operator. We denote by $A_n$ the operator $A_n = P_n A P_n$. Multiplying (8.35) from the left and right by $P_n$, we obtain

$$(X^2)_n + C_n X_n + X_n C_n = K_n. \tag{8.36}$$

By calculating the trace of the operators $C_n X_n$ and $X_n C_n$ in the basis $\{\xi_k\}$, we find that $\mathrm{Sp}\, C_n X_n = \mathrm{Sp}\, X_n C_n \geq \mu \, \mathrm{Sp}\, X_n$, where $\mu$ is a constant bounding the operator $C$ from below. (In obtaining this inequality we have made use of the fact that $X \geq 0$ and therefore the diagonal elements of $X$ in any basis are nonnegative.) Equating the traces of the both members in (8.36) and taking into account that $\mathrm{Sp}(X^2)_n \geq 0$, we obtain the inequality

$$\mathrm{Sp}\, X_n \leq \frac{1}{2\mu} \mathrm{Sp}\, K_n.$$

Since $X \geq 0$, $X_n = P_n X P_n$, $K_n = P_n K P_n$ and $K$ is a trace-class operator, it follows from this that $X$ is a trace-class operator.

Passing to the limit as $n \to \infty$, we find that

$$\mathrm{Sp}\, X \leq \frac{1}{2\mu} \mathrm{Sp}\, K. \tag{8.37}$$

We now consider the case when $K \leq 0$. In this case it follows from (8.34) that $X \leq 0$. Let $K_1 = -K$, $X_1 = -X$, $C_1 = (C^2 - K_1)^{1/2}$. In the new notation (8.34) can be rewritten in the form

$$X_1 = (C_1^2 + K_1)^{1/2} - C_1.$$

Applying the above result we find that $X_1$ is a trace-class operator, for which

$$\mathrm{Sp}\, X_1 \leq (1/2\mu_1) \mathrm{Sp}\, K_1. \tag{8.37'}$$

Now let $K$ be an arbitrary trace-class operator. We represent it in the form $K = K_1 - K_2$, where $K_1 \geq 0$, $K_2 \geq 0$. Starting from (8.34) we obtain for $X$ the expression

$$X = [((C^2 + K_1)^{1/2})^2 - K_2]^{1/2} - C$$
$$= (C^2 + K_1)^{1/2} - C - X_2 = X_1 - X_2,$$

where $X_1$ and $X_2$ are trace-class operators, and moreover it follows from (8.37) and (8.37') that

$$\operatorname{Sp} X_2 \leq (1/2\mu_1) \operatorname{Sp} K_2, \qquad \operatorname{Sp} X_1 \leq (1/2\mu) \operatorname{Sp} K_1.$$

Let $A$ be an arbitrary self-adjoint trace-class operator with $\operatorname{Sp} |A| = \sum_k |\lambda_k|$, where $\lambda_k$ are eigenvalues of the operator $A$. Evidently if $A = A_1 - A_2$, $A_1 \geq 0$, $A_2 \geq 0$, then $\operatorname{Sp}|A| \leq \operatorname{Sp} A_1 + \operatorname{Sp} A_2$, and in addition $A_1$ and $A_2$ can be so chosen that this inequality turns into an equality. Let $K_1$, $K_2$ be selected in accordance with the condition $\operatorname{Sp}|K| = \operatorname{Sp} K_1 + \operatorname{Sp} K_2$. Then we obtain for $\operatorname{Sp}|X|$ the estimate

$$\operatorname{Sp}|X| \leq \operatorname{Sp}|K|/\min(\mu, \mu_1). \tag{8.38}$$

We now remove the condition that $C$ has a pure point spectrum. For this purpose we consider a sequence of operators $C_n$ with pure point spectra such that

(1) The domain of definition $D_n$ of the operator $C_n$ is included in the domain of definition $D$ of the operator $C$.

(2) $C_n > \mu(n)E$, $C_n^2 + K > \mu_1^2(n)E, \mu(n) \to \mu$, $\mu_1(n) \to \mu_1$ for $n \to \infty$[15].

Evidently the sequence of operators $X_n = (C_n^2 + K)^{1/2} - C_n$ on elements of $D$ converges strongly to $X = (C^2 + K)^{1/2} - C$, and moreover $X$ is a trace-class operator and $\operatorname{Sp}|X|$ satisfies inequality (8.38).

We proceed to the second assertion. Let $K$ be a Hilbert-Schmidt operator, $\|K\|_2 = (\operatorname{Sp} KK^*)^{1/2}$. Consider first the case when $\|K\|_2 < \mu - (\delta/2)$, where $\delta > 0$ and $\mu$ is a constant bounding the operator $C$. Evidently we may assume without loss of generality that $\mu = 1 + (\delta/2)$.

We denote by $\Gamma$ the operation $X \to CX + XC$ in the space of Hilbert-Schmidt operators. It is evident that $\Gamma > (2 + \delta)E$. By equation (8.35)

---

[15] Such a sequence can be constructed as follows: Let $\xi_1, \ldots, \xi_n, \ldots, \xi_n \in D$, be an orthonormal basis in the space, and let $P_n$ be the projection operator onto the subspace spanned by the vectors $\xi_1, \ldots, \xi_n$. As $C_n$ one can take the operator $C_n = P_n C P_n + \mu(E - P_n)$ (for sufficiently large $n$).

we have $X = \Gamma^{-1}(K - X^2)$. We shall show that the operator on the right satisfies the condition for the principle of contraction mappings inside the ball $\|X\|_2 < 1$. We remark first of all that $\|A^2 - B^2\|_2 \leq \|A - B\|_2(\|A\|_2 + \|B\|_2)$. In fact, it is evident that $A^2 - B^2 = (A - B)A + B(A - B)$. Passing to the norm, we obtain from this the required inequality. Now let $X_1 = \Gamma^{-1}(K - Y_1^2)$, $X_2 = \Gamma^{-1}(K - Y_2^2)$, $\|Y_1\|_2 < 1$, $\|Y_2\|_2 < 1$. By making use of the inequality just obtained, we find

$$\|X_1 - X_2\|_2 \leq \|\Gamma^{-1}\| \, \|Y_2 - Y_1\|_2(\|Y_2\|_2 + \|Y_1\|_2)$$

$$\leq 2\|\Gamma^{-1}\| \, \|Y_2 - Y_1\|_2 = \varepsilon\|Y_2 - Y_1\|_2, \qquad \varepsilon < 1$$

where $\|\Gamma^{-1}\|$ signifies the norm of the operator $\Gamma^{-1}$ in the Hilbert space of Hilbert-Schmidt operators, and $\varepsilon < 1$ because $\Gamma > (2 + \delta)E$ and accordingly $\|\Gamma^{-1}\| < \frac{1}{2}$.

We now set $X_n = \Gamma^{-1}(K - X_{n-1}^2)$ with $X_1 = \Gamma^{-1}K$. Evidently $\|X_n\|_2 < 1$. Therefore the sequence $X_n$ converges in the norm $\| \ \|_2$ to a Hilbert-Schmidt operator $X$ which is a solution of equation (8.35).

Let us pass to the general case. Let $k_i$ be eigenvalues of the operator $K$ ordered in such a way that $|k_i| \geq |k_{i+1}|$. We denote by $P_n$ the projection operator onto the subspace $H_n$ spanned by eigenvectors of $K$ with eigenvalues $k_1, \ldots, k_n$. We represent the operator $K$ in the form $K = K_n' + K_n''$, where $K_n' = P_nKP_n$, $K_n'' = Q_nKQ_n$ and $P_n + Q_n = E$. Evidently $\|K_n''\|_2 \to 0$ for $n \to \infty$, but the operator $K_n'$ for any $n$ is finite-dimensional and accordingly it is of trace class.

We choose $n$ so large that the inequalities $C^2 + K_n' > [\mu_1^2 - (\delta/2)]E > 0$ and $\|K_n''\|_2 < \mu - (\delta/2)$ are satisfied. Under these conditions we have $(C^2 + K)^{1/2} = [((C^2 + K_n'')^{1/2})^2 + K_n']^{1/2} = (C^2 + K_n'')^{1/2} + X_1 = C + X_2 + X_1$, where $X_1$ is a trace-class operator, and accordingly it is a Hilbert-Schmidt operator, in view of the first assertion of the lemma. The operator $X_2$ is a Hilbert-Schmidt operator as long as $\|K_n''\|_2 < \mu - (\delta/2)$. Thus $(C^2 + K)^{1/2} - C$ is a Hilbert-Schmidt operator. The lemma is proved.

## Chapter IV

# Thirring's Model in Quantum Field Theory

The Thirring model[1] is the simplest relativistically invariant model in quantum field theory. As always in present-day theory, the calculation of physically important quantities—matrix elements of the scattering operator—leads to characteristic "infinities." It is possible to get the correct result only after eliminating the infinities.

The Thirring model is distinct from real theories in the respect that it does not contain the so-called *paradox of a vanishing charge.* Apparently this peculiarity is connected with the fact that the model is one-dimensional. Thanks to the absence of the paradox a presentation can be made within the framework of an operator theory in a Hilbert space with a definite metric.

In this chapter the reason infinities appear in the Thirring model is made clear and the statement of the problem is modified so as to lead to a definitive answer without discarding infinities.

I have endeavored to make all arguments as clear as possible. These can, without a great deal of difficulty, be brought into a modern representation with satisfactory mathematical rigor.

All the exposition is founded on the Hamiltonian formalism, in which the relativistic invariance is not apparent.

## 9. Thirring's Four-Fermion Model

1. PRELIMINARY REMARKS. *Thirring's four-fermion model* with a form factor is described by the operator

$$\hat{H} = \hat{H}_0 + g\hat{V}. \tag{9.1}$$

[1] Cf. Thirring [1].

Here

$$\hat{H}_0 = \frac{1}{i} \int \left( \hat{\psi}_1{}^*(x) \frac{\partial \hat{\psi}_1}{\partial x} - \hat{\psi}_2{}^*(x) \frac{\partial \hat{\psi}_2}{\partial x} \right) dx \qquad (9.2)$$

is the operator of the free field and

$$\hat{V} = 2 \int \hat{\psi}_1{}^*(x_1)\hat{\psi}_2{}^*(x_2) f(x_1 - x_2)\hat{\psi}_2(x_2)\hat{\psi}_1(x_1)\, dx_1\, dx_2 \qquad (9.2')$$

is the interaction operator. $x$ in formulas (9.1) and (9.2) runs along the real axis; $f(x)$ is a real function called a *form factor*. Originally the Thirring model (without a form factor) corresponds to the case[2] $f(x) = \delta(x)$. Only in this case is the model relativistically invariant.

The operators[3] $\hat{\psi}_i(x)$, $\hat{\psi}_i{}^*(x)$ ($i = 1, 2$) satisfy the Fermi commutation relations. They are expressed in terms of creation and annihilation operators of physical particles, $\hat{a}^*$, $\hat{b}^*$, $\hat{a}$, $\hat{b}$, by the formulas

$$\hat{\psi}_1(x) = \frac{1}{(2\pi)^{1/2}} \int e^{ipx}[\theta(p)\hat{a}(p) + \theta(-p)\hat{b}^*(-p)]\, dp,$$

$$\hat{\psi}_2(x) = \frac{1}{(2\pi)^{1/2}} \int e^{ipx}[\theta(-p)\hat{a}(p) + \theta(p)\hat{b}^*(-p)]\, dp, \qquad (9.3)$$

$$\theta(p) = \begin{cases} 1 & \text{for} \quad p \geq 0, \\ 0 & \text{for} \quad p < 0. \end{cases}$$

The expression for the adjoint operators is omitted.

We observe that formulas (9.3) give an improper canonical transformation. We denote by $\mathscr{H}_\psi$ the state space in which the operators $\hat{\psi}_i$, $\hat{\psi}_i{}^*$ serve for annihilation and creation operators, and by $\mathscr{H}_a$ the state space in which $\hat{a}^*$, $\hat{b}^*$, $\hat{a}$, $\hat{b}$ serve for creation and annihilation operators. $\mathscr{H}_a$ is the state space of physical particles, and $\mathscr{H}_\psi$ is an auxiliary space whose elements do not have a direct physical meaning.[4]

---

[2] The equality $f(x) = \delta(x)$ means physically a point interaction.

[3] Strictly speaking, these are not operators but operator-generalized functions.

[4] The space $\mathscr{H}_\psi$ is characterized by the presence of a vacuum vector relative to the operators $\hat{\Psi}_i(x)$, i.e., a vector $\hat{\Phi}_0 \neq 0$ satisfying the equations $\hat{\Psi}_1(x)\hat{\Phi}_0 = 0$, $\hat{\Psi}_2(x)\hat{\Phi}_0 = 0$. The space $\mathscr{H}_a$ is characterized by the presence of a vacuum vector $F_0 \neq 0$ relative to the operators $\hat{a}$, $\hat{b}$: $\hat{a}(p)\hat{F}_0 = 0$, $\hat{b}(p)\hat{F}_0 = 0$. Since the transformation (9.3) is improper, there does not exist in $\mathscr{H}_\psi$ a vector $\hat{\Phi} \neq 0$ satisfying the conditions $\hat{a}(p)\hat{\Phi} = \hat{b}(p)\hat{\Phi} = 0$, and there does not exist in $\mathscr{H}_a$ a vector $\hat{F} \neq 0$ satisfying the conditions $\hat{\Psi}_1(x)\hat{F} = \hat{\Psi}_2(x)\hat{F} = 0$.

We agree to denote by $\hat{H} = \hat{H}_0 + g\,\hat{V}$ the operator given by formulas (9.1)–(9.2') in $\mathcal{H}_\psi$, and by $\hat{H} = \hat{H}_0 + g\,\hat{V}$ the polynomial of operators $\hat{a}$, $\hat{b}$, $\hat{a}^*$, $\hat{b}^*$ in $\mathcal{H}_a$ which are obtained by substituting (9.3) into (9.1)–(9.2').

The problem is how to find the scattering operator $\hat{S}(\hat{H}, \hat{H}_0)$. We shall give a definition of the scattering operator.[5] If $A$ and $B$ are self-adjoint operators, the scattering operator $S(A, B)$ is defined by the formulas

$$S(A, B) = V_+ V_-{}^*, \qquad V_+ = \lim_{t \to +\infty} e^{-itB} e^{itA},$$

$$V_- = \lim_{t \to -\infty} e^{-itB} e^{itA}, \tag{9.4}$$

under the condition that the limits $V_+$ and $V_-$ exist in the strong sense. From (9.4) it follows easily that $V_\pm A = B V_\pm$. Therefore, $BS = SB$.

As we shall see later, the calculation of the scattering operator $\hat{S}(\hat{H}, \hat{H}_0)$ by means of the formulas (9.4) is impossible; it leads to infinities. Only after discarding the infinities can one get a result regarded as acceptable from the physical point of view. The appearance of the infinities is connected principally with the fact that $\hat{H}$ is not an operator, and so the expression $e^{it\hat{H}}$ entering into (9.4) loses its operator meaning. In distinction from $\hat{H}$, $\hat{H}$ is a self-adjoint operator. In fact, subspaces with a fixed number of particles are invariant with respect to $\hat{H}$, and in each of these subspaces $\hat{H}$ is a simple differential operator, the self-adjointness of which may be ascertained without difficulty.[6]

[5] More precisely, the operator of elastic scattering. In the Thirring model inelastic scattering does not occur, and therefore we can restrict ourselves to the definition to be given below. For the details of the scattering operator, see, for example, the book by Schweber [1]. The fundamental role of this operator was established by Heisenberg [1].

[6] In the limiting case when $f(x) = \delta(x)$, the expression (9.1) does not have a direct operator meaning in the space $\mathcal{H}_\psi$. It is possible, however, to attach a meaning to it by starting from the following argument. Consider in the state space a set of vectors $\Phi$ satisfying the condition $\hat{V}\Phi = 0$. The operator $\hat{H}_0$, considered on this set, is symmetric. Its self-adjoint extension is indeed such an operator that corresponds to (9.1) in the case $f(x) = \delta(x)$. Not all extensions are equally important. The most interesting one is obtained from the operators (9.1) for $f(x) \neq \delta(x)$ by means of the limiting operation $f(x) \to \lambda\delta(x)$. The well-known inconsistency in the results of Thirring [1] and Glaser [1] is caused by the fact that these authors used different extensions in their own calculations. (Concerning the description of a point interaction with the aid of extensions, cf. Berezin [4] and Berezin et al. [1].

The calculation of the scattering operator $\hat{S}(\hat{H}, \hat{H}_0)$ connected with $\hat{H}$ does not lead to any difficulty.

If the canonical transformation (9.3) were proper, then $\hat{H}$ and $\hat{H}_0$ should be operators unitary equivalent to $\hat{H}$ and $\hat{H}_0$; consequently the scattering operator $\hat{S}(\hat{H}, \hat{H}_0)$ should be unitary equivalent to the operator $\hat{S}(\hat{H}, \hat{H}_0)$ and the infinities would not appear in its calculation. Thus all difficulties originate from the fact that the transformation (9.3) is improper.

In the following two subsections field operators (see below) are constructed first in the space $\mathcal{H}_\psi$ and then, by means of a canonical transformation and by discarding infinities, in the space $\mathcal{H}_a$. In Subsection 4 the field operators in $\mathcal{H}_a$ are constructed by avoiding the discarding of infinities. The scattering operator is constructed in Subsection 5.

2. Field Operators in the Space $\mathcal{H}_\psi$.[7] These are the operators $\hat{\psi}_{k\tau}(x, t) = e^{-it\hat{H}_0}e^{i(t+\tau)\hat{H}}\hat{\psi}_k(x)\, e^{-i(t+\tau)\hat{H}}e^{it\hat{H}_0}$. The scattering operator is constructed more simply by means of field operators than by making direct use of the definition (9.4). The connection between $\hat{\psi}_{k\tau}(x, t)$ and the scattering operator will be mentioned in Subsection 5.

Differentiating $\hat{\psi}_{k\tau}(x, t)$ with respect to $t$, we find for $\hat{\psi}_{k\tau}$ the differential equations

$$\frac{1}{i}\frac{d\hat{\psi}_{k\tau}}{dt} = [\hat{H}_\tau, \hat{\psi}_{k\tau}], \quad \text{where} \quad \hat{H}_\tau = e^{-it\hat{H}_0}\hat{H}e^{it\hat{H}_0}. \tag{9.5}$$

By means of an argument similar to that on page 145, it may be shown that $\hat{H}_\tau$ coincides with the operator obtained from the operator $\hat{H}$ defined by equations (9.1)–(9.2') by the replacement $\hat{\psi}_k(x) \to \hat{\psi}_{k\tau}(x, t)$. Equations (9.5) are called the *Heisenberg equations*.

We remark that $\hat{\psi}_{k\tau}(x, t)$ is the solution of (9.5) under the initial condition $\hat{\psi}_{k\tau}(x, -\tau) = e^{-it\hat{H}_0}\hat{\psi}_k(x)e^{it\hat{H}_0}$. It can be readily verified that[8]

$$e^{-it\hat{H}_0}\hat{\psi}_1(x)e^{it\hat{H}_0} = \hat{\psi}_1(x + \tau), \; e^{-it\hat{H}_0}\hat{\psi}_2(x)e^{it\hat{H}_0} = \hat{\psi}_2(x - \tau). \tag{9.5'}$$

Evidently, $\hat{\psi}_{k\tau}(x, t)$ for every fixed $t$ satisfy the Fermi commutation

[7] In this subsection we follow Glaser [1].

[8] Equalities (9.5') follow easily from equations (9.6) to be derived below, if one put $g = 0$ therein.

relations. Therefore we can calculate the commutator in the right member of (9.5). As a result we obtain[9]

$$\frac{1}{i}\frac{\partial\hat{\psi}_{1\tau}}{\partial t} = -\frac{1}{i}\frac{\partial\hat{\psi}_{1\tau}}{\partial x} - 2g\int\hat{\psi}_{2\tau}^*(x_2)\hat{\psi}_{2\tau}(x_2)f(x-x_2)\,dx_2\hat{\psi}_{1\tau}(x),$$

$$\frac{1}{i}\frac{\partial\hat{\psi}_{2\tau}}{\partial t} = \frac{1}{i}\frac{\partial\hat{\psi}_{2\tau}}{\partial x} - 2g\int\hat{\psi}_{1\tau}^*(x_1)\hat{\psi}_{1\tau}(x_1)f(x_1-x)\,dx_1\hat{\psi}_{2\tau}(x).$$

$$(9.6)$$

Everywhere in these formulas $\hat{\psi}_{k\tau} = \hat{\psi}_{k\tau}(x) = \hat{\psi}_{k\tau}(x,t)$. It is convenient to denote the operator $\hat{\psi}_{k0}(x,0) = \hat{\psi}_k(x)$ by $\hat{\phi}_k(x)$. With these notations the initial data for the system (9.6) takes the form

$$\hat{\psi}_{1\tau}(x,-\tau) = \hat{\phi}_1(x+\tau), \qquad \hat{\psi}_{2\tau}(x,-\tau) = \hat{\phi}_2(x-\tau). \qquad (9.6')$$

It is not difficult to verify immediately that the solutions of the system (9.6) under the initial conditions (9.6') are given by the operators

$$\hat{\psi}_{1\tau}(x,t) = \hat{\phi}_1(x-t)\exp\left[-ig\int K_{1\tau}(x,t\,|\,s)\hat{\phi}_2^*(s)\hat{\phi}_2(s)\,ds\right],$$

$$\hat{\psi}_{2\tau}(x,t) = \hat{\phi}_2(x+t)\exp\left[ig\int K_{2\tau}(x,t\,|\,s)\hat{\phi}_1^*(s)\hat{\phi}_1(s)\,ds\right],$$

$$(9.7)$$

where

$$K_{1\tau}(x,t\,|\,s) = \int_{x-t-2\tau}^{x+t} f(\xi-s)\,d\xi,$$

$$K_{2\tau}(x,t\,|\,s) = \int_{x+t+2\tau}^{x-t} f(s-\xi)\,d\xi.$$

$$(9.8)$$

3. FIELD OPERATORS IN THE SPACE $\mathscr{H}_a$. In this subsection it will be necessary for us to go beyond the limits of the set of operators in the space $\mathscr{H}_a$. We consider the ring of formal power series[10] of operators $\hat{a}(p)$, $\hat{a}^*(p)$, $\hat{b}(p)$, $\hat{b}^*(p)$. Some of these series define operators in $\mathscr{H}_a$. Evidently, if formal series $\hat{A}$ and $\hat{B}$ define operators in $\mathscr{H}_a$, then their sum and product define the sum and product of the corresponding

---

[9] Here and in what follows the expressions for the operators $\psi_k^*$ will be omitted, since they can be obtained in an obvious way from the expressions for $\psi_k$.

[10] Cf. Section 6.2 for the definition of the formal power series.

operators (provided the sum and product of these operators exists).[11]

In manipulating formal power series we must keep in mind certain well-known precautions. We shall speak of them in detail at the beginning of the next subsection. The aim of this subsection is to obtain the field operators in the space $\mathscr{H}_a$ by "discarding infinities."

Here and later, until the end of this section, letters with carets will signify formal power series of $\hat{a}(p)$, $\hat{a}^*(p)$, $\hat{b}(p)$, $\hat{b}^*(p)$.

We write the Heisenberg equation:

$$\frac{1}{i}\frac{d\hat{\psi}_k}{dt} = [\hat{H}, \hat{\psi}_k]. \tag{9.9}$$

Evidently the solution of equation (9.9) can be obtained from (9.7) by expressing $\varphi_k(x)$, $\varphi_k{}^*(x)$ in terms of $\hat{a}(p)$, $\hat{b}(p)$, $\hat{a}^*(p)$, $\hat{b}^*(p)$ with the help of (9.3):

$$\hat{\varphi}_k(x) = \frac{1}{(2\pi)^{1/2}} \int e^{ipx} \hat{c}_k(p) dp.$$

$$\hat{c}_1(p) = \theta(p)\hat{a}(p) + \theta(-p)\hat{b}^*(-p), \tag{9.10}$$

$$\hat{c}_2(p) = \theta(-p)\hat{a}(p) + \theta(p)\hat{b}^*(-p).$$

As a result we obtain for the exponents in formulas (9.7) the expressions

$$\int K_{1\tau}(x, t\,|\,s)\hat{\varphi}_2{}^*(s)\hat{\varphi}_2(s)\,ds = \int F(\sigma)e^{i\sigma(x-\tau)}\,(\sin \sigma(t+\tau)/\sigma)\,\hat{Q}_2(-\sigma)\,d\sigma,$$

$$\int K_{2\tau}(x, t\,|\,s)\hat{\varphi}_1{}^*(s)\hat{\varphi}_1(s)\,ds = -\int F(\sigma)e^{-i\sigma(x+\tau)}\,(\sin \sigma(t+\tau)/\sigma)\,\hat{Q}_1(\sigma)\,d\sigma,$$

---

[11] The simplest example of power series which does not define an operator in $\mathscr{H}_a$ is

$$\hat{A} = \int \hat{a}(p)\hat{a}^*(p)\,dp.$$

(This is not even a series, but is a polynomial of second degree.) In fact,

$$\hat{A} = -\int \hat{a}^*(p)\hat{a}(p)\,dp + \delta(0)\int dp = -\hat{A}' + \delta(0)\int dp,$$

$\hat{A}'$ is evidently a self-adjoint operator with a dense domain of definition. Since $\hat{A}$ differs from $\hat{A}'$ by the infinite term $\delta(0) \int dp$, it cannot have the meaning of an operator.

where

$$F(\sigma) = \frac{1}{\pi} \int f(x) e^{-i\sigma x} dx,$$

$$\hat{Q}_1(\sigma) = \int \hat{c}_1{}^*(p)\hat{c}_1(p - \sigma)\, dp$$

$$= \int [\theta(p)\hat{a}^*(p) + \theta(-p)\hat{b}(-p)]$$

$$\times [\theta(p - \sigma)\hat{a}(p - \sigma) + \theta(-p + \sigma)\hat{b}^*(-p + \sigma)]\, dp \quad (9.11)$$

$$\hat{Q}_2(\sigma) = \int \hat{c}_2{}^*(p)\hat{c}_2(p - \sigma)dp$$

$$= \int [\theta(-p)\hat{a}^*(p) + \theta(p)\hat{b}(-p)]$$

$$\times [\theta(-p + \sigma)\hat{a}(p - \sigma) + \theta(p - \sigma)\hat{b}^*(-p + \sigma)]\, dp.$$

Arranging the operators $\hat{a}$, $\hat{b}$, $\hat{a}^*$, $\hat{b}^*$, in (9.11) in the normal order, we find that

$$\hat{Q}_1(\sigma) = \hat{Q}_1{}'(\sigma) + \delta(\sigma) \int \theta(-p)\, dp,$$

$$\hat{Q}_2(\sigma) = \hat{Q}_2{}'(\sigma) + \delta(\sigma) \int \theta(p)\, dp,$$

where

$$\hat{Q}_1{}'(\sigma) = \int [\theta(p)\theta(p - \sigma)\hat{a}^*(p)\hat{a}(p - \sigma)$$

$$- \theta(-p)\theta(-\tau + \sigma)\hat{b}^*(-p + \sigma)\hat{b}(-p)$$

$$+ \theta(p)\theta(-p + \sigma)\hat{a}^*(p)\hat{b}^*(-p + \sigma)$$

$$+ \theta(-p)\theta(p - \sigma)\hat{b}(-p)\hat{a}(p - \sigma)]\, dp,$$

$$\hat{Q}_2{}'(\sigma) = \int [\theta(-p)\theta(-p + \sigma)\hat{a}^*(p)\hat{a}(p - \sigma) \quad (9.12)$$

$$- \theta(p)\theta(p - \sigma)\hat{b}^*(-p + \sigma)\hat{b}(-p)$$

$$+ \theta(-p)\theta(p - \sigma)\hat{a}^*(p)\hat{b}^*(-p + \sigma)$$

$$+ \theta(p)\theta(-p + \sigma)\hat{b}(-p)\hat{a}(p - \sigma)]\, dp.$$

Thus

$$\int K_{1\tau}(x, t\,|\,s)\hat{\phi}_2{}^*(s)\hat{\phi}_2(s)\,ds = \int F(\sigma)e^{i\sigma(x-\tau)}\,(\sin \sigma(t + \tau)/\sigma)\,\hat{Q}_2{}'(-\sigma)\,d\sigma$$

$$+ (t + \tau)F(0)\int \theta(-p)\,dp,$$

(9.13)

$$\int K_{2\tau}(x, t\,|\,s)\hat{\phi}_1{}^*(s)\hat{\phi}_1(s)\,ds = -\int F(\sigma)e^{-i\sigma(x+\tau)}\,(\sin \sigma(t + \tau)/\sigma)\,\hat{Q}_1{}'(\sigma)\,d\sigma$$

$$-(t + \tau)F(0)\int \theta(p)\,dp.$$

We impose on the form factor the requirement

$$\int \frac{|F(\sigma)|^2}{|\sigma| + 1}\,d\sigma < \infty.$$

(9.14)

Under this condition the first terms in the right members of (9.13) are self-adjoint quadratic normal forms, and hence, according to Theorem 6.1, define self-adjoint operators in $\mathscr{H}_a$. In fact, the formal self-adjointness of the expression

$$\int F(\sigma)e^{i\sigma(x-\tau)}\frac{\sin \sigma(t + \tau)}{\sigma}\,\hat{Q}_2{}'(-\sigma)\,d\sigma$$

(9.15)

is evident. The term in (9.15) containing the product of two creation operators has the form (after an obvious change of variables)

$$\int F(p + q)e^{i(p+q)(x-\tau)}\frac{\sin(p + q)(t + \tau)}{p + q}\,\theta(-p)\theta(-q)\hat{a}^*(p)\hat{b}^*(q)\,dp\,dq.$$

In order that the expression (9.15) be a quadratic normal form, it is sufficient that the inequality

$$\int_{-\infty}^{0}\int_{-\infty}^{0}|F(p + q)|^2\frac{\sin^2(p + q)\,(t + \tau)}{(p + q)^2}\,dp\,dq < \infty$$

(9.16)

be fulfilled. Inequality (9.16) evidently follows from (9.14). In a similar way it may be ascertained that

$$\int F(\sigma) e^{-i\sigma(x+\tau)} \frac{\sin \sigma (t + \tau)}{\sigma} \hat{Q}_1{}'(\sigma) \, d\sigma$$

is a self-adjoint operator.[12]

We return to the field operator $\hat{\psi}_{k\tau}(x, t)$. From what has been mentioned, it is clear that the operators $\hat{\psi}_{k\tau}(x, t)$ are representable in the form

$$\hat{\psi}_{k\tau}(x, t) = \hat{\psi}'_{k\tau}(x, t) \exp[-i(t + \tau)gF(0) \int \theta(\mp p) \, dp], \qquad (9.17)$$

$$\hat{\psi}'_{1\tau}(x, t) = \hat{\phi}_1(x - t) \exp\left[ -ig \int F(\sigma) \exp[i\sigma(x - \tau)] \right.$$

$$\times [\sin \sigma(t + \tau)/\sigma] \hat{Q}_2{}'(-\sigma) \, d\sigma \right],$$

$$\hat{\psi}'_{2\tau}(x, t) = \hat{\phi}_2(x + t) \exp\left[ -ig \int F(\sigma) \exp[-i\sigma(x + \tau)] \right.$$

$$\times [\sin \sigma(t + \tau)/\sigma] \hat{Q}_1{}'(\sigma) \, d\sigma \right].$$

$$(9.17')$$

[The upper sign in the exponent of (9.17) corresponds to $k = 1$, the lower sign to $k = 2$.] Evidently, $\hat{\psi}'_{1\tau}(x, t)$ and $\hat{\psi}'_{2\tau}(x, t)$ are operators (more exactly, operator-generalized functions) in $\mathcal{H}_a$.

Thus the solutions $\hat{\psi}_{k\tau}(x, t)$ of the Heisenberg equations (9.9) are not operators; they differ from the operators $\hat{\psi}'_{k\tau}(x, t)$ by the "infinite phase factors" $\exp[-i(t + \tau)gF(0) \int \theta(\pm p) \, dp]$. Those factors show that it is impossible to put the Hamiltonian $H$ into the basis of a mathematically consistent theory—it can be used only for heuristic considerations to construct a more rigorous Hamiltonian. Such a Hamiltonian $H'$ will be constructed in the following subsection. Infinities do not appear in the calculations with $H'$ (always in the presence of a form factor). However, these calculations are significantly more complicated.

---

[12] It is not difficult to verify that if inequality (9.16) is violated, then the conditions of Theorem 7.1, *necessary* for the formally self-adjoint expression (9.15) to define a self-adjoint operator, are not fulfilled.

4. EQUATIONS FOR FIELD OPERATORS IN THE SPACE $\mathscr{H}_a$. In this subsection many calculations with formal power series will be carried out. First we shall give an explanatory remark. At first glance it seems natural to regard two formal power series as equal if one can go over from one to the other by a finite number of applications of the identities

$$\{\hat{a}^*(p), \hat{a}(p')\} = \delta(p - p'), \qquad \{\hat{b}^*(p), \hat{b}(p')\} = \delta(p - p'),$$

and thereby no infinities appear. However, it turns out that, by such a definition of equality, all formal power series are equal to each other![13] This inconvenience can be avoided, for example, as follows.

[13] We shall prove this. It is more convenient to use as the argument a discrete parameter rather than a continuous one. Let $\hat{a}^*(n)$, $\hat{a}(n)$ be Fermi creation and annihilation operators, $n = 0, \pm 1, \pm 2, \ldots$. Consider the operators

$$\hat{A} = \Sigma f(n)\hat{a}^*(n)\hat{a}(n + k), \qquad \hat{B} = \Sigma g(n)\hat{a}(n - k)\hat{a}^*(n),$$

where $f(n) = \theta(n)\theta(n + k)$, $g(n) = \theta(n)\theta(n - k)$, and $k > 0$ is a fixed integer.

Let us calculate the commutation relation for the operators $\hat{A}$ and $\hat{B}$.

$$\begin{aligned}
\hat{A}\hat{B} &= \Sigma f(n)g(m)\hat{a}^*(n)\hat{a}(n + k)\hat{a}(m - k)\hat{a}^*(m) \\
&= -\Sigma f(n)g(m)\delta_{n+k-m}\hat{a}^*(n)\hat{a}(m - k) \\
&\quad + \Sigma f(n)g(m)\hat{a}^*(n)\hat{a}(m - k)\hat{a}^*(m)\hat{a}(n + k) \\
&= -\Sigma f(n)g(m)\delta_{n+k-m}\hat{a}^*(n)\hat{a}(m - k) \\
&\quad + \Sigma f(n)g(m)\delta_{n+k-m}\hat{a}^*(m)\hat{a}(n + k) + \hat{B}\hat{A}.
\end{aligned}$$

Hence

$$[\hat{A}, \hat{B}] = \Sigma (f(n - k)g(n) - f(n)g(n + k))\hat{a}^*(n)\hat{a}(n).$$

Now we may calculate the same commutator in an alternative manner.

$$\begin{aligned}
\hat{A}\hat{B} &= -\Sigma f(n)g(m)\delta_{n-m+k}\hat{a}(n + k)\hat{a}^*(m) \\
&\quad + \Sigma f(n)g(m)\hat{a}(n + k)\hat{a}(m - k)\hat{a}^*(n)\hat{a}^*(m) \\
&= -\Sigma f(n)g(m)\delta_{n-m+k}\hat{a}(n + k)\hat{a}^*(m) \\
&\quad + \Sigma f(n)g(m)\delta_{n+k-m}\hat{a}(m - k)\hat{a}^*(n) + \hat{B}\hat{A}.
\end{aligned}$$

Thus we have

$$[\hat{A}, \hat{B}] = \Sigma (f(n)g(n + k) - f(n - k)g(n))\hat{a}(n)\hat{a}^*(n).$$

Comparing with the preceding result, and because of $\hat{a}(n)\hat{a}^*(n) + \hat{a}^*(n)\hat{a}(n) = 1$, we obtain

$$\Sigma (f(n)g(n + k) - f(n - k)g(n)) = 0.$$

On the other hand, by use of the explicit expression for the functions $f$, $g$, we obtain

$$\Sigma (f(n)g(n + k) - f(n - k)g(n)) = \Sigma (\theta(n)\theta(n + k) - \theta(n)\theta(n - k)) = k.$$

Thus $k = 0$. Clearly, with this result, one can establish that any power series is equal to zero.

Before beginning with the calculations we replace the formal power series $\hat{A}$, $\hat{B}$,..., which we are going to use for the calculations, by operators $\hat{A}_\alpha$, $\hat{B}_\alpha$,..., which converge in some sense or other to $\hat{A}$, $\hat{B}$,... as $\alpha \to \alpha_0$. Then we carry out the calculations with the operators $\hat{A}_\alpha$, $\hat{B}_\alpha$,... and in the final answer pass to the limit as $\alpha \to \alpha_0$.

To realize this program we first replace the improper canonical transformation (9.10) by

$$\hat{c}_i(p) = \int [\varphi_{i1}^{(\alpha)}(p, q)a(q) + \varphi_{i2}^{(\alpha)}(p, q)b(q)$$

$$+ \psi_{i1}^{(\alpha)}(p, q)a^*(q) + \psi_{i2}^{(\alpha)}(p, q)b^*(q)] \, dq,$$

which is proper. The functions $\hat{\varphi}_{ij}^{(\alpha)}$, $\hat{\psi}_{ij}^{(\alpha)}$ are so chosen that

$$\lim_{\alpha \to \alpha_0} \varphi_{11}^{(\alpha)}(p, q) = \lim_{\alpha \to \alpha_0} \psi_{22}^{(\alpha)}(p, q) = \delta(p - q)\,\theta(p),$$

$$\lim_{\alpha \to \alpha_0} \varphi_{21}^{(\alpha)}(p, q) = \lim_{\alpha \to \alpha_0} \psi_{12}^{(\alpha)}(p, q) = \delta(p - q)\,\theta(-p),$$

$$\lim_{\alpha \to \alpha_0} \varphi_{i2}^{(\alpha)}(p, q) = \lim_{\alpha \to \alpha_0} \psi_{i1}^{(\alpha)}(p, q) = 0,$$

where

$$\int |p| \, |\psi_{ij}^{(\alpha)}(p, q)|^2 \, dp \, dq < \infty$$

It is not difficult to construct a family of proper canonical transformations satisfying this condition, and hence we shall not dwell on this.

Let an operator $\hat{A}$ be written in the normal form with respect to $\hat{c}^*$, $\hat{c}$. We denote by $\hat{A}^{(\alpha)}$ the result which is obtained from $\hat{A}$ by replacing $\hat{c}^*$, $\hat{c}$ by their expressions in terms of $\hat{a}$, $\hat{a}^*$, $\hat{b}$, $\hat{b}^*$. We rearrange in $\hat{A}^{(\alpha)}$ the operators $\hat{a}$, $\hat{a}^*$, $\hat{b}$, $\hat{b}^*$ in their normal order and discard such terms that have infinite limits as $\alpha \to \alpha_0$. The remaining terms will be denoted by $\hat{A}'^{(\alpha)}$. For $\alpha \to \alpha_0$ the operator $\hat{A}'^{(\alpha)}$ has a formal power series $\hat{A}'$ as its own limit. We apply this construction to the operators $\hat{Q}_i(\sigma)$ and $\hat{H}_0$:

$$\hat{Q}_1^{(\alpha)}(\sigma) = \hat{Q}_1'^{(\alpha)}(\sigma) + \int [\psi_{12}^{(\alpha)}(p - \sigma, q)\overline{\psi}_{12}^{(\alpha)}(p, q)$$

$$+ \psi_{11}^{(\alpha)}(p - \sigma, q)\overline{\psi}_{11}^{(\alpha)}(p, q)] \, dp \, dq,$$

$$\hat{Q}_2^{(\alpha)}(\sigma) = \hat{Q}_2'^{(\alpha)}(\sigma) + \int [\psi_{22}^{(\alpha)}(p - \sigma, q)\bar{\psi}_{22}^{(\alpha)}(p, q)$$

$$+ \psi_{21}^{(\alpha)}(p - \sigma, q)\bar{\psi}_{21}^{(\alpha)}(p, q)] \, dp \, dq,$$

$$\hat{H}_0^{(\alpha)} = \hat{H}_0'^{(\alpha)} + \int p[|\psi_{12}^{(\alpha)}(p, q)|^2 + |\psi_{21}^{(\alpha)}(p, q)|^2$$

$$- |\psi_{22}^{(\alpha)}(p, q)|^2 - |\psi_{21}^{(\alpha)}(p, q)|^2] \, dp \, dq.$$

The limits of $\hat{Q}_i'^{(\alpha)}(\sigma)$ for $\alpha \to \alpha_0$ are equal to the formal polynomials $\hat{Q}_i'(\sigma)$ defined by formulas (9.12), and the limit of $\hat{H}_0'^{(\alpha)}$ is equal to the operator $\hat{H}_0'$ to be defined below by formula (9.20). All formal power series in which we shall be interested in the sequel are expressed explicitly in terms of $\hat{Q}_i'(\sigma)$ and $\hat{H}_0'$, and their approximations by operators consist of replacing $\hat{Q}_i'(\sigma)$ by $\hat{Q}_i'^{(\alpha)}(\sigma)$ and $\hat{H}_0'$ by $\hat{H}_0'^{(\alpha)}$.

We turn our attention in particular to the Hamiltonian $\hat{H}'$ [see (9.20) and (9.21)]. Apparently it does not have an operator meaning (i.e., the conditions $\hat{\Phi} \in \mathcal{H}_a$ and $\hat{H}'\hat{\Phi} \in \mathcal{H}_a$ imply that $\hat{\Phi} = 0$). In any case, as will be shown at the end of this subsection, it is not a self-adjoint operator. However, the explicit form shows that it has meaning not only as a formal power series, but also as an Hermitian bilinear form defined on a dense set consisting of (not necessarily all) finite vectors. It is not difficult to see that the proposed approximation of the Hamiltonian $\hat{H}'$ is an approximation of this form:

$$(\hat{H}'^{(\alpha)}\hat{\Phi}_1, \hat{\Phi}_2) \to (\hat{H}'\hat{\Phi}_1, \hat{\Phi}_2).$$

We can observe that if the form factor satisfies the condition (9.14) and the canonical transformation converges strongly[14] to the transformation (9.10) as $\alpha \to \alpha_0$, then the field operators

$$\hat{\psi}_{k\tau}'^{(\alpha)}(x, t) = e^{-it\hat{H}_0'^{(\alpha)}} e^{i(t+\tau)\hat{H}'^{(\alpha)}} \hat{\psi}_k(x) e^{-i(t+\tau)\hat{H}'^{(\alpha)}} e^{it\hat{H}_0'^{(\alpha)}}$$

converge strongly to the operator (9.17') as $\alpha \to \alpha_0$.[15]

[14] Namely, the operator in the space $L$ defined by the matrix of limiting transformation converges strongly to the operator defined by the matrix of the limit transformation

[15] More precisely, the operators

$$\hat{\psi}_{k\tau}'^{(\alpha)}(f, t) = \int \hat{\psi}_k'^{(\alpha)}(x, t)f(x) \, dx \qquad \text{with} \qquad \int |f(x)|^2 \, dx < \infty$$

Thus the convergence is improved when one passes from the Hamiltonian $\hat{H}'^{(\alpha)}$ to the solution of the Heisenberg equation $\hat{\psi}_{k\tau}'^{(\alpha)}$.

In what follows, so as not to encumber the exposition by introducing an additional index $\alpha$, we shall directly manipulate formal power series, bearing in mind that the calculations to be carried out below have a strict meaning if we first replace the formal power series in them by the operators depending on $\alpha$ according to the rule we have just stated, and then carry out the calculations and in the final answer pass to the limit as $\alpha \to \alpha_0$.

It should be noted that the way of approximating formal power series by operators, which we have adopted, is natural, but it is by no means the only possible approximation. It is not impossible that another way of approximation may give a different final answer (the expressions for field operators and for the scattering operator). In such a case it

---

converge strongly. The proof of this fact follows immediately from the explicit form of $\hat{\psi}_{k\tau}'^{(\alpha)}$ which will be found in this subsection. Namely, we find that the operators $\hat{\psi}_{k\tau}'^{(\alpha)}$ are defined by formulas (9.17′) with $\hat{Q}_i'^{(\alpha)}(\sigma)$ in place of $\hat{Q}_i'(\sigma)$. Therefore, it suffices to establish that the sequence of operators

$$\hat{K}^{(\alpha)} = \exp\left[ -ig \int F(\sigma)e^{i\sigma(x-\tau)} \frac{\sin \sigma(t+\tau)}{\sigma} \hat{Q}_2'^{(\alpha)}(-\sigma) \, d\sigma \right]$$

converges strongly, and uniformly with respect to $x$, to the operator $\hat{K}'$ obtained from $\hat{K}^{(\alpha)}$ by replacing $\hat{Q}_2'^{(\alpha)}$ by $\hat{Q}_2'$. Passing to the functional, we find that there corresponds to the matrix form of $\hat{K}^{(\alpha)}$ a functional of the form

$$\tilde{K}^{(\alpha)} = c(\alpha) \exp[B^{(\alpha)}(a^* b^* \mid ab)],$$

where $c(\alpha)$ is a convergent numerical function and $B^{(\alpha)}(a^* b^* \mid ab)$ is a quadratic form whose matrix has a strong limit as $\alpha \to \alpha_0$. Consequently, matrix elements of $\hat{K}^{(\alpha)}$ have limits as $\alpha \to \alpha_0$ and $\hat{K}^{(\alpha)}$ converges weakly to $\hat{K}'$. Now let us calculate the functional $\tilde{K}_2^{(\alpha)}$ corresponding to the matrix form of the operator $\hat{K}_2^{(\alpha)} = (\hat{K}^{(\alpha)})^* \hat{K}^{(\alpha)}$. The calculation is evidently reduced to Gaussian quadrature, and the answer is

$$\tilde{K}_2^{(\alpha)} = c_2(\alpha) \exp[B_2^{(\alpha)}(a^*b^* \mid ab)].$$

Concerning $c_2(\alpha)$, $B_2^{(\alpha)}$, and $\tilde{K}_2^{(\alpha)}$, we have the same statements valid as for $c(\alpha)$, $B^{(\alpha)}$, and $K^{(\alpha)}$. As a consequence, the sequence of operators $\hat{K}_2^{(\alpha)} = (\hat{K}^{(\alpha)})^* \hat{K}^{(\alpha)}$, and accordingly the sequence $\hat{K}^{(\alpha)}$, converges strongly to $\hat{K}'$. Uniformity with respect to $x$ comes from an obvious estimate connected with the fact that in all the expressions $x$ appears only in the exponential $e^{i\sigma x}$.

The calculation of the functional $\tilde{K}^{(\alpha)}$ is conveniently carried out as follows. First, we find the functional corresponding to $\exp[-ig \int K_{1\tau}(x, t \mid s)\hat{\varphi}_2^*(s)\hat{\varphi}_2(s) \, ds]$ by using formula (6.38), then accomplish the canonical transformation by using (5.32) and discard a superfluous factor.

The calculation of the functional $\tilde{K}_2^{(\alpha)}$ can be carried out in the same way.

would be very interesting to investigate the set of all possible solutions
—for example, to establish whether it depends on a finite number of
parameters.

After these remarks we shall proceed to the fundamental problem of
this subsection.

We denote by $\hat{H}'$ the polynomial of $\hat{a}(p)$, $\hat{b}(p)$, $\hat{a}^*(p)$, $\hat{b}^*(p)$, obtained
by reducing $\hat{H}$ to the normal form and by discarding the infinite terms
which result:

$$\hat{H} = \hat{H}' - \left[ \delta(0) \int |k|\, dk + gF(0)\delta(0) \int \theta(-p)\theta(p')\, dp\, dp' \right.$$
$$\left. + gF(0)\left( \hat{Q}_1(0) \int \theta(p)\, dp + \hat{Q}_2(0) \int \theta(-p)\, dp \right) \right].$$

By making use of formula (9.3), $\hat{H}'$ can be written as a polynomial of
$\hat{\psi}_1(x)$, $\hat{\psi}_2(x)$. Replacing $\hat{\psi}_k(x)$ in this expression by $\hat{\psi}'_{k\tau}(x, t)$, we obtain
a polynomial of $\hat{\psi}'_{k\tau}(x, t)$, which will be denoted by $\hat{H}_\tau'$.

It turns out that the field operators $\hat{\psi}'_{k\tau}$ satisfy the equations

$$\frac{1}{i}\frac{d\hat{\psi}'_{k\tau}}{dt} = [\hat{H}_\tau', \hat{\psi}'_{k\tau}]. \tag{9.18}$$

For the proof it is sufficient to ascertain that

$$\hat{\psi}'_{k\tau}(x, t) = e^{-i\tau\hat{H}_0'}e^{i(t+\tau)\hat{H}'}\hat{\psi}_k(x)e^{-i(t+\tau)\hat{H}'}e^{i\tau\hat{H}_0'} \tag{9.19}$$

[The circumstance that the formal power series (9.19) satisfies equations
(9.18) is verified in literally the same way as was the similar assertion
concerning the operators $\hat{\psi}_{k\tau}(x, t)$ in Subsection 2.]

We remark that the Hamiltonian $\hat{H}'$ is representable in the form

$$\hat{H}' = \hat{H}_0' + g\hat{V}', \tag{9.20}$$

where

$$\hat{H}_0' = \int |p|[\hat{a}^*(p)\hat{a}(p) + \hat{b}^*(p)\hat{b}(p)]\, dp,$$
$$\hat{V}' = \int F(\sigma)\hat{Q}_1'(\sigma)\hat{Q}_2'(-\sigma)\, d\sigma. \tag{9.21}$$

Between $\hat{H}_0'$ and $\hat{Q}_i'$ the following commutation relations[16] hold:

[16] Let us clarify the meaning of these relations. It is not difficult to find a dense
set $D$ of finite vectors invariant with respect to $\hat{H}_0'$ and such that the formal expressions $\hat{Q}_i'(\sigma)$ have the meaning of bilinear forms on $D$. Clearly, the expressions
$\hat{H}_0'\hat{Q}_i'(\sigma)$, $\hat{Q}_i'(\sigma)\hat{H}_0'$ and $[\hat{H}_0', \hat{Q}_i'(\sigma)]$ have the same meaning. The commutator
$[\hat{H}_0', \hat{Q}_i'(\sigma)]$ can be transformed as usual, and thereby, no misunderstanding arises,

$$[\hat{H}_0', \hat{Q}_1'(\sigma)] = \sigma\hat{Q}_1'(\sigma), \qquad [\hat{H}_0', \hat{Q}_2'(\sigma)] = -\sigma\hat{Q}_2'(\sigma),$$
$$[\hat{Q}_i'(\sigma_1), \hat{Q}_j'(\sigma_2)] = 0. \tag{9.22}$$

By use of formulas (9.20)–(9.22), it is not difficult to verify immediately that

$$e^{it\hat{H}'} = e^{it\hat{H}_0'}\hat{U}(g, t), \tag{9.23}$$

where[17]

$$\hat{U}(g, t) = \exp\left[ig\int F(\sigma)\frac{1 - e^{-2it\sigma}}{2i\sigma}\hat{Q}_1'(\sigma)\hat{Q}_2'(-\sigma)\, d\sigma\right] \tag{9.24}$$

We temporarily denote the right member of (9.19) by $\hat{\psi}_{k\tau}''(x, t)$. Starting from (9.19) and (9.23) we obtain

$$\hat{\psi}_{k\tau}''(x, t) = e^{i(t+\tau)\hat{H}_0'}\hat{U}_\tau(g, t + \tau)\hat{\psi}_{k\tau}''(x, -\tau)$$
$$\times \hat{U}_\tau^{-1}(g, t + \tau)e^{-i(t+\tau)\hat{H}_0'}, \tag{9.25}$$

---

since expressions in every step have the meaning of bilinear forms on $D$. As a result of calculations one obtains the first two relations of (9.22).

The situation is different in equations $[\hat{Q}_i'(\sigma_1), \hat{Q}_j'(\sigma_2)] = 0$. An attempt to get them by formal use of the commutation relations leads to a paradox analogous to that mentioned in the previous footnote.

We now note that the relations similar to (9.22) are fulfilled for the operators $\hat{H}_0$ and $\hat{Q}_i(\sigma)$ (the verification is easy):

$$[\hat{H}_0, \hat{Q}_1(\sigma)] = \sigma\hat{Q}_1(\sigma), \qquad [\hat{H}_0, \hat{Q}_2(\sigma)] = -\sigma\hat{Q}_2(\sigma), \qquad [\hat{Q}_i(\sigma_1), \hat{Q}_j(\sigma_2)] = 0. \quad \text{(a)}$$

Therefore our approximation gives

$$[\hat{H}_0'^{(\alpha)}, \hat{Q}_1'^{(\alpha)}(\sigma)] = \sigma\hat{Q}_1'^{(\alpha)}(\sigma) + \varepsilon_1(\alpha, \sigma), \quad [\hat{H}_0'^{(\alpha)}, \hat{Q}_2'^{(\alpha)}(\sigma)] = -\sigma\hat{Q}_2'^{(\alpha)}(\sigma) + \varepsilon_2(\alpha, \sigma)$$
$$[\hat{Q}_i'^{(\alpha)}(\sigma_1), \hat{Q}_j'^{(\alpha)}(\sigma_2)] = 0. \quad \text{(b)}$$

From what has been stated above we see that $\lim_{\alpha\to\alpha_0}\varepsilon_i(\alpha, \sigma) = 0$ for any reasonable approximation. It can be verified that this condition is satisfied in our case. Strictly speaking, one should carry out all calculations in the following by using relations (b) and pass to the limit as $\alpha \to \alpha_0$ in the final answer. However, it is possible to observe that the answer will be the same as that obtained when one formally uses relations (9.22). Finally, we emphasize that the last relation of (9.22) depends on the approximation of $\hat{Q}_i'^{(\alpha)}(\sigma)$. For example, if one put

$$\hat{Q}_1^{(\alpha)}(\sigma) = \int \hat{Q}_1'(\sigma')f_\alpha(\sigma', \sigma)d\sigma' \qquad \text{with} \qquad \lim_{\alpha\to\alpha_0} f_\alpha(\sigma', \sigma) = \delta(\sigma' - \sigma),$$

then $\lim_{\alpha\to\alpha_0}[\hat{Q}_1'^{(\alpha)}(\sigma_1), \hat{Q}_2'^{(\alpha)}(\sigma_2)] = \sigma_2\delta(\sigma_1 + \sigma_2)$. It would be interesting to investigate all possibilities arising here.

[17] It is remarked that the formal power series $\hat{U}(g, t)$ $(t \neq 0)$ does not define a unitary operator, as is seen from the fact that one cannot reduce it to a normal form; we shall meet with infinities if we try to arrange $\hat{a}$, $\hat{b}$, $\hat{a}^*$, $\hat{b}^*$ in the series $\hat{U}(g, t)$ in the normal order. This is a consequence of the circumstance that the Hamiltonian $\hat{H}'$ is not a self-adjoint operator (see below).

where

$$\hat{U}_\tau(g, t) = e^{-it\hat{H}_0'}\hat{U}(g, t)e^{it\hat{H}_0'},$$

$$\hat{\psi}_{k\tau}''(x, -\tau) = e^{-it\hat{H}_0'}\hat{\phi}_k(x)e^{it\hat{H}_0'},$$

$$\hat{\phi}_k(x) = \hat{\psi}_{k0}''(x, 0) = \hat{\psi}_{k0}'(x, 0) = \hat{\psi}_{k0}(x, 0) = \hat{\psi}_k(x).$$

By using formulas (9.22) and (9.23) it is found that

$$\hat{U}_\tau(g, t + \tau) = \exp\left[ ig \int F(\sigma)e^{-2i\sigma\tau}\frac{1 - e^{-2i(t+\tau)\sigma}}{2i\sigma}\, \hat{Q}_1'(\sigma)\, \hat{Q}_2'(-\sigma)\, d\sigma \right]$$

$$(9.26)$$

We denote by $ig\hat{T}$ the exponent in formula (9.26), and the $\mathcal{T}$ the operator on formal power series: $\mathcal{T}\hat{A} = [\hat{T}, \hat{A}]$. Evidently

$$\hat{U}_\tau(g, t)\hat{A}\hat{U}_\tau^{-1}(g, t) = e^{ig\mathcal{T}}\hat{A}.$$

We now remark that[18] $e^{-it\hat{H}_0'}\hat{\phi}_1(x)e^{it\hat{H}_0'} = \hat{\phi}_1(x + \tau)$. Consider the formal power series

$$\hat{\chi}_{1\tau}(x, t) = \hat{U}_\tau(g, t + \tau)\hat{\phi}_1(x + \tau)\hat{U}_\tau^{-1}(g, t + \tau).$$

It follows from (9.25) that

$$\hat{\psi}_{1\tau}''(x, t) = \exp[i(t + \tau)\hat{H}_0']\hat{\chi}_{1\tau}(x, t)\exp[-i(t + \tau)\hat{H}_0'].    (9.27)$$

By making use of the expressions of $\hat{\phi}_1(x)$, $\hat{Q}_1'(\sigma)$, $\hat{Q}_2'(\sigma)$ in terms of $\hat{a}$, $\hat{b}$, $\hat{a}^*$, $\hat{b}^*$ [cf. (9.3) and (9.12)], we find that $\mathcal{T}\hat{\phi}_1(x + \tau) = [\hat{T}, \hat{\phi}_1(x + \tau)] = -\hat{\phi}_1(x + \tau)\int F(\sigma)e^{i(x-\tau)\sigma}\{[1 - e^{-2i(t+\tau)\sigma}]/2i\sigma\}\, \hat{Q}_2'(-\sigma)\, d\sigma$. Since $[\hat{\phi}_1(x + \tau), \hat{Q}_2'(\sigma)] = 0$, it follows from this that

$$\hat{\chi}_{1\tau}(x, t) = e^{ig(t+\tau)\mathcal{T}}\hat{\phi}_1(x + \tau)$$

$$= \hat{\phi}_1(x + \tau) \exp\left[ -ig \int F(\sigma)e^{i(x-\tau)\sigma} \right.$$

$$\left. \times \frac{1 - e^{-2i(t+\tau)\sigma}}{2i\sigma}\, \hat{Q}_2'(-\sigma)\, d\sigma \right]    (9.28)$$

[18] In fact, $\hat{H}_0' = \hat{H}_0 + c$, where $c$ is an infinite constant. Therefore $e^{-it\hat{H}_0'}\hat{\phi}_1(x)e^{it\hat{H}_0'} = e^{-it\hat{H}_0}\hat{\phi}_1(x)e^{it\hat{H}_0}$. As we have seen above, the last expression is equal to $\hat{\phi}_1(x + \tau)$. Of course, the calculation of $e^{-it\hat{H}_0'}\hat{\phi}_1(x)e^{it\hat{H}_0'}$ can be easily carried out without considering the infinite constant.

To calculate $e^{i(t+\tau)\hat{H}_0'}\hat{\chi}_{1\tau}(x,t)e^{-i(t+\tau)\hat{H}_0'}$, it evidently suffices to replace $\hat{\varphi}_1(x+\tau)$ in formula (9.28) by

$$\exp[i(t+\tau)\hat{H}_0']\,\hat{\varphi}_1(x+\tau)\exp[-i(t+\tau)\hat{H}_0'] = \hat{\varphi}_1(x-t)$$

and $\hat{Q}_2'(-\sigma)$ by $\exp[i(t+\tau)\hat{H}_0']\,\hat{Q}_2'(-\sigma)\,\exp[-i(t+\tau)\hat{H}_0'] =$ $\exp[i(t+\tau)\sigma]\,\hat{Q}_2'(-\sigma)$. [The first of these substitutions has already been encountered, and the second is an obvious consequence of formulas (9.22).]

Thus, using (9.27), we obtain for $\hat{\psi}_{1\tau}''(x,t)$ the final expression

$$\hat{\psi}_{1\tau}''(x,t) = \hat{\varphi}_1(x-t)\exp\left[-ig\int F(\sigma)\exp[i(x-\tau)\sigma]\right.$$

$$\left. \times (\sin(t+\tau)\sigma/\sigma)\hat{Q}_2'(-\sigma)\,d\sigma\right]. \tag{9.29}$$

Comparing (9.29) with (9.17') we find that $\hat{\psi}_{1\tau}''(x,t) = \hat{\psi}_{1\tau}'(x,t)$. Analogously it is established that $\hat{\psi}_{2\tau}''(x,t) = \hat{\psi}_{2\tau}'(x,t)$.

Thus equality (9.19) is proved and, with this, the Heisenberg equation (9.18) is verified.[19]

In spite of the fact that equation (9.18) allows the definition of field operators $\hat{\psi}_{1\tau}'$ without "discarding infinities," $\hat{H}'$ is not a self-adjoint

---

[19] Equations (9.18) may be verified in another way without using formal power series. For this purpose we write $\hat{H}_\tau'$ not in terms of $\hat{\psi}_{i\tau}(x,t)$, but in terms of the initial data $\hat{\psi}_{i\tau}(x,-\tau)$. As is easily seen, by expressing $\hat{\psi}_{1\tau}(x,-\tau) = \hat{\varphi}_1(x+\tau)$, $\hat{\psi}_{2\tau}(x,-\tau) = \hat{\varphi}_2(x-\tau)$ in terms of $\hat{a}$, $\hat{b}$, $\hat{a}^*$, $\hat{b}^*$, we obtain for $\hat{H}_\tau'$ an expression distinct from (9.20), (9.21) by the substitutions $\hat{a}(p) \to e^{i|p|\tau}\hat{a}(p)$, $\hat{b}(p) \to e^{i|p|\tau}\hat{b}(p)$. We now consider instead of the operator $\hat{\psi}_{1\tau}'(x,t)$ the functional $\psi_{1\tau}'(a^*, b^*, a, b\,|\,x, t)$ corresponding to its normal form. Passing in (9.18) from operators to functionals and using formulas (1.26), we obtain for $\psi_{1\tau}'(a^*, b^*, a, b\,|\,x, t)$ a linear equation in variational derivatives with the obvious initial condition

$$\psi_{1\tau}'(a^*, b^*, a, b\,|\,x, -\tau) = \varphi_1(x+\tau)$$

$$= \int e^{ip(x+\tau)}\,[\theta(p)a(p) + \theta(-p)b^*(-p)]\,dp.$$

The functional $\psi_{1\tau}'$ can be calculated starting from formulas (9.17') and (6.38). By calculating this functional we can show that it satisfies the above-stated equation together with the initial condition.

The method mentioned here, however, leads to essentially more complicated calculations than those given earlier on the basis of (9.22). R. A. Minlos drew my attention to relations (9.22).

operator, and the commutator in (9.18) should be understood formally, similarly for the commutator in the right member of (9.9). Now we shall ascertain that $\hat{H}'$ is not a self-adjoint operator.[20] Consider the momentum operator

$$\hat{P} = \int p(\hat{a}^*(p)\hat{a}(p) + \hat{b}^*(p)\hat{b}(p))\, dp. \tag{9.30}$$

It can be readily verified that $[\hat{P}, \hat{H}'] = 0$. (This relation represents the conservation law of momentum.)

It follows from (9.30) that the momentum operator has a unique eigenvector; it is the vacuum vector $\hat{F}_0$.

If $\hat{H}'$ were to be self-adjoint, then, since $\hat{H}'$ commutes with $\hat{P}$, it would follow that $\hat{F}_0$ not only enters into the domain of definition of $\hat{H}'$ but also is an eigenvector of $\hat{H}'$. From the explicit form of $\hat{H}'$ it follows, however, that

$$\hat{H}'\hat{F}_0 = g \int F(p-q)\theta(p)\theta(-q)\theta(p')\theta(-q')\delta(p+p'-q-q')$$
$$\times \hat{a}^*(p)\hat{b}^*(-q)\hat{a}^*(-p')\hat{b}^*(q')\, dp\, dp'\, dq\, dq'\, \hat{F}_0. \tag{9.31}$$

Thus $\hat{F}_0$ does not enter into the domain of definition of $\hat{H}'$, and accordingly $\hat{H}'$ is not a self-adjoint operator. In addition, it follows from (9.31) that $\hat{H}'$ cannot be made a self-adjoint operator by attaching to it an infinite constant.[21]

Using this last result, it can be shown that there does not exist a unitary operator $\hat{U}(t)$ in $\mathscr{H}_a$ such that

$$\hat{\psi}'_{kt}(x, t) = \hat{U}(t)\hat{\phi}_k(x)\hat{U}^{-1}(t), \qquad t \neq 0.$$

We shall not enter into its details.[22]

It is to be remarked that $\exp[it\hat{H}']$ is only a formal power series, apparently not having any operator meaning, but nevertheless $\exp[it\hat{H}']\hat{\phi}_1(x)\exp[-it\hat{H}']$ is an operator-generalized function. A similar situation has already been met in the study of quadratic operators, when $\hat{H}$ is an expression of the form (7.1) such that the system

---

[20] The idea of the proof given here is contained in essence in Haag's work [1].

[21] It appears that the natural domain of definition of $\hat{H}'$ consists only of the null vector. $\hat{H}'$ is, however, a bilinear form with a dense domain of definition. As for the initial Hamiltonian $\hat{H}$, it is impossible to even give such a meaning to it.

[22] This is a corollary of Haag's general theorem [1].

(7.2) has the solution (7.3), which defines an improper canonical transformation.

5. SCATTERING OPERATORS. We shall find the connection between field operators and scattering operators (cf., for example, Schweber's book [1]). Let $\mathscr{H}$ be the state space, $D$ be a collection of operators with a dense domain of definition, and $\hat{A}$ and $\hat{B}$ be self-adjoint operators in $\mathscr{H}$ such that there exists a scattering operator $\hat{S}(\hat{A}, \hat{B})$ defined by equation (9.4). Consider the operators

$$\hat{\alpha}_\tau(t) = e^{-i\tau B} e^{i(t+\tau)\hat{A}} \hat{\alpha}_{in} e^{-i(t+\tau)\hat{A}} e^{i\tau B}, \qquad \hat{\alpha}_{in} \in D. \qquad (9.32)$$

It follows from the definition of the scattering operator that there exists the strong limit on the dense set

$$\hat{\alpha}(t) = \lim_{\tau \to \infty} \hat{\alpha}_\tau(t) = \hat{V}_+ e^{it\hat{A}} \hat{\alpha}_{in} e^{-it\hat{A}} \hat{V}_+{}^*.$$

From (9.32) it follows that $\hat{\alpha}_\tau(t) = e^{it B} \hat{\alpha}_{in} e^{-it B}$ for $t = -\tau$. Therefore, it is natural to expect the weak asymptotic behavior

$$\hat{\alpha}(t) \sim e^{it B} \hat{\alpha}_{in} e^{-it B} \qquad \text{as} \qquad t \to -\infty. \qquad (9.33)$$

Furthermore,

$$\hat{\alpha}(t) = \hat{V}_+ e^{it\hat{A}} e^{-it B} e^{it B} \hat{\alpha}_{in} e^{-it B} e^{it B} e^{-it\hat{A}} \hat{V}_+{}^*$$

and $\lim e^{it\hat{A}} e^{-it B} = \hat{V}_-{}^*$ for $t \to \infty$. Therefore, it is natural to expect the weak asymptotic behavior as $t \to +\infty$:

$$\hat{\alpha}(t) \sim \hat{V}_+ \hat{V}_-{}^* e^{it B} \hat{\alpha}_{in} e^{-it B} \hat{V}_- \hat{V}_+{}^*. \qquad (9.34)$$

By definition $\hat{V}_+ \hat{V}_-{}^* = \hat{S}(\hat{A}, \hat{B})$. It has been noted on page 183 that $\hat{S}\hat{B} = \hat{B}\hat{S}$. Therefore, (9.34) can be rewritten in the form

$$\hat{\alpha}(t) \sim e^{it B} \hat{\alpha}_{out} e^{-it B} \qquad \text{for} \qquad t \to +\infty,$$

$$\hat{\alpha}_{out} = \hat{S} \hat{\alpha}_{in} \hat{S}^{-1}. \qquad (9.33')$$

Evidently, if the collection of operators $\hat{\alpha}_{in}$ is irreducible, then equality (9.33') defines a unitary operator $\hat{S}$ up to a factor equal to unity in modulus.

In the Thirring model, in the space $\mathscr{H}_a$, the role of $\hat{A}$ should be played by the Hamiltonian $\hat{H}'$ and the role of $\hat{B}$ by the noninteracting

Hamiltonian $\hat{H}_0' = \int |p| (\hat{a}^*(p)\hat{a}(p) + \hat{b}^*(p)\hat{b}(p))\, dp$. Since, however, $\hat{H}'$ is not a self-adjoint operator, it is impossible to obtain the scattering operator by using formulas (9.4).

But it turns out that by means of the asymptotic conditions (9.33) and (9.33') one can directly define the operators $\hat{\psi}'_{k\,\text{in}}$, $\hat{\psi}'_{k\,\text{out}}$. It is remarkable that although the operators $\hat{\psi}'_{k\tau}(x, t)$ and $\hat{\psi}'_{k\tau}(x, t')$ for finite $t \neq t'$ are not connected by a unitary transformation and thus do not give equivalent representations of the commutation relations, the operators $\hat{\psi}'_{k\,\text{in}}(x)$, $\hat{\psi}'_{k\,\text{out}}(x)$ can nevertheless be shown to be connected by a unitary transformation. Thus there arises the possibility of defining the scattering operator in the Thirring model, avoiding the definition (9.4), directly by means of the equalities

$$\hat{\psi}'_{k\,\text{out}}(x) = \hat{S}\hat{\psi}'_{k\,\text{in}}(x)\hat{S}^{-1}. \tag{9.35}$$

By making use of formulas (9.17') we find that

$$\hat{\psi}'_{1\,\text{in}}(x) = \hat{\phi}_1(x), \qquad \hat{\psi}'_{1\,\text{out}}(x) = \hat{\phi}_1(x)e^{-\pi i g F(0)\hat{Q}_2'(0)},$$
$$\hat{\psi}'_{2\,\text{in}}(x) = \hat{\phi}_2(x), \qquad \hat{\psi}'_{2\,\text{out}}(x) = \hat{\phi}_2(x)e^{-\pi i g F(0)\hat{Q}_1'(0)}. \tag{9.36}$$

The operators $\hat{\psi}'_{k\,\text{in}}(x) = \hat{\phi}_k(x)$ form an irreducible set, and hence equalities (9.35) define the operator $\hat{S}$ up to a factor $\theta$ ($|\theta| = 1$). Using (9.36) we obtain for the scattering operator the expression

$$\hat{S} = \theta \exp[-\pi i g F(0)\hat{Q}_1'(0)\,\hat{Q}_2'(0)]$$

$$= \theta \exp\left[-\pi i g F(0)\int \theta(p)[\hat{a}^*(p)\hat{a}(p) - \hat{b}^*(p)\hat{b}(p)]dp \right. \tag{9.37}$$

$$\left. \times \int \theta(-p)[\hat{a}^*(p)\hat{a}(p) - \hat{b}^*(p)\hat{b}(p)]\, dp \right].$$

Evidently $\hat{Q}_i'(0)$ are self-adjoint operators. Therefore formula (9.37) indeed defines a unitary operator. It should be noted that formulas (9.36), (9.37) are almost independent of the form factor $f$; they depend only on $\pi F(0) = \int f(x)\, dx$. Therefore, in these formulas one can pass to the limiting case of point interaction, when $f(x) = \delta(x)$ and hence $\pi F(0) = 1$.

Formula (9.37) may be verified by the same argument as that used for the calculation of the function $\hat{\chi}_{1\tau}(x, t)$ [cf. formula (9.28)]. We shall not go into details.

Formula (9.37) is not yet the final solution of the problem; it now remains to calculate the matrix elements of $\hat{S}$ or, what is the same thing, the functional $\tilde{S}(a^*, b^*, a, b)$. In the calculation of $\tilde{S}$ we shall put $\pi F(0) = \theta = 1$. Since the operators $\hat{Q}_1'(0)$ and $\hat{Q}_2'(0)$ commute, there follows the possibility of the integral representation for $\hat{S}$,

$$\hat{S} = \frac{1}{2\pi i} \int e^{z\hat{Q}_1'(0) - ig\bar{z}\hat{Q}_2'(0) - z\bar{z}} \, dz \, d\bar{z}. \tag{9.38}$$

The operator in the exponent is quadratic, Therefore one can use formula (6.38) for the calculation of the matrix elements of the exponential. As a result one obtains for $\tilde{S}$ the integral representation

$$\tilde{S}(a^*, b^*, a, b) = \frac{1}{2\pi i} \int \exp\left[\int \{\exp[z\theta(p) - ig\bar{z}\theta(-p)]\, a^*(p)a(p)\right.$$

$$\left. + \exp[-z\theta(p) + ig\bar{z}\theta(-p)]b^*(p)b(p)\} \, dp - z\bar{z}\right] dz \, d\bar{z}. \tag{9.39}$$

We note in conclusion that the idea of calculating the operator $\hat{S}$ by making use of the auxiliary space $\mathscr{H}_\psi$ and the improper canonical transformation (9.3) is contained in the original work of Thirring [1]. It was also used by Glaser [1].

6. RENORMALIZED FIELD OPERATORS. We turn back to formula (9.17'). The operators there can be brought to their normal form by using formulas (6.38) and (1.27). As a result we obtain for the corresponding functionals expressions of the form

$$\psi_{k\tau}'(x, t \,|\, a^*, b^*, a, b) = Z_{k\tau}(x, t)\, F_{k\tau}^{(1)} \exp F_{k\tau}^{(2)},$$

where $F_{k\tau}^{(1)} = F_{k\tau}^{(1)}(x, t \,|\, a^*, b^*, a, b)$ are linear, and $F_{k\tau}^{(2)}$ are quadratic functionals of $a, b, a^*, b^*$.

The expression $\Phi_{k\tau}' = Z_{k\tau}^{-1}\psi_{k\tau}'$ is called the *renormalized field operator*, and $Z_{k\tau}$ a *renormalization constant*. If the form factor tends to the limit of a $\delta$ function, then $Z_{k\tau}$ does not have a finite limit, but $F_{k\tau}^{(1)}$ and $F_{k\tau}^{(2)}$ have finite limits. Thus there arises a possibility of defining the "limiting renormalized operator" by means of the functionals $\Phi_{k\tau} = \lim \Phi_{k\tau}'$.

The functional $\Phi_{k\tau}$ does not, however, correspond to an operator or, apparently, to an operator-generalized function. We are to assume that the formal power series $\hat{\Phi}_{k\tau}(t) = \int \hat{\Phi}_{k\tau}(t, x)s(x)\, dx$ has a natural domain of definition consisting only of the zero vector. However, $\hat{\Phi}_{k\tau}(t)$ has the meaning of a bilinear form with a dense domain of definition $D$, independent of $t$ and $\tau$, and moreover there exists the $\lim_{\tau \to \infty} (\xi, \hat{\Phi}_{k\tau}\eta) = (\xi, \hat{\Phi}_k\eta)$, $\xi, \eta \in D$. By the use of explicit formulas it can be shown that $\hat{\Phi}_k(t, x)$ satisfies the asymptotic conditions

$$(\xi, \hat{\Phi}_k(t, x)\eta) \sim (\xi, \hat{\psi}'_{k^{in}_{out}}(x)\eta) \qquad \text{for} \quad t \to \mp \infty, \quad \xi, \eta \in D.$$

Thus the renormalized operators $\hat{\Phi}_k$ also may serve to construct the scattering operator.

*Appendix*

# Wick's Theorem[1]

The energy operators of physical systems usually have the form $\hat{H}$ $= \hat{H}_0 + \hat{V}$, where $\hat{H}_0$ is the simplest quadratic operator describing a free system and $\hat{V}$ is the interaction operator, which is usually a polynomial operator of third or fourth order in $\hat{a}$ and $\hat{a}^*$.

It becomes necessary to calculate the operator $e^{it\hat{H}}$ in a series of problems. To calculate this operator one may apply the so-called Wick's theorem, which reduces the operator $e^{it\hat{H}}$ to a relatively convenient series in perturbation theory or to an integral representation (in the form of a continual integral). In this Appendix we shall present a method of constructing the operator $e^{it\hat{H}}$ on the basis of Wick's theorem. The exposition is carried out formally in an algebraic way. We shall omit the analytical foundation.

In the following it is assumed that

$$\hat{H}_0 = \int \omega(k)\hat{a}^*(k)\hat{a}(k) \, dk,$$

$$\hat{V} = \sum \int V(p_1,\dots,p_r|q_1 \cdots q_s) \tag{1}$$

$$\times \hat{a}^*(p_1) \cdots \hat{a}^*(p_r)\hat{a}(q_1) \cdots \hat{a}(q_s) \, d^r p \, d^s q.$$

---

[1] In style almost all the exposition in this Appendix follows the article by Berestečkiĭ and Galanin [1]. The essential difference consists of the consistent application of functionals and the application of the Fermi continual integral, and these make it possible to attain complete uniformity in the Bose and Fermi cases.

203

We pay special attention to the simplest case when $k = (k_1, k_2, k_3)$ is a vector of three-dimensional space and

$$\omega(k) = k^2 = k_1{}^2 + k_2{}^2 + k_3{}^2,$$

$$\hat{V} = \int V(p_1 - q_1)\delta(p_1 + p_2 - q_1 - q_2) \tag{2}$$

$$\times \hat{a}^*(p_1)\hat{a}^*(p_2)\hat{a}(q_1)\hat{a}(q_2)\, d^2p\, d^2q.$$

In this case, by the Fourier transformation, the operator $\hat{H}$ takes the form

$$\hat{H} = -\int \hat{\varphi}^*(x)\Delta\hat{\varphi}(x)\, dx$$

$$+ \int u(x_1 - x_2)\hat{\varphi}^*(x_1)\hat{\varphi}^*(x_2)\hat{\varphi}(x_2)\hat{\varphi}(x_1)\, dx_1\, dx_2, \tag{3}$$

where

$$\hat{\varphi}(x) = \frac{1}{(2\pi)^{3/2}}\int e^{ipx}\hat{a}(p)\, dp,$$

$$\hat{\varphi}^*(x) = \frac{1}{(2\pi)^{3/2}}\int e^{-ipx}\hat{a}^*(p)\, dp,$$

$$u(x) = \int e^{-ipx}V(p)\, dp,$$

and $\Delta$ is the Laplace operator. Evidently the operator $\hat{H}$ leaves invariant subspaces with a fixed number of particles. Its value in $n$-particle space is denoted by $\hat{H}_n$. The operator $\hat{H}_n$ is given by the formula

$$\hat{H}_n K = [-\Delta_{x_1} - \cdots - \Delta_{x_n} + 2\sum u(x_i - x_j)]K; \tag{4}$$

i.e., it is the energy operator of the system of $n$ particles interacting pairwise.

The function $K = K(x_1,\ldots, x_n)$ is symmetric or antisymmetric according to whether the Bose or the Fermi case is concerned.[2]

---

[2] Formula (4) is obtained if one applies the operator (3) to a vector of the form

$$\hat{\Phi} = \int K(x_1,\ldots, x_n)\hat{\varphi}^*(x_1) \cdots \hat{\varphi}^*(x_n)\, d^nx\, \hat{\Phi}_0.$$

1. $T$ PRODUCT. Suppose that an operator $\hat{H}$ has the form $\hat{H} = \hat{H}_0 + \hat{V}$. We represent $e^{it\hat{H}}$ in the form $e^{it\hat{H}} = e^{it\hat{H}_0}\hat{U}(t)$, where $\hat{U}(t) = e^{-it\hat{H}_0}e^{it\hat{H}}$. Along with the operator $\hat{U}(t)$ we consider the more general operator[3]

$$\hat{U}(t, \tau) = e^{-it\hat{H}_0}e^{i(t-\tau)\hat{H}}e^{i\tau\hat{H}_0} = \hat{U}(t)\hat{U}^*(\tau).$$

Differentiating with respect to $t$, we find for $\hat{U}(t, \tau)$ the differential equation

$$\frac{1}{i}\frac{d\hat{U}(t, \tau)}{dt} = \hat{V}(t)\hat{U}(t, \tau), \qquad \text{where} \qquad \hat{V}(t) = e^{-it\hat{H}_0}\hat{V}e^{it\hat{H}_0}. \tag{5}$$

Using this equation and the initial condition $\hat{U}(\tau, \tau) = 1$, we obtain for $\hat{U}(t, \tau)$ the integral equation

$$\hat{U}(t, \tau) = 1 + i \int_{\tau}^{t} \hat{V}(t_1)\hat{U}(t_1, \tau)\, dt_1. \tag{6}$$

Starting from (6) we obtain for $\hat{U}(t, \tau)$ the series expansion $\hat{U}(t, \tau) = \sum \hat{U}_n(t, \tau)$, where $\hat{U}_0(t, \tau) = 1$, and for $n > 1$,

$$\hat{U}_n(t, \tau) = i^n \int \cdots \int_{t > t_1 > \cdots > t_n > \tau} \hat{V}(t_1) \cdots \hat{V}(t_n)\, dt_1 \cdots dt_n. \tag{7}$$

We consider the operator $T$ on operators which is defined for the time being only for operators of the form $\hat{V}(t_1)\hat{V}(t_2) \cdots \hat{V}(t_n)$:

$$T[\hat{V}(t_1) \cdots \hat{V}(t_n)] = \sum \theta(t_{i_1} > t_{i_2} > \cdots > t_{i_n})\hat{V}(t_{i_1}) \cdots \hat{V}(t_{i_n}), \tag{8}$$

where

$$\theta(t_1 > \cdots > t_n) = \begin{cases} 1 & \text{for } t_1 \geq t_2 \geq \cdots \geq t_n, \\ 0 & \text{otherwise.} \end{cases}$$

The sum extends over all permutations $i_1, \ldots, i_n$ of the indices $1, \ldots, n$. For clarity we display $T[\hat{V}(t_1)\hat{V}(t_2)]$:

$$T[\hat{V}(t_1)\hat{V}(t_2)] = \theta(t_1 > t_2)\hat{V}(t_1)\hat{V}(t_2) + \theta(t_2 > t_1)\hat{V}(t_2)\hat{V}(t_1).$$

---

[3] The operator $\hat{U}(t, \tau)$ is closely connected with the scattering operator: The strong limit (if it exists) $\hat{S} = \lim_{t \to +\infty, \tau \to -\infty} \hat{U}(t, \tau)$ is the elastic part of the scattering operator.

We observe that operators are commutable under the sign $T$:

$$T[\hat{V}(t_{i_1}) \cdots \hat{V}(t_{i_n})] = T[\hat{V}(t_1) \cdots \hat{V}(t_n)].$$

By the use of the operator $T$, formula (7) can be written in the form

$$\hat{U}_n(t, \tau) = \frac{i^n}{n!} \int_\tau^t \cdots \int_\tau^t T[\hat{V}(t_1) \cdots \hat{V}(t_n)] \, dt_1 \cdots dt_n. \qquad (9)$$

In fact, by substituting the value of $T[\hat{V}(t_1) \cdots \hat{V}(t_n)]$ into (9), we obtain in the right member of (9), $n!$ terms, each of which differs from the right member of (7) only by the designation of integration variables. The expression (8) appearing in the integrand of (9) is called the $T$ product of the operators $\hat{V}(t_1), \ldots, \hat{V}(t_n)$.

The next task is to transform the $T$ product to the normal form. The operator $\hat{V}(t)$ has the form [cf. (1)]

$$\hat{V}(t) = e^{-i\hat{H}_0 t} \hat{V} e^{i\hat{H}_0 t}$$

$$= e^{-i\hat{H}_0 t} \sum \int V(\dot{p}_1, \ldots, p_r \,|\, q_1, \ldots, q_s)$$

$$\times \hat{a}^*(p_1) \cdots \hat{a}^*(p_r) \hat{a}(q_1) \cdots \hat{a}(q_s) \, d^r p \, d^s q \, e^{i\hat{H}_0 t}$$

$$= \sum \int V(p_1, \ldots, p_r \,|\, q_1, \ldots, q_s)$$

$$\times \hat{a}^*(p_1, t) \cdots \hat{a}^*(p_r, t) \hat{a}(q_1, t) \cdots \hat{a}(q_s, t) \, d^r p \, d^s q, \qquad (10)$$

where

$$\hat{a}^*(p, t) = e^{-i\hat{H}_0 t} \hat{a}^*(p) e^{i\hat{H}_0 t}, \qquad \hat{a}(p, t) = e^{-i\hat{H}_0 t} \hat{a}(p) e^{i\hat{H}_0 t}.$$

By using the explicit form of the operator $\hat{H}_0$ [cf. (1)] we find $\hat{a}(p, t)$ and $\hat{a}^*(p, t)$:

$$\hat{a}(p, t) = e^{it\omega(p)} \hat{a}(p), \qquad \hat{a}^*(p, t) = e^{-it\omega(p)} \hat{a}^*(p). \qquad (11)$$

In the following it will be necessary for us to consider an expression of the form

$$\int c(p_1, t_1, \ldots, p_r, t_r \,|\, q_1, \tau_1, \ldots, q_s, \tau_s) \hat{a}^*(p_1, t_1) \cdots \hat{a}(q_s, \tau_s) \, d^r p \, d^s q \, d^r t \, d^s \tau.$$

$$(12)$$

Because of the specific dependence of the operators $\hat{a}(p, t)$ and $\hat{a}^*(p, t)$ on $t$, the function $c$ is not defined uniquely by the expression (12), even if it satisfies the necessary condition of symmetry. This causes an inconvenience, which we shall circumvent by introducing instead of the operators $\hat{a}(p, t)$, $\hat{a}^*(p, t)$ the symbols $\tilde{a}(p, t)$, $\tilde{a}^*(p, t)$, for which it is required only that they satisfy definite commutation relations. The equality

$$\int c(p_1, t_1, \ldots, p_r, t_r | q_1, \tau_1 \cdots q_s, \tau_s) \tilde{a}^*(p_1, t_1) \cdots \tilde{a}(q_s, \tau_s) \, d^r p \, d^s q \, d^r t \, d^s \tau = 0$$

is possible only if $c \equiv 0$, provided that $c$ satisfies the usual condition of symmetry, and hence the expression of the form (12), when the operators are replaced by the symbols, defines the function $c$ uniquely. All intermediate calculations will be carried out by means of $\tilde{a}^*$, $\tilde{a}$. To get the final answer it will be necessary, after completing all calculations, to replace the symbols $\tilde{a}^*(p, t)$ and $\tilde{a}(p, t)$ by the operators $\hat{a}^*(p, t)$ and $\hat{a}(p, t)$, respectively.

2. $T$ PRODUCT OF SYMBOLS. Let $\tilde{a}(p, t)$, $\tilde{a}^*(p, t)$ be symbols satisfying the relations

$$[\tilde{a}(p_1, t_1), \tilde{a}^*(p_2, t_2)] \equiv [\hat{a}(p_1, t_1), \hat{a}^*(p_2, t_2)]$$
$$= D(p_1, t_1 | p_2, t_2),$$
$$[\tilde{a}(p_1, t_1), \tilde{a}(p_2, t_2)] \equiv [\hat{a}(p_1, t_1), \hat{a}(p_2, t_2)] = 0, \qquad (13_B)$$
$$[\tilde{a}^*(p_1, t_1), \tilde{a}^*(p_2, t_2)] \equiv [\hat{a}^*(p_1, t_1), \hat{a}^*(p_2, t_2)] = 0$$

or

$$\{\tilde{a}(p_1, t_1), \tilde{a}^*(p_2, t_2)\} \equiv \{\hat{a}(p_1, t_1), \hat{a}^*(p_2, t_2)\}$$
$$= D(p_1, t_1 | p_2, t_2),$$
$$\{\tilde{a}(p_1, t_1), \tilde{a}(p_2, t_2)\} \equiv \{\hat{a}(p_1, t_1), \hat{a}(p_2, t_2)\} = 0, \qquad (13_F)$$
$$\{\tilde{a}^*(p_1, t_1), \tilde{a}^*(p_2, t_2)\} \equiv \{\hat{a}^*(p_1, t_1), \hat{a}^*(p_2, t_2)\} = 0.$$

Starting from (11) we obtain for the function $D$ in the Bose and Fermi cases the expression

$$D(p_1, t_1 | p_2, t_2) = \delta(p_1 - p_2) e^{i(t_1 - t_2)\omega(p_1)}. \qquad (14)$$

In this and the next subsections we define the $T$ product of symbols and reduce it to the normal form. The results obtained in this way are applied in Subsection 4 to the transformation of the $T$ product of operators. Symbols are called *boson* or *fermion symbols* according to whether they satisfy relations $(13_B)$ or $(13_F)$.

Suppose for definiteness the symbols $\tilde{a}$, $\tilde{a}^*$ satisfy relations $(13_B)$. We consider a linear combination of the products of $\tilde{a}(p, t), \tilde{a}^*(p,t)$ with various $p$ and $t$. By making use of relations $(13_B)$ one can achieve an expression in which every term contains factors with the asterisk * standing on the left of factors without an asterisk:

$$\tilde{A} = \sum c(p_1, t_1,..., p_r, t_r | q_1, \tau_1,..., q_s, \tau_s)$$
$$\times \tilde{a}^*(p_1, t_1) \cdots \tilde{a}^*(p_r, t_r) a(q_1, \tau_1) \cdots a(q_s, \tau_s). \tag{15}$$

The linear combination of products written in such form will be called the *normal form*. The definition of the normal form can be transferred without alteration to the Fermi case.

The way of writing $\tilde{A}$ in the normal form (15) is unique, if the coefficients $c(p_1, t_1,..., p_r, t_r | q_1, \tau_1,..., q_s, \tau_s)$ are symmetric or anti-symmetric with respect to the first group of variables $p_i$, $t_i$ and the second group of variables $q_j$, $\tau_j$, separately, for bosons or fermions, respectively.

We define the $T$ product of the symbols $\tilde{a}(p, t)$, $\tilde{a}^*(p, t)$. In the Bose case for $t_i \neq t_j$,

$$T[\tilde{a}^*(p_1, t_1) \cdots \tilde{a}^*(p_r, t_r) \tilde{a}(p_{r+1}, t_{r+1}) \cdots \tilde{a}(p_n, t_n)]$$
$$= \sum \theta(t_{i_1} > t_{i_2} > \cdots > t_{i_n})\alpha(p_{i_1}, t_{i_1}) \cdots \alpha(p_{i_n}, t_{i_n}), \tag{$16_B$}$$

where

$$\alpha(p_k, t_k) = \begin{cases} \tilde{a}^*(p_k, t_k) & \text{for} \quad k \leq r, \\ \tilde{a}(p_k, t_k) & \text{for} \quad k > r \end{cases}$$

and

$$\theta(t_1 > t_2 > \cdots > t_n) = \begin{cases} 1 & \text{for} \quad t_1 \geq t_2 \geq \cdots \geq t_n, \\ 0 & \text{otherwise.} \end{cases}$$

In the Fermi case for $t_i \neq t_j$,

$$T[\tilde{a}^*(p_1, t_1) \cdots \tilde{a}^*(p_r, t_r) \tilde{a}(p_{r+1}, t_{r+1}) \cdots \tilde{a}(p_n, t_n)]$$
$$= \sum \pm \theta(t_{i_1} > t_{i_2} > \cdots > t_{i_n})\alpha(p_{i_1}, t_{i_1}) \cdots \alpha(p_{i_n}, t_{i_n}), \tag{$16_F$}$$

where $\alpha(p, t)$ and $\theta(t_1 > \cdots > t_n)$ have the same meaning as in the Bose case. The sums in both cases extend over all permutations $i_1, \ldots, i_n$ of the indices $1, \ldots, n$, and $+$ or $-$ in the Fermi case is taken according to whether the permutation is even or odd.

If some of the $t_k$'s coincide, then in the Bose case as well as in the Fermi case it is assumed that the corresponding symbols $\tilde{a}^*, \tilde{a}$ should be placed in the normal order.

We note that the symbols $\tilde{a}, \tilde{a}^*$ under the sign of the $T$ product commute in the Bose case, and anticommute in the Fermi case, for example,

$$T[\tilde{a}^*(p_1, t_1)\tilde{a}(p_2, t_2)] = T[\tilde{a}(p_2, t_2)\tilde{a}^*(p_1, t_1)] \qquad \text{in the Bose case,}$$

$$T[\tilde{a}^*(p_1, t_1)\tilde{a}(p_2, t_2)] = - T[\tilde{a}(p_2, t_2)\tilde{a}^*(p_1, t_1)] \qquad \text{in the Fermi case.}$$

## 3. Reduction of the $T$ Product of Symbols to Normal Form (Wick's Theorem).

**A. Bose Case.** We first consider the simplest expression. For $t_1 \neq t_2$ we have

$$T[\tilde{a}^*(p_1, t_1)\tilde{a}(p_2, t_2)]$$
$$= \theta(t_1 > t_2)\tilde{a}^*(p_1, t_1)\tilde{a}(p_2, t_2)$$
$$\quad + \theta(t_2 > t_1)\tilde{a}(p_2, t_2)\tilde{a}^*(p_1, t_1)$$
$$= \theta(t_1 > t_2)\tilde{a}^*(p_1, t_1)\tilde{a}(p_2, t_2)$$
$$\quad + \theta(t_2 > t_1)[D(p_2, t_2 | p_1, t_1) + \tilde{a}^*(p_1, t_1)\tilde{a}(p_2, t_2)]$$
$$= \tilde{a}^*(p_1, t_1)\tilde{a}(p_2, t_2) + \theta(t_2 > t_1)D(p_2, t_2 | p_1, t_1).$$

For $t_1 = t_2$,

$$T[\tilde{a}^*(p_1, t_1)\tilde{a}(p_2, t_1)] = \tilde{a}^*(p_1, t_1)\tilde{a}(p_2, t_1)$$

by definition. We introduce for brevity the new function

$$\Delta(p_1, t_1 | p_2, t_2) = \begin{cases} D(p_1, t_1 | p_2, t_2) & \text{for} \quad t_1 > t_2, \\ 0 & \text{for} \quad t_1 \leq t_2. \end{cases} \qquad (17)$$

With this function we have for all $t_1, t_2$:

$$T[\tilde{a}^*(p_1, t_1)\tilde{a}(p_2, t_2)] = \tilde{a}^*(p_1, t_1)\tilde{a}(p_2, t_2) + \Delta(p_2, t_2 | p_1, t_1). \qquad (18)$$

By the use of the fact that $[\tilde{a}(p_1, t_1), \tilde{a}(p_2, t_2)] = 0$ and $[\tilde{a}^*(p_1, t_1), \tilde{a}^*(p_2, t_2)] = 0$, we find

$$T[\tilde{a}^*(p_1, t_1)\tilde{a}^*(p_2, t_2)] = \tilde{a}^*(p_1, t_1)\tilde{a}^*(p_2, t_2),$$
$$T[\tilde{a}(p_1, t_1)\tilde{a}(p_2, t_2)] = \tilde{a}(p_1, t_1)\tilde{a}(p_2, t_2). \tag{$18_1$}$$

Now suppose that there are $n$ symbols under the sign of the $T$ product and $t_i \neq t_j$ [cf. $(16_B)$]. We divide the $n$-dimensional space of variables $t_1, \ldots, t_n$ by the planes $t_i = t_j$ into $n!$ polyhedral angles $t_{i_1} > t_{i_2} > \cdots > t_{i_n}$. With every polyhedral angle there is associated a term of the right member of $(16_B)$: If the polyhedral angle is defined by the inequalities $t_{i_1} > t_{i_2} > \cdots > t_{i_n}$, then there corresponds to it the term $\theta(t_{i_1} > \cdots > t_{i_n})\alpha(p_{i_1}, t_{i_1}) \cdots \alpha(p_{i_n}, t_{i_n})$. We rearrange the term corresponding to the polyhedral angle $t_{i_1} > t_{i_2} > \cdots > t_{i_n}$ in the normal order. Among terms arising as a result of this rearrangement, there will be first

$$\theta(t_{i_1} > \cdots > t_{i_n})\tilde{a}^*(p_1, t_1) \cdots \tilde{a}^*(p_r, t_r)\tilde{a}(p_{r+1}, t_{r+1}) \cdots \tilde{a}(p_n, t_n).$$

The sum of all terms of this type over all polyhedral angles evidently gives

$$\tilde{a}^*(p_1, t_1) \cdots \tilde{a}^*(p_r, t_r)\tilde{a}(p_{r+1}, t_{r+1}) \cdots \tilde{a}(p_n, t_n).$$

Suppose for definiteness that $t_1 < t_{r+1}$ is within the selected polyhedral angle. In such a case, among terms arising from the reduction to the normal form, there will be

$$\theta(t_{i_1} > \cdots > t_{i_n})D(p_{r+1}, t_{r+1}|p_1, t_1)$$
$$\times \tilde{a}^*(p_2, t_2) \cdots \tilde{a}^*(p_r, t_r)\tilde{a}(p_{r+2}, t_{r+2}) \cdots \tilde{a}(p_n, t_n).$$

Evidently there are terms of the same type in all polyhedral angles situated in the half-space $t_1 < t_{r+1}$. Therefore, the sum of all these terms gives

$$\theta(t_{r+1} > t_1)D(p_{r+1}, t_{r+1}|p_1, t_1)$$
$$\times \tilde{a}^*(p_2, t_2) \cdots \tilde{a}^*(p_r, t_r)\tilde{a}(p_{r+2}, t_{r+2}) \cdots \tilde{a}(p_n, t_n).$$

Suppose, further, that within the polyhedral angle the inequality $t_2 < t_{r+2}$ is also satisfied. Then, among terms arising from the rearrangement, there will be

$$\theta(t_{i_1} > t_{i_2} > \cdots > t_{i_n})D(p_{r+1}, t_{r+1}|p_1, t_1)D(p_{r+2}, t_{r+2}|p_2, t_2)$$
$$\times \tilde{a}^*(p_3, t_3) \cdots \tilde{a}^*(p_r, t_r)\tilde{a}(p_{r+3}, t_{r+3}) \cdots \tilde{a}(p_n, t_n),$$

and moreover such terms will be in all polyhedral angles situated in the intersection of the half-spaces $t_1 < t_{r+1}$ and $t_2 < t_{r+2}$. Therefore, the sum of all these terms gives

$$\theta(t_{r+1} > t_1)\theta(t_{r+2} > t_2)D(p_{r+1}, t_{r+1}|p_1, t_1)D(p_{r+2}, t_{r+2}|p_2, t_2)$$

$$\times \tilde{a}^*(p_3, t_3) \cdots \tilde{a}^*(p_r, t_r)\tilde{a}(p_{r+3}, t_{r+3}) \cdots \tilde{a}(p_n, t_n). \quad (19)$$

Evidently, by continuing this process further, we cover all terms arising from the reduction of the $T$ product to the normal form. The result thus obtained can be written in the form

$$T[\tilde{a}^*(p_1, t_1) \cdots \tilde{a}^*(p_r, t_r)\tilde{a}(q_1, \tau_1) \cdots \tilde{a}(q_s, \tau_s)]$$

$$= \tilde{a}^*(p_1, t_1) \cdots \tilde{a}^*(p_r, t_r)\tilde{a}(q_1, \tau_1) \cdots \tilde{a}(q_s, \tau_s)$$

$$+ \sum \{\Delta(q_i, \tau_i|p_j, t_j)\tilde{a}^*(p_1, t_1) \cdots \tilde{a}^*(p_{j-1}, t_{j-1})\tilde{a}^*(p_{j+1}, t_{j+1}) \cdots$$

$$\tilde{a}^*(p_r, t_r)\tilde{a}(q_1, \tau_1) \cdots \tilde{a}(q_{i-1}, \tau_{i-1})\tilde{a}(q_{i+1}, \tau_{i+1}) \cdots \tilde{a}(q_s, \tau_s)\}$$

$$+ \frac{1}{2!} \sum \{\Delta(q_{i_1}, \tau_{i_1}|p_{j_1}, t_{j_1})\Delta(q_{i_2}, \tau_{i_2}|p_{j_2}, \tau_{j_2})$$

$$\times \tilde{a}^*(p_1, t_1) \cdots \tilde{a}^*(p_{j_1-1}, t_{j_1-1})\tilde{a}^*(p_{j_1+1}, t_{j_1+1}) \cdots$$

$$\tilde{a}^*(p_{j_2-1}, t_{j_2-1})\tilde{a}^*(p_{j_2+1}, t_{j_2+1}) \cdots \tilde{a}^*(p_r, t_r)$$

$$\times \tilde{a}(q_1, \tau_1) \cdots \tilde{a}(q_{i_1-1}, \tau_{i_1-1})\tilde{a}(q_{i_1+1}, \tau_{i_1+1}) \cdots$$

$$\tilde{a}(q_{i_2-1}, \tau_{i_2+1})\tilde{a}(q_{i_2+1}, \tau_{i_2+1}) \cdots \tilde{a}(q_s, \tau_s)\} + \cdots \quad (20)$$

The first sum extends over all possible pairs $(p_j, t_j|q_i, \tau_i)$ and the second sum over two such pairs, and the third over three such pairs, and so forth. The first and second indices forming a pair run independently through their own set of values. Therefore every term in the sum over $k$ pairs appears $k!$ times. Hence there is the factor $1/k!$ before the sum over $k$ pairs.

Formula (20) has been derived under the condition $t_i \neq t_j$, $\tau_i \neq \tau_j$, $t_i \neq \tau_j$. However, it is not difficult to verify that this holds for all cases. If some of $t_i$, $\tau_j$ are equal, then by the definition of the $T$ product the corresponding symbols are in the normal form and no further re-arrangement is needed. This circumstance can be taken into account by the fact that $\Delta(t_1, p_1 \,|\, t_2, p_2) = 0$ for $t_1 = t_2$. Formula (20) is called *Wick's formula*.[4]

Formula (20) can be written in a more compact form as follows. We consider complex-valued functions $a^*(p, t)$, $a(p, t)$ and put into correspondence with every normal product of symbols the corresponding product of functions:

$$\tilde{a}^*(p_1, t_1) \cdots \tilde{a}^*(p_r, t_r)\tilde{a}(q_1, \tau_1) \cdots \tilde{a}(q_s, \tau_s)$$
$$\leftrightarrow a^*(p_1, t_1) \cdots a^*(p_r, t_r)a(q_1, \tau_1) \cdots a(q_s, \tau_s).$$

By making use of this correspondence, we can rewrite formula (20) in the form

$$T[\tilde{a}^*(p_1, t_1) \cdots \tilde{a}^*(p_r, t_r)\tilde{a}(q_1, \tau_1) \cdots \tilde{a}(q_s, \tau_s)]$$
$$\leftrightarrow \exp\left[\int \frac{\delta}{\delta a(q, \tau)} \Delta(q, \tau \,|\, p, t) \frac{\delta}{\delta a^*(p, t)} \, dp \, dq \, dt \, d\tau\right]$$
$$\times a^*(p_1, t_1) \cdots a^*(p_r, t_r)a(q_1, \tau_1) \cdots a(q_s, \tau_s). \qquad (21_B)$$

The right member of formula $(21_B)$ is the result of operating by $\exp \int (\delta/\delta a) \Delta (\delta/\delta a^*) \, dp \, dq \, dt \, d\tau$ on the product $a^*(p_1, t_1) \cdots a(q_s, \tau_s)$.

The verification of formula $(21_B)$ is carried out by expanding the exponential into a series; the terms arising therein evidently correspond to the terms in the right member of (20).

**B. Fermi Case.** All arguments given above can be transferred to the Fermi case and lead to a formula almost identical in form with $(21_B)$:

$$T[\tilde{a}^*(p_1, t_1) \cdots \tilde{a}^*(p_r, t_r)\tilde{a}(q_1, \tau_1) \cdots \tilde{a}(q_s, \tau_s)]$$
$$\leftrightarrow \exp\left[\int \frac{\delta}{\delta_r a(q, \tau)} \Delta(q, \tau \,|\, p, t) \frac{\delta}{\delta_l a^*(p, t)} \, dp \, dq \, dt \, d\tau\right]$$
$$\times a^*(p_1, t_1) \cdots a^*(p_r, t_r)a(q_1, \tau_1) \cdots a(q_s, \tau_s). \qquad (21_F)$$

The difference consists of the fact that here $a^*(p, t)$, $a(p, t)$ are functions with anticommuting values (forming a Grassmann algebra), and $\delta/\delta_r a$,

---

[4] Wick's formula in this form is found in textbooks of quantum field theory. Cf., for example, the book by Ahiezer and Berestečkiĭ [1] or the book by Bogolyubov and Širkov [1].

$\delta/\delta_l a^*$ are the operators of right and left differentiation. The function $\Delta$ is defined in the same way as in the Bose case by equality (17).

4. APPLICATION OF WICK'S FORMULA TO THE CALCULATION OF THE OPERATOR $\hat{U}(t, \tau)$. Consider first the Bose case. It has been noted above that the operator $\hat{V}(t)$ is equal to

$$\hat{V}(t) = \sum \int V(p_1,\ldots,p_r | q_1,\ldots,q_s)$$
$$\times \hat{a}^*(p_1, t) \cdots \hat{a}^*(p_r, t)\hat{a}(q_1, t) \cdots \hat{a}(q_s, t) \, d^r p \, d^s q,$$

where $\hat{a}^*(p, t) = e^{-it\omega(p)}\hat{a}^*(p)$, $\hat{a}(p, t) = e^{it\omega(p)}\hat{a}(p)$. We assign to the operator $\hat{V}(t)$ the symbol

$$\hat{V}(t) = \sum \int V(p_1,\ldots,p_r | q_1,\ldots,q_s)$$
$$\times \tilde{a}^*(p_1, t) \cdots \tilde{a}^*(p_r, t)\tilde{a}(q_1, t) \cdots \tilde{a}(q_s, t) \, d^r p \, d^s q.$$

We have to find the normal form of the operator $T[\hat{V}(t_1) \cdots \hat{V}(t_n)]$. We shall solve an auxiliary problem: to find the normal form of the symbol $T[\tilde{V}(t_1) \cdots \tilde{V}(t_n)]$. It can be readily seen that if we reduce $T[\tilde{V}(t_1) \cdots (\tilde{V}t_n)]$ to the normal form and replace $\tilde{a}^*(p, t)$ by $\hat{a}^*(p, t) = e^{-it\omega(p)}\hat{a}^*(p)$ and $\tilde{a}(p, t)$ by $\hat{a}(p, t) = e^{it\omega(p)}\hat{a}(p)$ in the final answer, then we obtain the normal form of the operator $T[\hat{V}(t_1) \cdots \hat{V}(t_n)]$.

Therefore we can make use of the result of the preceding subsection. Consider arbitrary functions $a(p, t)$, $a^*(p, t)$ of independent variables $p$, $t$. We assign to the operator $\hat{V}(t)$ the functional of $a(p, t)$, $a^*(p, t)$:

$$V(t | a^*, a) = \sum \int \{V(p_1,\ldots,p_r | q_1,\ldots,q_s)$$
$$\times \delta(t - t_1) \cdots \delta(t - t_r)\delta(t - \tau_1) \cdots \delta(t - \tau_s)$$
$$\times a^*(p_1, t_1) \cdots a^*(p_r, t_r)a(q_1, \tau_1) \cdots a(q_s, \tau_s)\} \, d^r p \, d^s q \, d^r t \, d^s \tau$$

By applying Wick's theorem we find that

$$T[\hat{V}(t_1) \cdots \hat{V}(t_n)]$$
$$\leftrightarrow \exp\left[\int \frac{\delta}{\delta a(q, \tau)} \Delta(q, \tau | p, t) \frac{\delta}{\delta a^*(p, t)} \, dp \, dq \, dt \, d\tau\right] V(t_1) \cdots V(t_n).$$
$$(22)$$

Because of the connection between the normal form of the operator and the functionals, it is found that to get the functional corresponding to the normal form of the operator $T[\hat{V}(t_1) \cdots \hat{V}(t_n)]$, one should put

$$a^*(p, t) = e^{-it\omega(p)}a^*(p), \qquad a(p, t) = e^{it\omega(p)}a(p).$$

after the calculation of the right member of (22). Integrating the right and left members of (22) between the limits $\tau$ to $t$, we find

$$\int_\tau^t \cdots \int_\tau^t T[\hat{V}(t_1) \cdots \hat{V}(t_n)]dt_1 \ldots dt_n$$

$$\leftrightarrow \exp\left[\int \frac{\delta}{\delta a(p_1, t_1)} \Delta(p_1, t_1 | p_2, t_2) \frac{\delta}{\delta a^*(p_2, t_2)} dp_1 \, dp_2 \, dt_1 \, dt_2\right]$$

$$\times \left(\int_\tau^t V(s|a^*, a) \, ds\right)^n. \tag{23}$$

Recalling formula (9) we find the final expression for the functional $U(t, \tau | a^*, a)$ corresponding to the normal form of the operator $\hat{U}(t, \tau)$: $U(t, \tau | a^*, a)$ is the value of the functional $U_1(t, \tau | a^*, a)$ of the arbitrary functions $a(p, t)$, $a^*(p, t)$ at $a(p, t) = e^{it\omega(p)}a(p)$ and $a^*(p, t) = e^{-it\omega(p)} a^*(p)$, where

$$U_1(t, \tau | a^*, a)$$

$$= \exp\left[\int \frac{\delta}{\delta a(p_1, t_1)} \Delta(p_1, t_1 | p_2, t_2) \frac{\delta}{\delta a^*(p_2, t_2)} dp_1 \, dp_2 \, dt_1 \, dt_2\right]$$

$$\times \exp\left[i \int_\tau^t V(s|a^*, a) \, ds\right]. \tag{24_B}$$

In the Fermi case a similar formula holds:

$$U_1(t, \tau | a^*, a) = \exp\left[\int \frac{\delta}{\delta_r a(q, \tau)} \Delta(q, \tau | p, t) \frac{\delta}{\delta a_l^*(p, t)} dp \, dq \, dt \, d\tau\right]$$

$$\times \exp\left[i \int_\tau^t V(s|a^*, a) \, ds\right]. \tag{24_F}$$

Formulas $(24_B)$ and $(24_F)$ are utilized for expanding $\hat{U}(t, \tau)$ into a perturbation series and for obtaining an integral representation of $\hat{U}(t, \tau)$. For $t = \infty$ and $\tau = -\infty$ formulas $(24_B)$ and $(24_F)$ give the expression for the elastic part of the scattering operator.

5. INTEGRAL REPRESENTATIONS FOR THE OPERATORS $\hat{U}(t, \tau)$ AND $e^{it\hat{H}}$.
In this subsection we shall restrict ourselves to the case when the
operator $\hat{H}$ has a very simple form $\hat{H} = \hat{H}_0 + \hat{V}$, where

$$\hat{H}_0 = \int \omega(k)\hat{a}^*(k)\hat{a}(k) \, dk,$$

$$\hat{V} = \int V(p_1, p_2 \,|\, q_1, q_2)\hat{a}^*(p_1)\hat{a}^*(p_2)\hat{a}(q_1)\hat{a}(q_2) \, dp_1 \cdots dq_2 \,.$$

From now on we shall employ the abbreviation for integrals, e.g.,

$$a^*f = \int a^*(p, t)f(p, t) \, dp \, dt,$$

$$\frac{\delta}{\delta a} \Delta \frac{\delta}{\delta a^*} = \int \frac{\delta}{\delta a(p_1, t_1)} \Delta(p_1, t_1 \,|\, p_2, t_2) \frac{\delta}{\delta a^*(p_2, t_2)} \, dp_1 \, dp_2 \, dt_1 \, dt_2, \text{ etc.}$$

Calculations in the Fermi and Bose cases are completely identical, and
hence we shall study in detail only the Fermi case and limit ourselves
to giving only the final answer for the Bose case.

For the calculation of the operator $\hat{U}(t, \tau)$ one must make use of
formula $(24_F)$. Before applying it, we solve some auxiliary problems.

First of all, let us calculate the functional

$$T_1(a^*, a) = \exp\left(\frac{\delta}{\delta_r a} \Delta \frac{\delta}{\delta_l a^*}\right) \exp[f^*a + a^*f], \tag{25}$$

where $f^*$, $f$ anticommute with $a$, $a^*$ and with each other. We remark
that the functional $e^{f^*a + a^*f}$ is the eigenvector of the operator $(\delta/\delta_r a)$
$\Delta (\delta/\delta_l a^*)$ with the eigenvalue $f^* \Delta f$. Using this fact we find the functional $T_1$:

$$T_1(a^*, a) = \exp[f^* \Delta f + a^*f + f^*a]. \tag{26}$$

We shall now find the functional $T_2$ which is equal to

$$T_2(a^*, a) = \exp\left(\frac{\delta}{\delta_r a} \Delta \frac{\delta}{\delta_l a^*}\right) \exp[-a^*Ka].$$

To this end we use the identity

$$\exp[-a^*Ka] = (\det K_1)^{-1} \int \exp[f^*K_1 f + a^*f + f^*a] \, \Pi \, df^* \, df,$$

which is easily verified. Here $K_1 = K_1(p_1, t_1 | p_2, t_2)$ is the operator inverse to the operator $K$ and $\det K_1$ is the Fredholm determinant of the operator $K_1$. By making use of formula (26), we find

$$\exp\left(\frac{\delta}{\delta_r a} \Delta \frac{\delta}{\delta_l a^*}\right) \exp[-a^* K a]$$

$$= (\det K_1)^{-1} \int \exp[f^* K_1 f] \exp\left(\frac{\delta}{\delta_r a} \Delta \frac{\delta}{\delta_l a^*}\right) \exp[a^* f + f^* a] \, \Pi \, df^* \, df$$

$$= (\det K_1)^{-1} \int \exp[f^* K_1 f + f^* \Delta f + a^* f + f^* a] \, \Pi \, df^* \, df$$

$$= (\det K_1)^{-1} \det(K_1 + \Delta) \exp[-a^*(K_1 + \Delta)^{-1} a].$$

Recalling that $K_1 = K^{-1}$, we obtain the final expression for $T_2$:

$$T_2(a^*, a) = \det(1 + K\Delta) \exp[-a^*(K^{-1} + \Delta)^{-1} a]. \qquad (27)$$

Now we are in a position to calculate our functional. For this purpose we express it in terms of a functional of the type $T_2$, just as we have expressed these functionals in terms of a simpler functional of the type $T_1$:

$$\exp\left[i \int V(p_1, p_2 | q_1, q_2) a^*(p_1, t) a^*(p_2, t) a(q_1, t) a(q_2, t) \, d^2p \, d^2q \, dt\right]$$

$$= \int \exp\left\{-\int a^* [V_1(s) z(s, t) + V_2(s) z^*(s, t)] \, a \, ds \, dt\right.$$

$$\left. - \int z^* z \, ds \, dt\right\} \Pi \, dz^* \, dz,$$

where $z = z(s, t)$, $z^* = z^*(s, t)$ are complex-valued functions, $s$ is a certain parameter, and $V_1(s) = V_1(p, q | s)$ and $V_2(s) = V_2(s | p, q)$ are arbitrary functions satisfying the relation[5]

$$\int V_1(p_1, q_1 | s) V_2(s | p_2, q_2) \, ds = i V(p_1, p_2 | q_1, q_2).$$

---

[5] Such a decomposition is always possible: for example, if $s = (p, q)$, then one may choose $V_1(p_1, q_1 | s) = i V(p_1, p | q_1, q)$ and $V_2(s | p_2, q_2) = \delta(p_2 - p)\delta(q_2 - q)$.

Applying the result obtained earlier, we find

$$\exp\left(\frac{\delta}{\delta_r a} \Delta \frac{\delta}{\delta_l a^*}\right) \exp\left[i \int V(p_1, p_2 | q_1, q_2) a^*(p_1, t) a^*(p_2, t)\right.$$

$$\left. \times a(q_1, t) a(q_2, t) d^2p\, d^2q\, dt\right]$$

$$= \int \det(1 + R\Delta) \exp[-a^*(R^{-1} + \Delta)^{-1}a - zz^*] \prod dz^*\, dz,$$

where $R$ is an operator with the kernel

$$R(p_1, t_1 | p_2, t_2)$$

$$= \int [V_1(p_1, p_2 | s) z(s, t_1) + V_2(s | p_1\, p_2) z^*(s, t_2)]\, ds\, \delta(t_1 - t_2)$$

$$= R_1(p_1, p_2, t_1) \delta(t_1 - t_2). \tag{28}$$

This last formula gives the solution of the problem. Before writing it in final form, we observe that the determinant in the integrand is equal to unity. In fact

$$\text{sp } R\Delta = \int R_1(p_1, p_2, t) \Delta(p_2, t | p_1, t)\, dp_1\, dp_2\, dt = 0,$$

since $\Delta(p_2, t | p_1, t) = 0$. Further, we have

$$\text{sp}(R\Delta)^2 = \int R_1(p_1, p_2, t_1) \Delta(p_2, t_1 | p_3, t_2)$$

$$\times R_1(p_3, p_4, t_2) \Delta(p_4, t_2 | p_1, t_1)\, d^4p\, d^2t.$$

Recalling the definition of the function $\Delta$ we find that the integrand contains a factor which vanishes identically: $\theta(t_1 > t_2)\theta(t_2 > t_1)$. In a similar way it is confirmed that $\text{sp}(R\Delta)^n = 0$. Therefore, $\text{sp } \ln(1 + R\Delta) = 0$ and hence $\det(1 + R\Delta) = \exp \text{sp} \ln(1 + R\Delta) = 1$.

Thus we obtain the final expression for the functional $U_1(t, \tau | a^*, a)$ in the form of the continual integral:

$$U_1(t, \tau | a^*, a) = \int \exp[-a^*(R^{-1} + \Delta)^{-1}a - zz^*] \prod dz^*\, dz,$$

where $R$ is the operator whose kernel is given by formula (28). To obtain the functional $U(t, \tau | a^*, a)$ corresponding to the normal form of the operator $\hat{U}(t, \tau)$, we have to put in this formula

$$a(p, t) = e^{it\omega(p)}a(p), \qquad a^*(p, t) = e^{-it\omega(p)}a^*(p).$$

As a result we obtain

$$U(t, \tau | a^*, a) = \int \exp[-a^*T(z^*, z)a - z^*z] \, \Pi \, dz^* \, dz, \qquad (29)$$

where

$$T(z^*, z) = T(z^*, z | t, \tau | p_1, p_2)$$

$$= \int_\tau^t \int_\tau^t \exp[i(t_2\omega(p_2) - t_1\omega(p_1))] \, S(p_1, t_1; p_2, t_2 | z^*, z) \, dt_1 \, dt_2.$$

$$(29_1)$$

$S(p_1, t_1; p_2, t_2 | z, z^*)$ is the kernel of the operator $S = (R^{-1} + \Delta)^{-1} = R(1 + \Delta R)^{-1}$, and $R$ is defined by formula (28).

Formula (29) is valid in the Fermi case as well as in the Bose case. In conclusion we note the case when

$$V(p_1, p_2 | q_1, q_2) = V(p_1 - q_1)\delta(p_1 + p_2 - q_1 - q_2). \qquad (30)$$

As was noted above, the function (30) induces an interaction operator in the many-particle problem. In this case the functions $V_1$ and $V_2$ defining the operator $R$ can be expressed as

$$V_1 = V_1(p_1 - q_1)\delta(p_1 - q_1 - s),$$
$$V_2 = V_2(q_2 - p_2)\delta(p_2 - q_2 + s),$$
$$(31)$$

where $V_1(p)$ and $V_2(p)$ are arbitrary functions satisfying the condition

$$V_1(p)V_2(p) = iV(p).$$

The operator $R$ corresponding to the function (31) is given by the kernel $R(p_1, t_1 | p_2, t_2) = R_1(p_1, p_2, t_1) \, \delta(t_1 - t_2)$, where

$$R_1(p_1, p_2, t) = V_1(p_1 - p_2)z(p_1 - p_2, t) + V_2(p_2 - p_1)z^*(p_2 - p_1, t).$$
$$(32)$$

6. OPERATOR $e^{it\hat{H}}$. The operator $\hat{H}_0$ has the form

$$\hat{H}_0 = \int \omega(k)\hat{a}^*(k)\hat{a}(k) \, dk.$$

Therefore, according to formulas (6.22) and (6.38), the operator $e^{it\hat{H}_0}$ is given by the functional corresponding to the normal form:

$$\exp{(it\hat{H}_0)} \leftrightarrow \exp\left[\int (\exp[it\omega(k)] - 1)a^*(k)a(k)\,dk\right]. \qquad (33)$$

By using this expression, formula (29) for $\tau = 0$ and the formula for the multiplication of operators, after simple transformations leading to singling out a complete square and the calculation of the Gauss integral, we find the functional corresponding to the normal form of the operator $e^{it\hat{H}}$:

$$e^{it\hat{H}} \leftrightarrow \int\left[\exp[a^*(e^{it\omega}(1 - T) - 1)a - zz^*\right]\Pi\,dz\,dz^*, \qquad (34)$$

where $T = T(z, z^*)$ is defined by formula $(29_1)$. Formula (34) is valid in the Bose case as well as in the Fermi case.

7. EXPRESSION OF PARTITION FUNCTIONS IN THE FORM OF CONTINUAL INTEGRALS. The function

$$\Xi(\beta, \mu) = \mathrm{Sp}\ e^{-\beta(\hat{H} + \mu\hat{N})},$$

is called the (grand) partition function in quantum statistical mechanics. Here $\hat{H}$ is the energy operator of the system, $\hat{N}$ the number operator of particles, $\beta$ a quantity inversely proportional to the absolute temperature, and $\mu$ the chemical potential. A typical case is given by the energy operator of the form[6]

$$\hat{H} = \sum \omega(k)\hat{a}^*(k)\hat{a}(k)$$

$$+ \frac{1}{\Omega}\sum V(p_1 - q_1)\delta_{p_1 + p_2 - q_1 - q_2}\hat{a}^*(p_1)\hat{a}^*(p_2)\hat{a}(q_1)\hat{a}(q_2),$$

where $k$, $p$, $q$ run through a lattice in a three-dimensional space with the volume of an elementary cell equal to $1/\Omega$. Putting $t = i\beta$ and because of the related changes in the calculations, we obtain from (34)

---

[6] The operators $\hat{a}(k)$, $\hat{a}^*(k)$ satisfy the relations $[\hat{a}(k), \hat{a}^*(k')] = \delta_{k-k'}$ in the Bose case and $\{\hat{a}(k), \hat{a}^*(k')\} = \delta_{k-k'}$ in the Fermi case, and $\delta_{k-k'} = 1$ for $k = k'$ and $\delta_{k-k'} = 0$ for $k \neq k'$.

Recall that the number operator of the particles is $\hat{N} = \sum \hat{a}^*(k)\hat{a}(k)$. Therefore the operator $\hat{H} + \mu\hat{N}$ is obtained from $\hat{H}$ by replacing $\omega(k)$ by $\omega(k) + \mu$.

and the formulas for the trace (2.34) and (3.72) an expression for the partition function: In the Bose case,

$$\Xi = \int \det[1 - \exp[-\beta(\omega + \mu)] (1 - T)]^{-1} \exp[-zz^*] \, \Pi \, dz \, dz^*. \quad (35_B)$$

In the Fermi case,

$$\Xi = \int \det[1 + \exp[-\beta(\omega + \mu)] (1 - T)] \exp[-zz^*] \, \Pi \, dz \, dz^*. \quad (35_F)$$

The operator $T$ is given in both cases by the kernel

$$T(p_1, p_2 | \beta)$$

$$= \int_0^\beta \int_0^\beta \exp[t_1(\omega(p) + \mu) - t_2(\omega(p_2) + \mu)] \, S(p_1, t_1; p_2, t_2) \, dt_1 \, dt_2,$$

$$(36)$$

$S(p_1, t_1; p_2, t_2)$ is the kernel of the operator $S = R(1 + \Delta R)^{-1}$, and $R$ is defined by formula (32), in which $V_1(p)V_2(p) = -(1/\Omega)V(p)$, and

$$\Delta = \Delta(p_1, t_1 | p_2, t_2) = \theta(t_1 - t_2)\delta_{p_1 - p_2} e^{(t_2 - t_1)(\omega(p_2) + \mu)},$$

$$\theta(t) = \begin{cases} 1 & \text{for } t > 0, \\ 0 & \text{for } t \le 0. \end{cases} \quad (37)$$

The operator $e^{-\beta(\omega + \mu)}(1 - T)$ under the sign of the determinant in formulas $(35_B)$ and $(35_F)$ allows a curious interpretation. We observe first of all that

$$e^{-\beta(\omega(p_1) + \mu)} \int_0^\beta e^{t_1(\omega(p_1) + \mu)} S(p_1, t_1; p_2, t_2) \, dt_1$$

$$= \sum_q \int_0^\infty \Delta(p_1, \beta | q, t_1) S(q, t_1; p_2, t_2) \, dt_1;$$

i.e., this is the kernel of the operator $\Delta S = \Delta R(1 + \Delta R)^{-1}$. We denote the kernel of this operator by $S_1(p_1, \beta; p_2, t_2)$. It follows from (36) that $e^{-\beta(\omega + \mu)}(1 - T)$ can be written in the form

$$\int_0^\infty [\delta(\beta - t_2)\delta_{p_1 - p_2} - \theta(\beta - t_2)S_1(p_1, \beta; p_2, t_2)] e^{-t_2(\omega(p_2) + \mu)} \, dt_2.$$

In the square brackets, evidently, there is the kernel of the operator

$$1 - \Delta S = 1 - \Delta R(1 + \Delta R)^{-1} = (1 + \Delta R)^{-1}.$$

We denote this kernel by $\tilde{G}(p_1, t_1; p_2, t_2)$. Thus we have

$$e^{-\beta(\omega+\mu)}(1 - T) = \int_0^\infty \tilde{G}(p_1, \beta; p_2, t)e^{-t(\omega(p_2)+\mu)} \, dt. \tag{38}$$

Suppose that a function $f(p, t)$ is connected with $g(p, t) = g(p)$ $e^{-t(\omega(p)+\mu)}$ $(0 \le t \le \beta)$ by the integral relation

$$f(p, t) = \sum_q \int_0^\infty \tilde{G}(p, t; q, \tau)g(q, \tau) \, d\tau. \tag{39}$$

By solving this equation with respect to $g$, we find that $g = (1 + \Delta R)f$. Because of the explicit form of the functions $\Delta$ and $R$, we obtain from this

$$f(p, t) + \sum_q \int_0^t e^{-(t-\tau)(\omega(p)+\mu)}R_1(p, q, \tau)f(q, \tau) \, d\tau = g(p, t). \tag{40}$$

Multiplying both members of this equality by $e^{t(\omega(p)+\mu)}$ and differentiating, we find

$$\frac{df}{dt} + (\omega(p) + \mu)f + \sum_q R_1(p, q, t)f(q, t) = 0. \tag{41}$$

(Here we have taken into account that $g(p, t) = g(p)e^{-t(\omega(p)+\mu)}$ and hence that $(d/dt)[g(p, t)e^{t(\omega(p)+\mu)}] = 0$.)

Integral equation (40) for $t = 0$ gives $f(p, 0) = g(p, 0) = g(p)$. Thus $f(p, t)$ is the solution of the Cauchy problem of equation (41) with the initial condition $f(p, 0) = g(p)$.

We denote by $G(p, q | t)$ the Green's function of the Cauchy problem for equation (41). Then

$$f(p, t) = \sum_q G(p, q | t)g(q).$$

On the other hand, according to (39),

$$f(p, t) = \sum_q \int_0^t \tilde{G}(p, t; q, \tau)e^{-\tau(\omega(q)+\mu)}g(q) \, d\tau.$$

As a consequence we have

$$\int_0^t \tilde{G}(p, t; q, \tau)e^{-\tau(\omega(q)+\mu)} \, d\tau = G(p, q | t).$$

This last relation holds for $0 \leq t \leq \beta$, in particular for $t = \beta$.
Recalling formula (38), we finally find from this that

$$e^{-\beta(\omega+\mu)}(1 - T) = G(p, q \mid \beta). \qquad (42)$$

Recalling also formulas $(35_B)$ and $(35_F)$, we obtain the expression for the partition function[7]

$$\Xi = \int \det(1 - G)^{-1} \exp[-zz^*] \, \Pi \, dz \, dz^* \qquad (43_B)$$

for bosons and

$$\Xi = \int \det(1 + G) \exp[-zz^*] \, \Pi \, dz \, dz^* \qquad (43_F)$$

for fermions.

In these formulas $G$ is the operator, depending on the parameter $\beta$, with the kernel $G(p, q \mid \beta)$, which is the Green's function for the Cauchy problem of Eq. (41). The function $R_1(p, q, t)$ entering into Eq. (41) is equal to

$$R_1(p, q, t) = V_1(p - q)z(p - q, t) + V_2(q - p)z^*(q - p, t),$$

where $V_1$, $V_2$ are arbitrary functions connected by the relation

$$V_1(p)V_2(p) = -\frac{1}{\Omega} \, V(p)$$

---

[7] R. A. Minlos drew my attention to the possibility of expressing the partition function in the form $(43_B)$, $(43_F)$.

# References

AHIEZER, A. I., and BERESTEČKIĬ, V. B.
[1] "Quantum Electrodynamics" (in Russian). Gostehizdat, Moscow, 1959; English transl., Wiley, New York, 1965.

AHIEZER, N. I.
[1] Infinite Jacobi Matrices and the Problem of Moments (in Russian). *Usp. Mat. Nauk* **9** 126–156 (1941).

AHIEZER, N. I., and GLAZMAN, I. M.
[1] "Spectral Theory of Linear Operators" (in Russian). Gostehizdat, Moscow-Leningrad, 1950; English transl., Ungar, New York, 1961.

BARGMANN, V.
[1] Remarks on a Hilbert Space of Analytic Functions. *Proc. Natl. Acad. Sci. U.S.* **2**, 199–204 (1962).
[2] On a Hilbert Space of Analytic Functions and an Associated Integral Transform, Part I. *Comm. Pure. Appl. Math.* **14**, 187–214 (1961).

BERESTEČKIĬ, V. B., and GALANIN, L. D.
[1] Introductory article to "Problems of Modern Physics" (in Russian). No. 3 5–27 (1955).

BEREZIN, F. A.
[1] On the Thirring Model (in Russian). *Zh. Eksperim. i Teor. Fiz.* **40**, 885–894 (1961).
[2] Canonical Transformations in the Representation of Second Quantization (in Russian). *Dokl. Akad. Nauk SSSR* **137**, 311–314 (1961).
[3] On the Lee Model (in Russian). *Dokl. Akad. Nauk SSSR* **143**, 811–814 (1962).
[4] On the Lee Model (in Russian). *Mat. Sb*, **60**, 425–446 (1963).
[5] Canonical Transformations in the Representation of Second Quantization (in Russian). *Dokl. Akad. Nauk SSSR* **150**, 959–962 (1963).
[6] Operators in the Representation of Second Quantization (in Russian). *Dokl. Akad. Nauk SSSR* **154**, 1063–1066 (1964).
[7] On Exactly Soluble Model in Quantum Field Theory (in Russian). *Usp. Mat. Nauk* **18**, No. 5 (113), 225–226 (1964).

BEREZIN, F. A., MINLOS, R. A., and FADDEEV, L. D.
[1] Quantum Mechanics of Systems with Many Degrees of Freedom (in Russian). *Proc. Fourth All-Union Math. Congr.* 1961, Nauka, Moscow 1964, Vol. II, pp. 532–540.

BOGOLYUBOV, N. N., and ŠIRKOV, D. V.
[1] "Introduction to the Theory of Quantized Fields" (in Russian). Gostehizdat, Moscow, 1957. English transl., Wiley (Interscience), New York, 1959.

CARLEMAN, T.
[1] "Les Fonctions quasi-analytiques." Gauthier-Villars, Paris 1926.

223

DIRAC, P. A. M.
[1] Theory of the Emission and Absorption of Radiation. *Proc. Roy. Soc.* (*London*) **A144**, 243–262 (1927).

DUNFORD, N., and SCHWARTZ, J. T.
[1] "Linear Operators," Part II. Wiley (Interscience), New York, 1963.

EDWARDS, S. F., and PEIERLS, R. E.
[1] Field Equations in Functional Form. *Proc. Roy. Soc.* (*London*), **A224**, 24–33 (1954).

FOCK, V. A.
[1] Konfigurationsraum und zweite Quantelung, *Z. Physik* **75**, 622–647 (1932).
[2] Zur Quantenelektrodynamik, *Soviet Phys.* **6**, 425 (1934).

FRADKIN, E. S.
[1] The Method of Green's Functions in the Theory of Quantized Fields and in the Quantum Statistics (in Russian). *Tr. Fiz. Inst. Akad. Nauk SSSR* **29**, 1–138 (1965).

FRIEDRICHS, K. O.
[1] "Mathematical Aspects of the Quantum Theory of Fields." Wiley (Interscience), New York, 1953.

GÅRDING, L., and WIGHTMAN, A. S.
[1] Representation of the Anticommutation Relations. *Proc. Natl. Acad. Sci. U.S.* **40**, 617–621 (1954).
[2] Representation of the Commutation Relations. *Proc. Natl. Acad. Sci. US.* **40**, 622–626 (1954).

GEL'FAND, I. M., and KOSTYUČENKO, A. G.
[1] Expansion by Eigenfunctions of Differential and Other Operators (in Russian). *Dokl. Akad. Nauk SSSR* **103**, 349–352 (1955).

GEL'FAND, I. M., and ŠILOV, G. E.
[1] "Generalized Functions," Vol. 2 (in Russian). Fizmatgiz, Moscow, 1958.

GEL'FAND, I. M., and VILENKIN, N. YA.
[1] "Generalized Functions," Vol. 4 (in Russian). Fizmatgiz, Moscow, 1958. English transl., Academic Press, New York, 1964.

GEL'FAND, I. M., and YAGLOM, A. M.
[1] Integration in Functional Spaces and Its Applications in Quantum Physics (in Russian). *Usp. Mat. Nauk* **11**, No. 1 (67), 77–114 (1956). English transl., *J. Math. Phys.* **1**, 48–69 (1960).

GLASER, V.
[1] An Explicit Solution of the Thirring Model. *Nuovo Cimento* **9**, 990–1006 (1958).

GREENBERG, O. W., and SCHWEBER, S. S.
[1] Clothed Particle Operators in Simple Models of Quantum Field Theory. *Nuovo Cimento* **8**, 378–406 (1958).

HAAG, R.
[1] On Quantum Field Theories. *Kgl. Danske Videnskab. Selskab, Mat.-Fys. Medd.* **29**, No. 12, 1–37 (1955).

HALATNIKOV I. M.
[1] Representation of the Green Functions in Quantum Electrodynamics (in Russian). *Zh. Eksperim. i. Teor. Fiz.* **28**, 635–638 (1954).

HEINZ, E.
[1] Beiträge zur Störungstheorie der Spektralzerlegung. *Math. Ann.* **123**, 415–438 (1951).

HEISENBERG, W.
[1] Die "beobachten Grössen" in die Theoric der Elementarteilchen. *Z. Physik* **120**, 513–538, 673–702 (1943).

HENLEY, E., and THIRRING, W. E.
[1] "Elementary Quantum Field Theory." McGraw-Hill, New York, 1962.

JORDAN, P., and WIGNER, E. P.
[1] Über das Paulishe Äquivalenzverbot. *Z. Physik* **47**, 631–658. (1928).

LANDAU, L. D., and LIFSHITZ, E. M.
[1] "Quantum Mechanics" (in Russian). Fizmatgiz, Moscow, 1962. English transl., Pergamon Press, New York, 1958.

MARTIN, J. L.
[1] Generalized Classical Dynamics, and the "Classical Analogue" of a Fermi Oscillator. *Proc. Roy. Soc.* (*London*) **A251**, 536–542 (1959).

MINLOS, R. A.
[1] Generalized Stochastic Processes and Their Extension to Measure (in Russian). *Tr. Mosk. Mat. Obšč.* **8**, 497–518 (1959).

NAIMARK, M. A.
[1] "Normed Rings" (in Russian). Gostehizdat, Moscow, 1956. English transl., Noordhoff, Groningen, 1959.

PLESNER, A. I., and ROHLIN, V. A.
[1] Spectral Theory of Linear Operators, II (in Russian). *Usp. Mat. Nauk* **1** No. 1 (11), 71–191 (1946).

SALAM, A., and MATTHEWS, P. T.
[1] The Green's Functions of Quantized Fields. *Nuovo Cimento* **12**, 563–565 (1954).

SCHWEBER, S. S.
[1] "An Introduction to Relativistic Quantum Field Theory." Harper & Row, New York, 1961.

SEGAL, I. E.
[1] Distributions in Hilbert Space and Canonical Systems of Operators. *Trans. Am. Math. Soc.* **88**, 12–41 (1954).

SIEGEL, C. L.
[1] Analytic Functions of Several Complex Variables, Lecture notes at the Institute for Advanced Study, Princeton, New Jersey, 1948–1949. Russian transl., Automorphic Functions of Several Complex Variables, IL, Moscow, 1954, pp. 1–167.

THIRRING, W. E.
[1] A Soluble Relativistic Field Theory. *Ann. Phys.* (*N.Y.*) **3**, 91–112 (1958).

Tomonaga, S.
[1] On the Effect of the Field Reaction on the Interaction of Mesotrons and Nuclear Particles, I. *Progr. Theoret. Phys.* (*Kyoto*) **1**, 83–91 (1946).

Van Hove, L.
[1] Les Difficultés de divergences pour un modèle particulier de champ quantifié. *Physica* **18**, 145–152 (1952).

Vivier, M. M.
[1] Sur quelques théorèmes d'algèbre extérieure. *Ann. Sci. École Norm. Sup.* (3) **73**, 203–281 (1956).

Von Neumann, J.
[1] Die Eindeutigkeit der Schrödingerschen Operatoren. *Math. Ann.* **104**, 570–578 (1931).
[2] On Infinite Direct Product. *Compositio Math.* **6**, 1–77 (1938).

Weyl, H.
[1] "The Classical Groups, Their Invariants and Representations." Princeton Univ. Press, Princeton, New Jersey, 1946.

# Index